Matsuoka
Relaxation Phenomena in Polymers

SPE Books from Hanser Publishers

Relaxation Phenomena in Polymers

Edited by
Shiro Matsuoka

With 121 Illustrations

Hanser Publishers, Munich Vienna New York Barcelona

Distributed in the United States of America and in Canada
by Oxford University Press New York

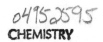

CHEMISTRY

The Author:
Shiro Matsuoka, AT&T, 600 Mountain Avenue, Murray Hill, NJ 07974-0636, USA

Distributed in USA and in Canada by
Oxford University Press
200 Madison Avenue
New York, NY 10016, USA

Distributed in all other countries by
Carl Hanser Verlag
Kolbergerstrasse 22
D-8000 München 80

The use of general descriptive names, trademarks, etc., in this publication, even if the former are not especially identified, is not to be taken as a sign that such names, as understood by the Trade Marks and Merchandise Marks Act, may accordingly be used freely by anyone.

While the advice and information in this book are believed to be true and accurate at the date of going to press, neither the authors nor the editors nor the publisher can accept any legal responsibility for any errors or omissions that may be made. The publisher makes no warranty, express or implied, with respect to the material contained herein.

Die Deutsche Bibliothek – CIP-Einheitsaufnahme
Matsuoka, Shiro:
Relaxation phenomena in polymers / Shiro Matsuoka. –
Munich ; Vienna ; New York ; Barcelona ; Hanser, 1992
  ISBN 3-446-17111-8

ISBN 3-446-17111-8 Carl Hanser Verlag, Munich Vienna New York Barcelona
ISBN 0-19-520957-5 Oxford University Press New York
Library of Congress Catalog Card Number 92-053927

TO   NORMA

and ● ● ●

Foreword

It is with particular pleasure that the Society of Plastics Engineers sponsors and endorses "Relaxation Phenomena in Polymers." Its author, Dr. Shiro Matsuoka, embodies the technical excellence which the Society strives to achieve. He was one of the first recipients of SPE's Award in Engineering and Technology and is one of only 90 Fellows of the Society. In addition, he has long served on the Advisory Board of Polymer Engineering and Science.

Most importantly, however, is his membership in the National Academy of Engineering. He is among the few with a background in polymers and plastics elected to this prestigious body. Who then can be better qualified to author this volume, particularly in view of his 35 years of experience in writing and presenting technical dissertations.

SPE, through its Technical Volumes Committee, has long sponsored books on various aspects of plastics and polymers. Its involvement has ranged from identification of needed volumes to recruitment of authors. An ever-present ingredient, however, is review of the final manuscript to insure accuracy of the technical content.

This technical competence pervades all SPE activities, not only in publication of books but also in other activities such as technical conferences and educational programs. In addition, the Society publishes periodicals – *Plastics Engineering, Polymer Engineering and Science, Polymer Processing and Rheology, Journal of Vinyl Technology* and *Polymer Composites* – as well as conference proceedings and other selected publications, all of which are subject to the same rigorous technical review procedure.

The resource of some 37,000 practicing plastics engineers has made SPE the largest organization of its type worldwide. Further information is available from the Society at 14 Fairfield Drive, Brookfield, Connecticut 06804, U.S.A.

Robert D. Forger
Executive Director
Society of Plastics Engineers

Technical Volumes Committee
Raymond J. Ehrig, Chairperson
Aristech Chemical Corporation

Preface

I have been fortunate to spend thirty years of my career at AT&T Bell Laboratories in close contact with world-class scientists, while keeping in touch with some of the most interesting engineering projects in industry. I recall that the dielectric properties of the ultrapure polyethylene being considered for the transoceanic submarine cable were so critical that we introduced an empirical equation: 10 microradian of $\Delta \tan \delta$ = \$1M of savings in the repeater cost. Aside from such special applications, AT&T was consuming 100 million dollars worth of plastics every year. Even though those times were exciting enough, the use of polymers has taken another dimension since then. Today, the optical fiber cables utilizing all sorts of polymers have replaced the coaxial cables; a miniature ultra-dense computer package with performance comparable to a Cray computer is being tested; the twenty Stealth bombers made of polymer composites have done more than 70% of destruction in the gulf war. The technology has made remarkable progress, and many new applications have emerged, and polymers are more than ever the essential part of new advances in the new technologies.

To predict engineering properties of polymers from their molecular structure is everyone's ambition. There are two main theories that are crucial to the work presented in this book. One is the process of the cooperative conformational relaxation. The basic relaxation rate is determined by the chemical potential of the transition state, but the required simultaneous cooperative relaxation among the neighboring molecular segments reduces the probability of successful relaxation by zth power, where z is the number of the cooperating and interlocked segments. The temperature dependence of the relaxation time does not follow the Arrhenius formula because the number z for the cooperating segments increases with the decreasing temperature, resulting in an enormous (and changing) value for the observed temperature coefficient near T_g. From the model distribution of domain size based on free volume fluctuations, we have obtained an equation for relaxation that fits data better than the Kohlrausch-Williams-Watts equation, especially in the high frequency range that is an important time range for the prediction of the mechanical properties of glassy polymers.

The second crucial theory we have incorporated is the theory of viscoplasticity. Stress is a manifestation of the elastic or stored free energy. The yield phenomenon occurs when the elastic energy exceeds the breaking strength of those domains. However, if strained slowly, the work energy is dissipated through the relaxation process before the yield stress is reached. The behavior, as described above, combines the features of linear viscoelasticity at low stresses and classical plasticity at high stresses; hence, it is termed viscoplasticity (elastico-visco-plasticity might have been more appropriate but cumbersome). Because the fraction that relaxes before reaching the yield (and never goes through yield) depends on the relaxation spectrum at a given strain rate, this apparently nonlinear behavior can be accurately predicted from the linear viscoelastic relaxation spectrum. Prediction of the yield stress at a given strain rate and temperature is possible. We have also shown that the non-Newtonian flow behavior of the polymer melts is in fact the viscoplastic behavior, only different from the solids in the level of the critical levels of stress and strain. Two computer programs have been included in this book with which many kinds of engineering properties can be calculated from the actual stress-strain data.

For the work presented in this book, I owe so much to so many of my friends and colleagues. First and foremost, Xina Quan, who has co-authored some crucial papers that became the basic part of this book, steadfastly declined to allow her name to be used as the co-author, although I feel her contribution was an essential part of this book. Harvey Bair, Ed Johnson and Jim Ryan have been my constant companions for all of the work included here. I have been lucky to have worked closely in the past with Graham Williams (University College of Wales at Swansea), Takeo Furukawa (Institute of Physical and Chemical Research in Tokyo) and Yoichi Ishida (deceased, formerly Kyushu University). Bryce Maxwell (Princeton University), Lee Blyler, and Bob Staats-Westover (retired) have taught me much on polymer engineering. My association with Glenn Frederickson (now at University of California, Santa Barbara) was particularly fruitful, giving me much needed insight to the concept of intermolecular cooperative relaxation. In fact, the molecular model in Chapter 2 can be described with the parameters from the Frederickson-Anderson Ising model. Yasu Koike (Keio University) and Takumi B. Tanaka (UNITIKA) have helped me on many related subjects while undertaking their extended visits at Bell Laboratories. Jehuda Rosenberg

(Israel) and Hany Ghoneim (Rochester Institute of Technology) spent their postdoctoral years at Bell Laboratories, teaching me applied mechanics. I had the world's brightest summer undergraduate program student from Princeton, Jack Hergenrother, who helped me on viscoplasticity of polymer melts. He subsequently went to Cambridge on the Marshall Scholarship, then went on to Harvard to study physics.

And then there is a group of notable names with whom I have spent time at Bell Laboratories: Bill Slichter (deceased), Dave McCall, Dean Douglas, Stretch Winslow, Frank Bovey, Linc Hawkins (retired), Doug Keith (U. Conn), Frank Padden, Andy Lovinger, Dale Pearson (UCSB), Gene Helfand, Henry Wang (Rutgers), Alan Tonelli (NC State U), Gary Patterson (Carnegie-Mellon), T. K. Kwei (Polytech U., NY), Lou Manzione, Reddy Raju, Sanjay Patel, Karl Amundson, Ken Takahashi, Ron Larson, Frank Bates (U. Minnesota), Susan Muller (UCB), Arturo Hale, Faith Morrison (Mich Tech U), Carl Taylor, Charles Aloisio, Paul Kelleher (retired), Phil Hubbauer, and I am sure I missed some names. I owe to names that I can't even begin to cite. I can only make a second-hand quotation from Chris Macosko (U. Minnesota) who quoted Lee Blyler who said, "I would like to thank all those people, whom I neglected to acknowledge over many years, whose original ideas have shaped my thinking and enabled me to make advances in the engineering and technology of plastics ...."

Shiro Matsuoka
Murray Hill, New Jersey
February, 1992

Table of Contents

1

Stress and Strain

This chapter presents a collection of mathematical tools that will be useful when relating molecular structure to phenomenologically observed behavior. These tools are utilized throughout this volume.

1.1 Free Energy and Stress

The word "potential" is a relative term. On the earth's surface, altitude is a kind of potential. By international agreement, altitude is expressed relative to sea level, but a local altitude might also be expressed relative to a nearby lake. Thus, altitude is a measure of a relative work potential, and potential energy depends on what we decide to be the ground potential.

The same principle of the relative nature of the potential applies to the *free energy* of a material. At 0 °C, 1 mole of gas contained in a 22.4 liter vessel will exert a pressure of 1 atmosphere on the inside wall, and we refer to this thermodynamic state as the standard condition, a sort of zero level potential. If this vessel has a piston, we can increase the pressure to 2 atmospheres by using an external force, and the volume of the gas will be reduced by half. The work performed on the gas is

$$W = \int_{V/2}^{V} p \, dV \qquad (1.1.1)$$

This compressed state has a potential to do work, because when the external force is removed and the pressure is reduced back to 1 atmosphere, the entire amount of work W will be returned by the gas. The gas under a pressure of 2 atmospheres tries to come back to the original standard condition as if it were a compressed spring. The energy that can be returned in this manner is free energy.

A solid material typically behaves like a spring when an external force is applied. In this case the zero energy level state is the state under zero external force. In many hard solid materials, the entire amount of work done by the external force results in a temporary deformation of the material but the original state always returns when the force is removed. Such materials are called *perfectly elastic*. Although many substances behave nearly perfectly elastically when the deformation is small, they will either fracture or yield when deformed beyond certain limits. The recoverable elastic strain energy is one type of free energy. Its quantity can be calculated in the same manner as the free energy in the compressed gas was calculated above. Let us consider pulling a rectangular bar of length l_0 from both ends. When the force is increased from 0 to F, the length will increase from l_0 to l. The work done, W, is equal to

$$W = \int_{l_0}^{l} F \, dl \tag{1.1.2}$$

For the energy density, i.e., the work per unit volume, the stress σ (the force per unit area) is integrated with respect to the strain ε (the deformation per unit length):

$$\Psi = \int_{0}^{\varepsilon} \sigma \, d\varepsilon \tag{1.1.3}$$

In the discussion above, only the simplest case of uniaxial tension was cited. The stresses vary depending on the choice of the angle of the cross-sectional area, even if the external force remains the same. The stress considered in the example was in the plane perpendicular to the direction of pull. Because of this choice of angle, there were no shear components in the plane. If we now consider a plane inclined 45° from the direction of pull, there will be shear stresses. The free energy in either case nevertheless remains the same, since energy is a scalar quantity. This is a very important principle, meaning that the total of all stress components at a point depends only on the boundary condition. It also means that if the stresses are known for three orthogonal planes at a point, all stress components for another set of orthogonal planes can be calculated.

Free energy in thermodynamics is expressed as Helmholtz energy $U - TS$ (U is the internal energy, T is the temperature, and S is the entropy) or as Gibbs energy $H - TS$ (H is the enthalpy). Because $H = U + PV$, the Helmholtz energy can be conveniently viewed as a special case of the Gibbs energy in which the pressure-volume effect is minimal. When a solid material is stressed, its springlike response is typically a result of an increased internal energy U. This mechanical energy is predominantly associated with a change of shape, although a small contribution may come from the strain-induced volume change. There is another type of strain energy that is not attributable to a raised internal energy. Polymer scientists are familiar with such an exceptional case with rubbery polymers in which the deformation hardly affects the internal energy U, but results in the decrease of entropy S, thus raising the Helmholtz energy. In all these cases, the mechanical energy is viewed as a type of thermodynamic free energy. Similarly, the electrically raised energy in dielectrics is also a type of free energy. Dielectric relaxation means that a stored (capacitive) free energy is dissipated as heat (resistive). If the resistance were zero, the entire energy could be stored and returned, and we would have a perfect capacitor.

Finally, one important comment should be made on a practical aspect of the strain energy when it is subject to relaxation. When a material capable of relaxation is strained, the stress will decay even when the strain is held constant. The elastic free energy is being dissipated as the molecules transit from the initially raised energy level (strained state) to the final equilibrium state. With the pressure-volume model, this is comparable to allowing the compressed gas to leak through a small hole in the chamber wall; the density will decay back to the uncompressed equilibrium value in time. However, at each step during this decay process in which the free energy is decaying (i.e., NOT in equilibrium), the precise thermodynamic relationship between the pressure and the specific volume is maintained. Similarly, even though the final equilibrium value of the relaxing stress is 0, at each step during the decay of stress, the precise relationship according to the law of *elasticity* is maintained between the stress and the free energy. This free energy is a measure of how much capacity to do work remains in the material but *not* how much work has been done to the material. The measurable (laboratory) strain is a measure of work that has been done, and it is *not* the strain ε in Equation 1.1.3. Rather, ε in that equation is the *elastic* portion of the measurable strain, and the equation can be considered to be the implicit definition of this parameter.

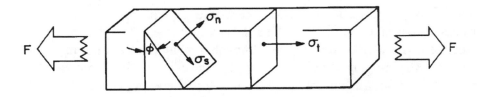

Figure 1.2.1 Force F on the rectangular bar induces the stress, the magnitude of which depends on the choice of the angle of cross section.

1.2 Interrelationships Among the Stresses in an Elastic Body[1]

We stated in the preceding section that the elastic (free) energy density Ψ at a point within the material is equal to the total sum of all stress components at the point. Since there are three orthogonal planes at each point and one normal stress and two shear stress components in each plane, nine stress components completely describe the state of stress at each point. The value of each stress component depends on the choice of the directions of the three orthogonal planes with respect to the external forces acting upon the body, but the elastic energy is constant as long as the external forces are constant. It is possible to consider several classes of elastic energy. For example, there is the energy that is related only to the hydrostatic stresses. The strain related to this kind of energy is compressive or expansive. The sum of three stresses, each normal to one of the three orthogonal planes, is independent of the angles and is called the *invariant.* By the same reasoning, the sum of all stresses that contribute toward changing the shape of the body is another type of invariant. Later we will use these invariants in stress analyses involving viscoelastic and viscoplastic behavior; here, we illustrate how the concept of invariants is used in simple elastic stress analyses. Consider a rectangular bar being pulled by forces F at both ends, as shown in Figure 1.2.1. For the plane perpendicular to the direction of F, the stress

1. Timoshenko, S., and Young, D. H., *Elements of Strength of Materials,* 5th ed., Van Nostrand Reinhold Co., New York, 1968

σ_t acting normal to this plane is the only component that is not 0. There are no shear stresses. Two other planes orthogonal to this plane have no stress components either. Thus for this choice of three planes, there is only one stress component and it is σ_t, which equals F/A.

Now, consider another plane which makes an angle ϕ with F. There are two components this time, the normal stress σ_n and the shear stress σ_s. The intensities of these stresses are:

$$\sigma_n = \frac{F}{A}\cos^2\phi \tag{1.2.1}$$

and

$$\sigma_s = \frac{F}{A}\sin\phi\cos\phi = \frac{1}{2}\frac{F}{A}\sin 2\phi \tag{1.2.2}$$

Thus, when ϕ is 45°, $\sigma_s = \sigma_n = (F/2A)$, and it is the maximum value for σ_s. The plane that makes an angle of -45° is orthogonal to the plane above. The stresses are a mirror image of those above, meaning the normal stresses are in the opposite directions and the shear stresses are in the same direction. The sum of all stress components, four in all, is again F/A, since the third orthogonal plane has no stresses. Thus, the sum of the stresses is always found to be equal to F/A. The choice of the coordinates does not alter the sum.

Here is another example. We will now consider a two-dimensional problem with a plate subjected to two forces, F_1 and F_2 that are perpendicular to each other as shown in Figure 1.2.2. For the plane that makes angle ϕ with F_1, the two stresses are

$$\sigma_{n1} = \frac{F_1}{A_1}\cos^2\phi + \frac{F_2}{A_2}\sin^2\phi \tag{1.2.3}$$

and

$$\sigma_{s1} = \frac{1}{2}\frac{F_1}{A_1}\sin 2\phi - \frac{1}{2}\frac{F_2}{A_2}\sin 2\phi \tag{1.2.4}$$

and for the plane orthogonal to the above plane, stresses are:

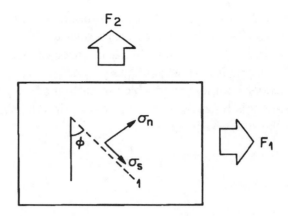

Figure 1.2.2   The stress resulting from two orthogonal forces F_1 and F_2 on area represented by the dotted line and marked as 1.

$$\sigma_{n2} = \frac{F_2}{A_2}\cos^2\phi + \frac{F_1}{A_1}\sin^2\phi \qquad (1.2.5)$$

and

$$\sigma_{s2} = \frac{1}{2}\frac{F_2}{A_2}\sin 2\phi - \frac{1}{2}\frac{F_1}{A_1}\sin 2\phi \qquad (1.2.6)$$

hence we obtain

$$\sigma_{n1} + \sigma_{n2} = \frac{F_1}{A_1} + \frac{F_2}{A_2} \qquad (1.2.7)$$

and

$$\sigma_{s1} = -\sigma_{s2} \qquad (1.2.8)$$

and the total of all stress components equals $F_1/A_1 + F_2/A_2$. When $\phi = 0$, $\sigma_{n1} = F_1/A_1$, $\sigma_{n2} = F_2/A_2$, and all shear stress components are zero. The stresses σ_{n1} and σ_{n2} for this case are the *principal* stresses, and will be noted by σ_1 and σ_2.

Equations 1.2.3 and 1.2.4 can be written in the form:

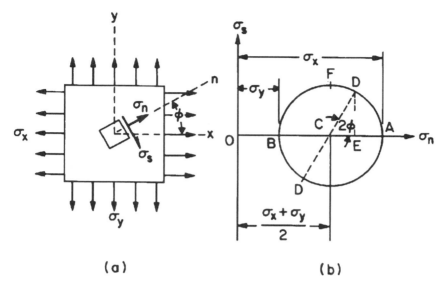

(a)   (b)

Figure 1.2.3   The two dimensional stresses in (a) can be calculated from the Mohr's circle shown in (b), which represents Equations 1.2.9 and 1.2.10.

$$\sigma_{n1} = \frac{1}{2}(\sigma_1 + \sigma_2) + \frac{1}{2}(\sigma_1 - \sigma_2)\cos 2\phi \tag{1.2.9}$$

$$\sigma_{s1} = \frac{1}{2}(\sigma_1 - \sigma_2)\sin 2\phi \tag{1.2.10}$$

Equations 1.2.9 and 1.2.10 are represented by "Mohr's circle" as shown in Figure 1.2.3 (b). Here the directions 1 and 2 were replaced by the x and y coordinates, such that the two principal stresses are σ_x and σ_y. In this diagram, σ_n corresponds to distance OE, and σ_s is distance DE. Negative values for tension mean compression, and for shear they mean clockwise moment with respect to a center inside the element.

The reason for showing these elementary mechanics of elastic behavior is that these relationships apply to the recoverable part of the strain energy (which is the free energy) in viscoelastic media as well. We shall be dealing with static and quasi-static states almost exclusively; i.e., the inertial effects are neglected. For these cases the stress components can be calculated quite accurately by using the mathematics of elasticity. This is true even for polymer melts, where the inertial components of flow are very small compared to the unrelaxed stress components.

1.3 Viscoelasticity

A model of springs and dashpots has a serious deficiency. If it is made to fit a set of real relaxation data, it cannot fit the creep data for the same material. A valid mathematical model must fit all experimental data without changing the values of the parameters. No combinations of numbers of springs and dashpots can satisfy this simple requirement!

1.3.1 Stress Relaxation

In the preceding sections, we have stated that for an elastic material, the level of the free energy remains constant indefinitely, as long as the external forces remain unchanged. In contrast, when external forces are applied to a liquid, the energy is immediately spent through irreversible deformation, and when the forces are removed no strain energy is left to be returned. We are interested here in materials that are partly like elastic solids, since they can retain the elastic or recoverable strain energy *partially,* but are also partly like liquids, since they dissipate energy if the external force is maintained; hence they are called *viscoelastic* materials.

We now consider a special mechanical experiment. First, a sample of viscoelastic material is deformed to a shear strain γ_0 *instantly,* and then, while maintaining this deformation, the stress is measured as it decays from the initial value of σ_0. This is a stress relaxation experiment. The *macroscopic* strain γ_0 is maintained constant, but the strain energy will be dissipated through the rearrangement of molecules into a lower free energy state. The *microscopic* strain, γ_e in Figure 1.3.1, is the recoverable strain, and it continues to return toward the zero level even as the macroscopic strain is maintained at a constant level. The remaining free energy is the work that can be given back by elastic recovery. We consider a Maxwell model in which the stress is uniformly distributed throughout the body: i.e., the stress is common to the spring and dashpot elements, but the macroscopic strain is the sum of elastic and viscous deformations (i.e., the strains and their time derivatives in the spring and the dashpots are added to make up the total strain). As shown in Figure 1.3.1, when the strain is suddenly raised from 0 to γ_0 at $t = 0$, the spring will elongate to γ_0, while the dashpot has not moved yet. The stress will jump to the initial value σ_0, and this stress is borne by both the spring and the dashpot. As the total deformation is maintained at γ_0, however, the spring will shrink back and the dashpot will extend, and the stress will fall progressively. The extension of the spring γ_e is representative

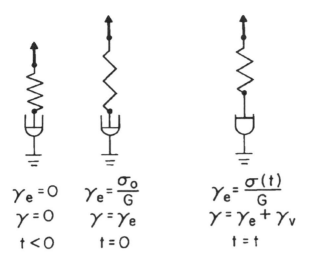

$$\gamma_e = 0 \qquad \gamma_e = \frac{\sigma_0}{G} \qquad \gamma_e = \frac{\sigma(t)}{G}$$
$$\gamma = 0 \qquad \gamma = \gamma_e \qquad \gamma = \gamma_e + \gamma_v$$
$$t < 0 \qquad t = 0 \qquad t = t$$

Figure 1.3.1   Linear viscoelastic stress relaxation modeled with a single spring and a single dashpot. The energy stored in the spring is equivalent to the free energy raised in the molecule.

of the molecular deformation, which is proportionalt to the *stress* and will disappear at $t \to \infty$, when the free energy will return to the initial unstrained level. The rate of the decay of the stress can be formulated by a first-order equation, because the decay rate for the perturbed species is proportional to the total number of the remaining perturbed species, and the stress is proportional to the population of these perturbed species:

$$\frac{d\sigma}{dt} = -\frac{G_0}{\eta}\sigma \qquad (1.3.1)$$

where G_0 is the elastic constant of the spring and η is the friction coefficient of the dashpot. We must clarify here that the Maxwell model is consistent with Equation 1.3.1 *only* in the stress relaxation experiment; it is inconsistent with the creep behavior of the same material. Thus, it cannot be overemphasized that the Maxwell element mimics material behavior only under limited sets of conditions. The ratio η/G_0 has the dimension of time and is defined as the relaxation time λ. The solution of Equation 1.3.1 can be written as:

$$\sigma(t) = \sigma_0 \exp\left(-\frac{t}{\lambda}\right) \tag{1.3.2}$$

The relaxation time λ is the "time constant" for the stress decay process; γ_e is the elastic (i.e., microscopic and recoverable) strain, and it corresponds to the remaining unrelaxed extension in the spring. Hence γ_e is proportional to $\sigma(t)$. Since the free energy Ψ is proportional to the square of the relaxing stress,

$$\Psi = \int_0^{\gamma_e} [\sigma(t)]_t \, d\gamma_e = \frac{1}{2G_0} [\sigma(t)]^2 \tag{1.3.3}$$

and the free energy Ψ decays at twice the rate of the stress relaxation, as the apparent time constant is halved. This principle has been found useful in predicting the time for slow crack or craze growth processes.

The elastic strain γ_e can be considered a perturbation in molecular configuration. The relaxation modulus $G(t)$ is a measure of the concentration of the perturbed (i.e., with higher than the equilibrium energy state) molecules (G_0 is the instantaneous modulus), and it represents the time dependent decay of the perturbed state toward the unstressed equilibrium state, e.g.,

$$G(t) = G_0 \exp\left(-\frac{t}{\lambda}\right) \tag{1.3.4}$$

Equation 1.3.4 is a basic formula for the relaxation process, and goes beyond the Maxwell model. To illustrate this point, we cite that the creep rate under a constant stress is predicted to be always constant by the Maxwell model, while the creep rate calculated from Equation 1.3.4 (utilizing the formulas in Section 1.3.2) is not constant with time. The inconsistency manifest in the Maxwell model is in fact inherent in all combinations of springs and dashpots.

For polymer melts, the value of G_0 is on the order of 10^6 dynes/cm^2, whereas for glassy polymers it is four orders of magnitude greater. Yet, as we shall discuss in subsequent chapters, relaxation processes are part of an extremely long and continuous process. In a polymer melt, the glasslike high modulus process relaxes so rapidly that only the low modulus process typical of the rubbery state is observed.

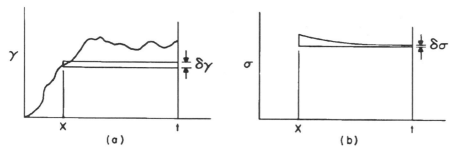

Figure 1.3.2   Schematic illustration of the convolution integral of Equation 1.3.6, below. The stress at time t is the sum of the unrelaxed stresses $\delta\sigma$ as a result of many incremental stress relaxation tests variably started at time x with the incremental strain $\delta\gamma$ and lasting variably for the time duration $t - x$.

1.3.2 Superposition of the Stress-Strain History

We have treated G_0 and λ as constants, i.e, as independent of the magnitude of the strain γ_0. This is a reasonable assumption when the stress, and therefore γ_e also, is small. This situation is comparable to the behavior of an elastic material within the elastic limit. Later we will discuss how small γ_e must be, but the limit turns out to be which is several percent strain for the glassy state and a few hundred percent for the melt. If the material meets the foregoing condition, which we call *linear viscoelasticity,* then the principle of superposition of the strain history applies. This principle states that the entire history of the stress can be reconstructed by adding the stress histories that correspond to individual bits of a strain history. The generalized superposition principle is illustrated in Figure 1.3.2. The history of the *macroscopic* strain γ is shown in Figure 1.3.2a, from which we wish to calculate the stress at time t, using the experimentally obtained $G(t)$. $\delta\gamma$ is an incremental strain added at $t = x$, and is equal to the product of the strain rate $\dot{\gamma} = d\gamma/dt$ and δx. This incremental strain has contributed to raising the stress to $G_0\delta\gamma$ at $t = x$, but it has decayed to $G(t - x)\delta\gamma$ by the time t is reached. Thus the incremental stress at t is:

$$\delta\sigma = G(t - x)\delta\gamma = G_0\exp\left[-\frac{t - x}{\lambda}\right]\frac{d\gamma}{dx}\delta x \qquad (1.3.5)$$

By integrating for the stress, we have

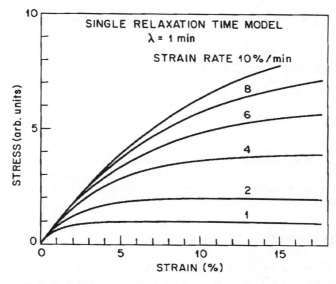

Figure 1.3.3   Linear viscoelastic stress built up under the strain being increased at a constant rate of strain (for a single relaxation time).

$$\sigma = \int_{0}^{t} G(t-x) \frac{d\gamma}{dx} \, dx \tag{1.3.6}$$

Equation 1.3.6 is one of the four forms of the *convolution* integrals. They are valid only within the linear viscoelastic limits. Many types of dynamic formula can be derived by making use of Equation 1.3.6. For example, for the dynamic strain $\gamma(t) = \gamma_0 \sin \omega t$, where ω is the circular frequency in radians per second, the steady state stress can be obtained from this equation by setting the lower limit of the integral to $-\infty$,

$$\sigma = G_0 \gamma_0 \left[\frac{\omega^2 \lambda^2}{1 + \omega^2 \lambda^2} \sin \omega t + \frac{\omega \lambda}{1 + \omega^2 \lambda^2} \cos \omega t \right] \tag{1.3.7}$$

The dynamic mechanical stress in this equation consists of a $\sin \omega t$ term and a $\cos \omega t$ term that are 90° out of phase from each other. The sine term is *in phase* with the strain, and the cosine term precedes the strain by $\pi/2$. The derivative of the cosine term with respect to the strain is zero, whereas the derivative of the sine term with respect to the strain rate is zero. Thus the sine term is an elastic stress, whereas the cosine term is a viscous or (energy) loss stress. The coefficient for the cosine term reaches a maximum

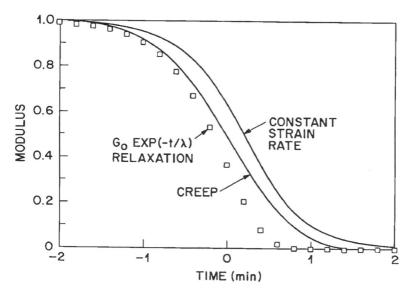

Figure 1.3.4 Comparison of three kinds of "modulus" (the stress divided by the strain): under constant strain (stress relaxation), under constant stress (creep), and under constant rate of strain (constant flow rate), for the single relaxation time model.

value when the frequency ω is equal to the reciprocal of the relaxation time λ^{-1}. Thus the maximum degree of relaxation is experienced when the dynamic strain rate is equal to the "rate constant" $\sim\lambda^{-1}$ for the relaxation process.

As another dynamic viscoelastic experiment, we consider a case when the strain is increased at a constant rate, $\dot{\gamma}$=constant, and we obtain by substituting Equation 1.3.4 into Equation 1.3.6:

$$\sigma(\gamma) = G_0\dot{\gamma}\lambda\left[1 - \exp\left(-\frac{\gamma}{\dot{\gamma}\lambda}\right)\right] \qquad (1.3.8)$$

The stress-strain curves at constant rates of strain are shown in Figure 1.3.3. The curves scale with the product $\dot{\gamma}\lambda$. The steady state stress is thus proportional to the strain rate and is equal to $G_0\dot{\gamma}\lambda$. Since the stress is *always* equal to $G_0\gamma_e$, the recoverable strain is equal to $\dot{\gamma}\lambda$. The viscosity $\sigma/\dot{\gamma}$ is equal to $G_0\lambda$ and is independent of $\dot{\gamma}$, exhibiting *Newtonian* behavior. The steady state value of this viscosity is equal to the friction coefficient η of the dashpot in the Maxwell model or, more precisely, the integral of the relaxation modulus with respect to time to infinity.

Another familiar type of viscoelastic experiment is found in the creep experiment. In this experiment, the stress is applied at time 0 and is maintained constant while the strain increases with time. The creep compliance, the strain divided by the stress, is *not* the reciprocal of the relaxation modulus. There is an exact relationship[2] between the linear viscoelastic creep compliance $J(t)$ and the linear viscoelastic modulus $G(t)$:

$$\int_0^t G(t-x)\dot{J}(x)\,dx = 1 \tag{1.3.9}$$

To satisfy this equation, the creep rate $\dot{J}(t)$ cannot be constant, and it is immediately clear that the Maxwell model, which satisfies the viscoelastic relaxation at constant strain, cannot predict the creep behavior *of the same material*.[3] The creep behavior of this material can be numerically calculated by continuously adding an incremental elastic strain $\Delta\gamma$ to maintain a constant stress σ_0. With each addition of $\Delta\gamma$, the stress increases slightly but decays back to σ_0 in time Δt. By repeating this step, the creep strain $\gamma(t)$ is calculated from the formula:

$$\gamma(t) = \frac{\sigma_0}{G_0}\left[1 + \sum\exp\left(-\frac{\Delta t}{\lambda}\right)\right] \tag{1.3.10}$$

The creep modulus $\sigma_0/\gamma(t)$ thus calculated is compared against the relaxation modulus and the modulus obtained under the constant rate of strain, all against the logarithmic elapsed time, in Figure 1.3.4. It is evident that, even for a material with a single relaxation time, the creep relaxation time, or the retardation time, is different from the stress relaxation time. The constant strain rate relaxation time is still different from either of the two, as shown in Figure 1.3.4. It depends on the strain rate, of course, and

---

2. The relationship can be derived from the reciprocity between the complex dynamic mechanical modulus $G^*(\omega)$ and the dynamic compliance $J^*(\omega)$. [See Hopkins, I. L., and Hamming, R. W., *J. Applied Phys.* **28**, 906 (1957)]

3. In fact, no matter how many springs and dashpots are used in any combination, Equation 1.3.9 will not be satisfied.

when $\dot{\gamma} = \lambda^{-1}$ is chosen, that relaxation time is about 2λ, which is about the same as the (creep) retardation time. This is related to the fact that, to arrive at the identical state of elastic stored energy, we put in the most energy in the relaxation experiment and the least in the constant strain rate experiment. The creep modulus is close to the relaxation modulus at $t \ll \lambda$, but approaches the constant $\dot{\gamma} = \lambda^{-1}$ modulus as $t \to \infty$, since the steady state condition should be the same for the latter two cases. Thus it is true that the product of the relaxation modulus and the creep compliance is less than 1. However, the creep modulus is closer to the relaxation modulus when the distribution of relaxation times is broad.

SUMMARY

The crucial point to be recognized in this section is that the Maxwell model portrays a single relaxation time process only in the stress relaxation experiment, but it fails to predict creep behavior of the same sample. Modifying the Maxwell model by increasing the number of the elements does not change the picture. A materially consistent approach is

1.   to set the molecular relaxation as follows:

$$\phi(t) = \exp\left(-\frac{t}{\lambda} \right) \tag{1.3.11}$$

2.   to recognize that the creep formula must satisfy the convolution integral such as Equation 1.3.9, and

3.   to forget about springs and dashpots.

1.4 The Relaxation Spectrum

The three stages of the relaxation process are (1) local segmental relaxation, (2) relaxation of dynamic molecules without entanglement, and (3) with entanglement or reptation.

1.4.1 Phenomenological Aspects

In the foregoing sections, practically all viscoelastic calculations were carried out with the single mode relaxation function:

$$G(t) = G_0 \exp\left(-\frac{t}{\lambda}\right) \tag{1.3.4}$$

In other words, we were assuming that a single time constant λ could be used to characterize the viscoelastic behavior. This is not true for real polymers, however. Since polymer molecules can perform many modes of motions, they can exhibit many modes of relaxation processes. The ith mode of relaxation is characterized by the relaxation time λ_i, and the probability for each mode determines the weighting factor, which is the modulus G_i. The relaxation modulus is the sum of all these modes of relaxation, i.e.,

$$G(t) = \sum_i G_i \exp\left(-\frac{t}{\lambda_i}\right) \tag{1.4.1}$$

The "master curve" for the relaxation modulus $G(t)$ for polyisobutylene, obtained by Catsiff and Tobolsky,[4] is shown in Figure 1.4.1. The x- and y-axes are both in logarithmic scale. The modulus $G(t)$ is seen to decrease by more than six orders of magnitude over the time range of 16 decades. A master curve such as this one is typically constructed from the data obtained over a wide range of temperatures by utilizing the time-temperature superposition principle, also known as the principle of reduced variables. The temperature dependence of relaxation processes is discussed in the chapters that follow. This curve in Figure 1.4.1 is plotted for the reference temperature of -76 °C, which is about 5 °C below the commonly accepted T_g for polyisobutylene. By knowing how a temperature change will shift the relaxation time, the relaxation modulus $G(t)$ for any temperature can be predicted from a master curve such as this. This enormously broad spectrum of relaxation times is typical of amorphous polymers in the equilibrium state (i.e., above T_g). The long time end ($t > 10^4$ hours) of the spectrum depends on the molecular weight,[5] and the elastic modulus G_0 is in the order of 10^6 dynes/cm^2, which is a typical value for rubberlike elasticity: 10^6 dynes/cm^2 = 1 atmosphere; this is a very weak elastic constant. For $t < 10^4$ hours, the

4. Catsiff, E, and Tobolsky, A. V., *J. Colloid Sci.* **10**, 375 (1955).
5. Marin, G., and Graessley, W. W., *Rheol. Acta*, **16**, 527 (1977).

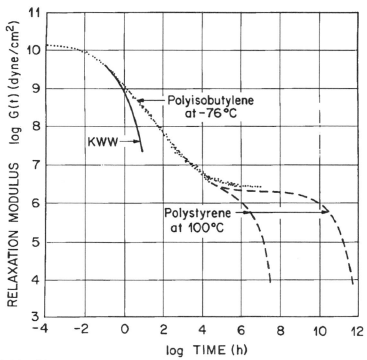

Figure 1.4.1   Master relaxation modulus curve of amorphous polymer constructed as a composite of polyisobutylene data by Catsiff and Tobolsky (Ref. 4) and polystyrene data by Marin and Graessley (Ref. 5) which encompass all three stages: stage 1 for segmental relaxation, stage 2 for the transition zone that bridges to the slow stage 3, which involves the entangled molecules. Line KWW stands for the Kohlrausch-Williams-Watts equation, which typically applies to stage 1.

value of the modulus becomes progressively greater at a shorter t, until G_0 of the glassy state exceeding 10^{10} dynes/cm^2 is reached. This value is comparable to the moduli of soft metals, and no entropic moduli for dynamic chains can give rise to such a high rigidity. Such a large value for the zero-time modulus G_0 is an indication of how difficult it is for the molecules to relax at high frequencies and low temperatures, because the strong intermolecular couplings hinder relaxation. For estimating the theoretical upper limit value for the modulus, the resistance encountered in bending of the carbon-carbon covalent bond would be a reasonable limit of rigidity. Diamond is the ultimate "organic" material from this point of view. Its modulus is in the order of 10^{13} dynes/cm^2. The moduli of a high pressure extruded polyethylene by Porter and coworkers,[6] and Kevlar, a highly oriented liquid crystalline fiber, are not very far below this ultimate value. In contrast, isotropic glassy polymers typically exhibit a modulus in the order of 10^{10} dynes/cm^2. The primary reason for such a comparatively low modulus value lies in the predominant effect of the soft degree of freedom originating from the rotation of the backbone carbon-carbon bonds, according to a computer-simulated study by Theodorou and Suter.[7] This is an important conclusion for the relaxation process also, because it implies that viscoelastic relaxation probably is dominated by the irreversible rotations of the carbon bonds. The measured relaxation time is in minutes, not in picoseconds, however.

1.4.2 The Three Stages of Relaxation

The reason for the extremely long relaxation time is that the relaxation process requires cooperative motions between neighboring segments. Through this kind of analysis one can understand why there are close relationships between molecular motions and the mechanical, dielectric, and thermodynamic relaxation phenomena.

The master curve in Figure 1.4.1 can be divided into three stages: stage 1, the short time, solidlike relaxation process in the time range from 0 to 1 hour; stage 2, the intermediate time range known as the transition zone from 1 hour to 10^4 hours; and stage 3, the plateau zone for times longer than 10^4 hours.

Stage 1 is not unique to polymers but is observed in nonpolymeric glass-forming liquids of all sorts. The distribution of relaxation times is skewed favoring the persisting short time end (the high frequency end) of the spectrum. The Kohlrausch-Williams-Watts equation[8] is the best known equation to fit this stage of the relaxation process:

---

6. Porter, R. S., ed, "Strength and Stiffness of Polymers", Dekker, (1983)
7. Theodorou, D. N., and Suter, U. W., *Macromolecules, 18* (1985).
8. Williams, G., and Watts, D. C., *Trans. Faraday Soc.* **67,** 1323 (1971).

$$G(t) = G_0 \exp\left[-\left(\frac{t}{\lambda_c}\right)^{\beta}\right] \qquad (1.4.2)$$

where the parameter β is often found to be approximately $\frac{1}{2}$ for polymers. The characteristic relaxation time λ_c is specific to the form of this equation, and its reciprocal value is frequently found to be nearly equal to the radial frequency for the dielectric loss maxima for the glass transition. The KWW equation fits well with experimental data near $t = \lambda_c$. Or, it is more correct to say that the adjustable parameters λ_c and β can be chosen in such a way that the equation will give excellent fit over a substantial portion of data near $t \approx \lambda_c$, where $G(t) \approx G_0/e$. In the extremely short time range of $t < \lambda_c/100$, the KWW equation with such a choice of λ_c and β begins to fail; even though its principal feature is to emphasize the high frequency end of a spectrum, it still underestimates the very high frequency portion of the spectrum. This point is discussed in relation to the persistence of subcritical domain sizes for the cooperative relaxation process in Chapter 2. The basic reason for the overall success of the KWW equation is that this equation is unsymmetrical around the characteristic relaxation time λ_c, with a sharp cutoff toward the longer time but with a long, persisting tail toward the short time. This is a typical feature of cooperative relaxation processes among relaxing units in a restricted environment, as we shall discuss in Chapter 2. The KWW equation is particularly suited for describing dielectric relaxation, viscoelastic relaxation in solids for $t \ll \lambda_c$, hypersonic relaxation,[9] and dynamic bulk relaxation.[10] Dielectric data for nonpolymeric liquids also agree with the KWW equation.[11] Among the nonpolymeric glass-forming liquids, the so-called fragile-glass type liquids tend to agree with the KWW equation, whereas others known as the strong glass-type tend to exhibit a single relaxation time.[12] The strong glass-type liquids exhibit a constant activation energy and Arrhenius-type temperature dependence, whereas the fragile

9. Patterson, G. D., *Macromolecules*, **14**, 83 (1981).

10. McKinney, J., and Goldstein, M., *J. Res. NBS*, **78a**, 331 (1974).

11. Johari, G. P., *J. Chem. Phys.* **58**, 1966 (1973).

12. Angell, C. A., and Sichina, W., *Ann. N.Y. Acad. Sci.* **279**, 53 (1976).

glass-type liquids exhibit a Vogel-type temperature dependence with the activation energy increasing at progressively lower temperatures toward an apparent limiting temperature T_0:

$$\ln \frac{\lambda_c}{\lambda_{\text{ref}}} = \frac{H}{R} \left[\frac{1}{T - T_0} - \frac{1}{T_{\text{ref}} - T_0} \right] \tag{1.4.3}$$

which is an equation associated with the aforementioned cooperative relaxation process. The subscript "ref" is referred to the reference temperature.

The value of parameter β in Equation 1.4.2 is a measure of the narrowness of the distribution ($\beta = 1$ means the single relaxation time) This β remains nearly constant against a temperature change as long as the polymer is in the equilibrium state, but its value drops precipitously with a temperature decrease in the nonequilibrium glassy state; i.e., the distribution becomes broader. This is observed both in viscoelastic[13] and dielectric relaxation.[14] The thermodynamically nonequilibrium glassy state tends to *recover* toward the equilibrium state. This process is also known as the physical aging process. The thermodynamic recovery process has been extensively studied by Kovacs[15] through measurements of volume versus time and temperature. The kinetics of the thermodynamic recovery process is nonlinear, since the ongoing relaxation time is affected by the thermodynamic structure. The structure is represented by the specific volume, which changes with time. When the data are properly analyzed, one finds, significantly, that the decay of the perturbed volume toward the equilibrium is governed by the distribution of relaxation times, which again fits the KWW equation.

In summary, stage 1 is a process common to polymers and nonpolymers. This stage of relaxation starts at a very short time range and ends abruptly near $t \approx \lambda_c$, except in the case of viscoelastic relaxation in

13. Matsuoka, S., *Polym. Eng. Sci.* **18**, 1073 (1978).

14. Mashimo, S., Nozaki, R., Yagihara, S., and Takeishi, S., *J. Chem. Phys.* **77**(12), 6259 (1982).

15. Kovacs, A. J.; *Fortschr. Hochpolym. Forsch.* **3** 394, (1963)

polymers, which extends into stage 2, as discussed below. The KWW
equation is a convenient approximation, though it fails to fit data at the
extremely short time range. An alternative formula is proposed in the next
chapter.

In the equilibrium state, the linear viscoelastic relaxation modulus for
an amorphous polymer starts out with the KWW formula but extends
beyond its time range. We have called this extended relaxation stage 2.
Stage 2 is molecular weight dependent, and it has been thought of as unique
to viscoelastic relaxation in polymers. It is absent in the dielectric relaxation
of polymers with dipoles in the perpendicular direction to the chain axis[16] as
well as in thermodynamic recovery for polymers and nonpolymers. It is also
absent in the viscoelastic relaxation of monomers and oligomers. On the
master curve in Figure 1.4.1, stage 2 is the portion with a constant slope in
the shape of a wedge, obeying the power law:

$$G(t) = \frac{G_0}{e} \left[\frac{t}{\lambda_c} \right]^{-n} \tag{1.4.4}$$

where e is the base for the natural logarithm, and typically $n \simeq \frac{1}{2}$ when in
equilibrium. Interestingly, a KWW formula and a power law formula can be
joined at $t = \lambda_c$ and $G(t = \lambda_c) = G_0/e$ with a slope of $-\beta = -n$. Thus, the
master viscoelastic relaxation curve can be represented by the composite of
two equations: Equation 1.4.2 when $t < \lambda_c$, and Equation 1.4.4 when $t > \lambda_c$
with the value of the power $n = \beta$. The value of β in equilibrium liquids is
typically nearly $\frac{1}{2}$. The smaller values are observed in the nonequilibrium
glassy state at lower temperatures.

A few physical and molecular models have been proposed to explain
why the relaxation data fit the KWW equation, but none of them predicts the
changeover to power law behavior at longer times. In the time range where
two different relaxation mechanisms can overlap, the characteristic

---

16. This is a Class A polymer according to the classification proposed by Stockmeyer, W. H.,
    Pure Appl. Chem. **15**, 539 (1967). Class B comprises those with the dipoles in the direction
    of the chain backbone, and the normal mode relaxation processes stages 2 and 3, which
    depend on molecular weight, are observed with dielectric measurement.

relaxation times and the activation energies of the two mechanisms must be equal at the overlapping point. Stage 1 is a cooperative mode among the individual segments. The frictional character of this type of process has been termed by de Gennes[17] as *internal* friction, in contrast to the slipping of a polymer molecule past its neighbors, which he calls *external* friction. The slipping of a molecule does not necessarily mean a whole molecule; it could be only a part of a molecule. The internal and external friction coefficients are comparable in magnitude only when the number of segments involved in the two processes is very small (i.e., in the order of 1). It turns out from our study that the number in the cooperative domain is typically 5 near the glass transition. Stage 2 is called the transition zone. This stage is nearly absent when the molecular weight is very small, but it extends further as the molecular weight is increased. The range of the relaxation time and the modulus indicate that in this stage the viscosity increases proportionately with the molecular weight. The slope of -1/2 for the relaxation modulus coincides with the slope predicted by Rouse's theory,[18] but the unrelaxed modulus in the Rouse model is the rubberlike elastic modulus with the range of 10^6 dynes/cm^2, instead of 10^9 dynes/cm^2. The rubbery modulus is the unrelaxed modulus in stage 3, which is the next topic of discussion.

Stage 3, the plateau and terminal zone, is also molecular weight dependent. Unlike the transition zone, the "unrelaxed" modulus for the maximum relaxation time remains independent of the molecular weight. The plateau zone is absent in polymers with molecular weights of less than the critical value, which depends on the polymer species. This part of the spectrum is most important for melt rheology, but also for the strength of a solid polymer, as the molecular weight of the polymer will affect the toughness. The particular type of intermolecular interaction that gives rise to the plateau zone is known as the entanglement effect, since this behavior has been modeled after the chemically crosslinked networks of polymer chains. Stage 3 is discussed in detail in Chapter 4.

---

17. de Gennes, P.-G., *Scaling Concepts in Polymer Physics*, Cornell University Press, Ithaca, NY, 1979.
18. Rouse, P. E. Jr., *J. Chem. Phys.* **21**, 1272 (1953).

1.4.3 Molecular Interpretation

1.4.3.1 Conformational Relaxation Without Cooperativity

At a very high (extrapolated) temperature, which will be shown to be about 500 °C for the segmental rotation in a polymer chain, polymer segments are conceived as capable of rotating without being encumbered by the neighboring chains. As will be shown later, the segments pack more densely at lower temperatures, and interference from neighbors will affect such thermodynamic properties as the increased specific heat and T_g, and such dynamic properties as the enormous increase in the relaxation time.

The very high temperature regime may not be actually realizable in the laboratory because chemical degradation may occur at this temperature even in a nitrogen atmosphere. Hence this is strictly an extrapolated limiting temperature, which will be helpful in interpreting the relaxation behavior at lower temperatures.

When the bulk polymer is stressed, the mechanical energy at the boundary is transmitted through the chain molecules primarily along the chain. Even in the shear field, the primary mode of stress propagation is the tension in the chain molecules. A molecule will always tend to deform by the softest degree of freedom, which, in this case, is the rotation of adjacent conformers. This has been demonstrated by the computer simulation of the glassy polymer molecules by Therodorou and Suter (see note 7, above). The relaxation process in this case is accomplished when the molecule is untwisted as the tension mounts until, finally, the strain energy exceeds the barrier energy and the segment will rotate to a new position, and this unkinking dissipates and relieves the accumulated strain energy.

The relaxation process as a rate process thus involves two steps: the reversible increase in free energy by the external force followed by the irreversible dissipation when the energy barrier is overcome and a new low energy state is attained. The process possibly may be considered to be a transition from a *gauche* to a *trans* conformation, although this is perhaps an oversimplification, since the stress may be relieved when a *trans* conformation is changed into a *gauche* conformation, depending on the local configuration of the chain. The foregoing picture of molecular relaxation is based on the site model[19] invoking the theory of rate processes.

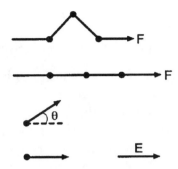

Figure 1.4.2 Comparison of the unkinking of a polymer segment by the stress and the orientation of a dipole under the electrical field.

Alternatively, it can be based on the concept of friction as the mechanism for the dissipation of free energy, where the process of conformational relaxation is termed the "internal" friction[20] as opposed to the external friction, which involves the translational migration (diffusion) of segments. For modes of relaxation that involve a larger unit of relaxation with more conformers, the latter begin to outweigh the former significantly, so that the local conformational relaxation can be neglected when considering the relaxation of the whole polymer molecule as a dynamic chain. Stage 1 thus involves the local conformational relaxation or the internal viscosity, while stages 2 (transition zone) and 3 (entanglement or reptation zone) are concerned with the larger scale conformational relaxation and the external viscosity. When the static electrical field is imposed on polymer having permanent dipoles along the chain, a simple analogy can be easily drawn with the stress-induced reorientation of conformers, as shown in Figure 1.4.2. When the segment having length a is unkinked through the reduction of its angle with the direction of the force from θ to 0, the work done is $Fa \cos \theta$; that is, the potential energy in the oriented state V is

19. Hoffman, J. D., *J. Chem. Phys.* **23**, 1331 (1955).
20. de Gennes (see note 17, above).

$$V = -Fa\cos\theta \tag{1.4.5}$$

The probability for finding the segment with angle θ is

$$P(\theta) = \exp\left[-\frac{V}{kT}\right] = \exp\left[\frac{Fa\cos\theta}{kT}\right] \tag{1.4.6}$$

The average of the projections of the segment in the direction of the force which we call x-axis is:

$$\langle a_x\rangle = \frac{\displaystyle\int_{-a}^{a} xP(\theta)dx}{\displaystyle\int_{0}^{a} P(\theta)dx} = \frac{\displaystyle\int_{0}^{\pi} a\cos\theta\, e^{(Fa\cos\theta)/kT}\,da\cos\theta}{\displaystyle\int_{0}^{\pi} e^{(Fa\cos\theta)/kT}\,da\cos\theta}$$

$$= \frac{\displaystyle\int_{0}^{\pi} a^2\cos\theta\, e^{(Fa\cos\theta)/kT}\sin\theta\,d\theta}{\displaystyle\int_{0}^{\pi} a\, e^{(Fa\cos\theta)/kT}\sin\theta\,d\theta}$$

$$= a\left[\coth\frac{Fa}{kT} - \frac{kT}{Fa}\right] = a\,\mathbf{L}\left[\frac{Fa}{kT}\right] \tag{1.4.7}$$

where $\mathbf{L}(x)$ denotes the Langevin function of x. Thus,

$$\frac{Fa}{kT} = \mathbf{L}^*\left[\frac{\langle a_x\rangle}{a}\right] = \frac{3\langle a_x\rangle}{a} + \frac{9}{5}\left(\frac{\langle a_x\rangle}{a}\right)^3$$

$$+ \frac{297}{175}\left(\frac{\langle a_x\rangle}{a}\right)^5 + \ldots \tag{1.4.8}$$

where $\mathbf{L}^*(x)$ is the inverse Langevin function of x.

The stress σ (dynes/cm^2) is the force per unit area, 1 cm^2 for 1 cm^3 of the conformer or the dipole, M_0/ρ, where M_0 is the molecular weight of the conformer and ρ the density (g/cm^3). The quantity $\langle a_x\rangle/a$ is the tensile strain ϵ. Thus, for very small strains, taking only the first term, we obtain:

$$\sigma = \frac{\rho RT}{3M_0}\, \varepsilon \tag{1.4.9}$$

which is the *equilibrium* equation of state at the very high temperature; it takes the form of rubberlike elasticity at small strains but predicts (quite correctly) the asymptotic increase in the modulus as the orientation is increased.[21] As the stress is increased, the stress-strain behavior will clearly take on the characteristics of nonlinear behavior, since the higher order terms in Equation 1.4.8 tend to increase the stress for a given strain. When shear stress is considered instead of the tensile stress, the factor 3 will be eliminated, since we are dealing with the "incompressible" case for which the Young's modulus is 3 times the shear modulus. We discuss the thermodynamics of the rubber elasticity in detail in Chapter 4, which deals with viscoelasticity of the dynamic molecules.

For the case of dielectric relaxation, the energy V due to the dipole orientation into the direction of the field E is $E\mu \cos \theta$, where μ is the dipole moment. Essentially, substitution of the internal field E_i for the force F above, and dipole moment μ for the segmental length a above, will yield the equation for the average moment $<m_x>$ resulting from the static field:

$$<m_x> = \frac{\mu^2 E_i}{3kT} \tag{1.4.10}$$

where $<m_x>$ is 0 when the field is zero, signifying the random state. This corresponds to the dielectric permittivity at very high frequencies, ε_∞. To change the conformation of segments from one equilibrium angle to another, the bond angle must go over the energy barrier.[22] The rate of conformational transition is expressed by the rate of the decreasing number n of species still remaining in the initial conformation:

---

21. Bueche, F., *Physical Properties of Polymers*, Wiley-Interscience, New York, 1962.

22. Alternative to this "site" model, a differential equation can be set up to account for the dissipation of energy as the viscous friction. When a sphere of radius r rotates in a liquid of internal friction ς, the frictional torque is $8\pi\varsigma r^3$, according to Stokes' law, and when proper numbers are assumed, the relaxation time of 3×10^{-11} second is obtained. (See Debye, P., *Polar Molecules*, Reinhold, New York, 1929, p 52.)

$$- \frac{dn}{dt} = \frac{n}{\lambda} \qquad (1.4.11)$$

where λ is the time constant or the reciprocal of the rate constant. After the voltage has been removed at $t = 0$, n will decrease from the initial value following the first-order equation as follows:

$$n(t) = n_0 \exp\left(- \frac{t}{\lambda} \right) \qquad (1.4.12)$$

where n_0 means the initial effective number of dipoles with the voltage on.

If the applied field energy is small compared to the barrier energy, then the rate of transition is essentially controlled by the dynamics of the segmental relaxation, as determined by the balance between the thermal agitation energy and the barrier height. When the voltage is suddenly decreased to zero after being maintained at a steady value for a long time, the decaying dipole orientation is described by the autocorrelation function:

$$\phi(t) = \frac{<m_x(t)\,m_x(0)>}{<m_x(0)\,m_x(0)>} = \exp\left(- \frac{t}{\lambda} \right) \qquad (1.4.13)$$

and

$$\lambda = \frac{h}{kT} \exp\left(\frac{\Delta\mu^*}{kT} \right) \qquad (1.4.14)$$

where $\Delta\mu^*$ is the barrier height, and h is Planck's constant. Equation 1.4.14 places the minimum value on λ at about 10^{-13} second for the limiting temperature of 500 °C. If $\Delta\mu^*$ of 3.5 kcal/mol of conformers is assumed, then the relaxation time of 10^{-11} second is obtained. These values have been observed in heptane.[23] Powles[24] arrives at λ of 10^{-11} second from the rotational relaxation of a nonpolymeric material for the critical temperature of 250 °C.

23. Abe and Flory (See note 1 in Chapter 2) for the activation energy, and Fröhlich, H., *Theory of Dielectrics,* Oxford University Press, London, 1958, for the relaxation time.
24. Powles, J. G., *The Relaxation of Molecular Orientation in Liquids,* Chemical Society Special Publication No. 20, The Chemical Society, London; Academic Press, 1966.

When the voltage V_0 is impressed on a parallel plate capacitor that includes a polymer as the dielectric, the charge Q will increase from the instantaneous initial value Q_i to the final value Q_f:

$$Q(t) = Q_i + (Q_f - Q_i)[1 - \phi(t)] \tag{1.4.15}$$

$$= \varepsilon_\infty C_0 V_0 - (\varepsilon_0 - \varepsilon_\infty)C_0 V_0\left[1 - \exp\left(-\frac{t}{\lambda}\right)\right]$$

where C_0 is the capacitance without the dielectric (the vacuum capacitance).

If, instead of applying the constant voltage, a sinusoidal voltage $V(t) = V_0\exp(j\omega t)$ is applied, then, by utilizing the convolution integral, we obtain:

$$Q(t) = \varepsilon_\infty C_0 V_0\exp(j\omega t)$$

$$+ (\varepsilon_0 - \varepsilon_\infty)C_0 \int_{-\infty}^{t} \frac{dV(x)}{dx}\left[1 - \exp\left(-\frac{t-x}{\lambda}\right)\right]dx$$

$$= \varepsilon_\infty C_0 V_0\exp(j\omega t)$$

$$+ j(\varepsilon_0 - \varepsilon_\infty)C_0\omega V_0 \int_{-\infty}^{t} \exp(j\omega x) - \exp\left[\left(j\omega + \frac{1}{\lambda}\right)x - \frac{t}{\lambda}\right]dx$$

$$= j\omega\,\varepsilon_0 C_0 V_0\exp(j\omega t) - \frac{j\omega}{j\omega + 1/\lambda}(\varepsilon_0 - \varepsilon_\infty)C_0 V_0\exp(j\omega t) \tag{1.4.16}$$

where the lower limit of integral was set at $-\infty$ to obtain the steady state value for $Q(t)$.

Since the current $I(t)$ is dQ/dt,

$$I(t) = j\omega\,C_0 V_0\exp(j\omega t)\left[\varepsilon_\infty + \frac{\varepsilon_0 - \varepsilon_\infty}{1 + \omega^2\lambda^2} - \frac{j\omega\lambda(\varepsilon_0 - \varepsilon_\infty)}{1 + \omega^2\lambda^2}\right] \tag{1.4.17}$$

Now, let

$$I(t) = j\omega\,\varepsilon^* C_0 V_0\exp(j\omega t) \tag{1.4.18}$$

and we obtain:

$$\varepsilon^* - \varepsilon_\infty = [\varepsilon_0 - \varepsilon_\infty]\left[\frac{1}{1 + \omega^2\lambda^2} - \frac{j\omega\lambda}{1 + \omega^2\lambda^2}\right] \tag{1.4.19}$$

For the conformational relaxation under stress, an expression similar to Equation 1.4.19 (except that the strain continues to increase indefinitely) is obtained for the dynamic compliance, since the charge Q is mathematically comparable to the strain ε, and the voltage V is comparable to the stress σ. The convolution integral to obtain the time-dependent stress from the relaxation modulus and the strain as an independent variable is preferred. This will lead to the dynamic mechanical modulus instead of the dynamic compliance.

1.4.3.2 Cooperativity in Stage 1 Relaxation

In the preceding section, the single relaxation time model was considered, and the resulting relaxation time of the order of teraseconds (10^{-12}) has been proposed. As we shall discuss in the next chapter, a concept of cooperative relaxation can explain how the basic mode with such a short relaxation time can become manifest in a slow and observable range of relaxation times. Cooperativity is required when there are interactive interferences among the neighboring conformers. In the condensed state, particularly at low temperatures, conformers will not be able to complete the rotational relaxation unless the neighboring conformers can rotate in a synchronized manner. If z conformers must relax together, the probability for the occurrence of such a simultaneous transition will be one zth power of the individual probability. Since the probability for the transition is $\exp(-\Delta\mu^*/kT)$, the apparent activation barrier for the *cooperative* relaxation time will be z times greater than the basic unhindered relaxation time, or $\Delta\mu^*z$.

As the temperature is decreased from the critical high temperature limit at which $z = 1$, the domain of cooperativity grows. When z gets to be 4 or 5, the glass transition occurs. As the size of the cooperative domain grows with the decreasing temperature, the temperature coefficient for the relaxation time will include not only the already large activation energy but also the term that is the derivative of z with respect to $1/T$, and the *apparent* activation energy can be found to exceed 100 kcal/mol! The continuously increasing temperature coefficient as the temperature is decreased, fits the Vogel-Fulcher equation, as shown in Chapter 2.

Another important aspect of cooperative relaxation is that the variation in domain size results in a broad distribution of relaxation times. As we shall see, the stretched exponential function can be obtained from assuming a certain distribution in domain size. In general, the greater the interference, the higher is T_g, and the broader the distribution of relaxation times. Ngai and coworkers[25] have proposed a universal scheme that establishes the relationship between the magnitude of the characteristic relaxation time to the spread of the distribution; their model works because, we believe, it takes advantage of the coupling of the fast unhindered mode to build the spectrum of slower modes in much the same way as our domain model is constructed.

1.4.3.3 External Viscosity: Stages 2 and 3

For translational relaxation, the correlation function $\phi(t)$ and the correlation time λ can be derived by the diffusion equation. The frictional coefficient ς, or the force over the velocity at steady state, is a molecular equivalent of the viscosity η and it is proportional to the length of the molecule, i.e.,

$$\varsigma = \frac{\varsigma_0 M}{M_0} \tag{1.4.20}$$

where the subscript 0 refers to one conformer, and M is the molecular weight of the polymer. ς_0 is the force required to move a conformer over a unit distance in a second. The effective local viscosity η_{eff} can be obtained based on Stokes' law for an isolated sphere of radius r :

$$\varsigma_0 = 6\pi\eta_{\text{eff}} r \tag{1.4.21}$$

For a typical polymer at ca., 100 °C above T_g, η_{eff} of 0.1 poise and λ of 10^{-12} seconds are obtained by assuming the reasonable values for Equations 1.4.20 and 1.4.21, as discussed in Chapter 2. Again, a polymer chain will exhibit a wide range of modes of relaxation depending on the number of segments that are involved in the diffusional relaxation. If we assume that there are equal numbers of conformers for the various modes, as we have done for the case of cooperative conformational relaxation, then the relaxation modulus

25. Ngai, K. L., Rendell, R. W., Rajagopal, A. K., and Teiler, S., *Ann. N.Y. Acad. Sci.* **484**, 150 (1986). Also, Ngai, K. L., and Plazek, D. J., *Macromolecules,* **213**, 4282 (1990).

that fits the power law with the exponent of $-\frac{1}{2}$ will be obtained. This is shown in Chapter 4.

1.5 Approximate Relations Among Linear Viscoelastic Functions

In the preceding sections, the spectrum of relaxation times was expressed by a discrete number of Dirac deltas (G_{0i}, λ_i). Experience has shown that it is best to space these deltas with equal intervals along the logarithmic time axis, i.e., $\Delta \ln \lambda$ = constant. The strength of each delta depends on the choice for the $\Delta \ln \lambda$ interval; hence the resolution is maximized by its proper choice. Some investigators prefer a continuous rather than a discrete spectrum. The continuous spectrum $H(\ln \lambda)$ is, at least in theory, unique. The relationship between the two is obvious:

$$\int_{\ln t}^{\ln t'} H(\ln \lambda) \, d\ln \lambda = \sum_{i}^{i'} G_{oi} \tag{1.5.1}$$

for any interval between $\ln t$ and $\ln t'$, where i and i' are such that $\ln t = \ln \lambda_i$ and $\ln t' = \ln \lambda_{i'}$. The relationship between the relaxation spectrum $H(\ln \lambda)$ and the relaxation modulus $G(t)$ is also self-evident:

$$G(t) = \int_{-\infty}^{+\infty} H(\ln \lambda) \exp\left(-\frac{t}{\lambda}\right) d\ln \lambda = \sum_{i} G_{0i} \exp\left(-\frac{t}{\lambda_i}\right) \tag{1.5.2}$$

The following is a list of *some* of the approximate relations among the linear viscoelastic functions, such as the dynamic and relaxation modulus and the spectrum,

$$H(\ln \lambda) \approx -\frac{dG(t)}{d\ln t} \tag{1.5.3}$$

From Equation 1.5.3, it can be shown that if the log-log plot of $G(t)$ is a straight line with the slope of $-n$, the spectrum is also a straight line with the same slope. Since the dynamic elastic modulus is a mirror image of $G(t)$, we can write

$$H(-\ln \lambda) \approx \frac{2}{\pi} \frac{dG'(\omega)}{d\ln \omega} \tag{1.5.4}$$

which means that a power law distribution will result in the power law plot for $\log G'$ vs. $\log \omega$, and

$$G(t) \approx G' \left(\omega = \frac{1}{t} \right) \tag{1.5.5}$$

where G' is the elastic (in-phase) dynamic modulus. These two approximations are not good for a narrow distribution of relaxation times. For a monodispersed polymer melt, the approximation breaks down at the terminal zone where the time-frequency range is comparable to the maximum relaxation time. In such a case, however, the slope can be easily obtained by assuming a single λ. The slope of $\ln G'(\omega)$ vs. $\ln \omega$ is obviously 2 when $\omega \ll \lambda^{-1}$.

The spectrum is approximated by the loss modulus G'' curve by substituting the relaxation time by reciprocal circular frequency.

$$H(-\ln\lambda) \approx \frac{2}{\pi} G''(\ln\omega) \tag{1.5.6}$$

Thus, from the plot of the loss modulus, one can obtain an estimate for the distribution of relaxation times. Also,

$$G^* = G' + jG'' = \frac{1}{J^*} = \frac{1}{J' - jJ''} \tag{1.5.7}$$

where the asterisk denotes a *complex* variable, and J denotes the compliance in shear. From this equation, one can obtain:

$$\int_0^t G(t-x)\dot{J}(x)dx = 1 \tag{1.3.9}$$

through a convolution integral, as we have discussed in Section 1.3, or

$$\int_0^t G(t-x)J(x)dx = t \tag{1.3.9a}$$

The tangential modulus $d\sigma/d\gamma$ under the constant rate of strain $\dot{\gamma}$ is

$$\left(\frac{d\sigma}{d\gamma} \right)_{\dot{\gamma}} = \sum_i G_i \exp\left(-\frac{t}{\lambda_i} \right) = G(t) \tag{1.5.8}$$

and similarly, the tangential compliance $d\gamma/d\sigma$ under the constant rate of stress $\dot{\sigma}$ is

$$\left(\frac{d\gamma}{d\sigma}\right)_{\dot{\sigma}} = J(t) \tag{1.5.9}$$

where $J(t)$ is the creep compliance. The time constant for the creep process is called the retardation time. For a single relaxation mechanism, the retardation time is slightly longer than the relaxation time, as shown in Section 1.3. However, with multiple relaxation mechanisms, the "dominant" relaxation or retardation time is strongly influenced by the shape of the distribution of relaxation or retardation times. For example, in the wedge-shaped transition zone, the relaxation spectrum is a wedge with its peak at the shortest time, whereas the retardation spectrum is a wedge with its peak at the longest time. The loss peak for the retardation spectrum, such as the dielectric loss, can occur at a substantially lower frequency than for the relaxation spectrum, such as the loss modulus. This is discussed in Section 4.3 for the relaxation without entanglement, and again in Section 6.3 for the polymer solutions.

The linear viscoelastic steady state viscosity is obtained by

$$\eta = \frac{\sigma(\infty)}{\dot{\gamma}} = \frac{1}{\dot{\gamma}} \int_0^\infty G(t) \dot{\gamma} \, dt = \int_0^\infty G(t) \, dt \tag{1.5.10}$$

Often a stress relaxation test is conducted following a constant strain rate $\dot{\gamma}$ to reach the strain γ, but well before reaching the steady state. In such a case, the apparent relaxation modulus $G_a(t)$ is smaller than the true relaxation modulus $G(t)$ for the instantaneously raised strain:

$$G_a(t) \approx G\left(t + \frac{\gamma}{2\dot{\gamma}}\right) \tag{1.5.11}$$

On the other hand, if the test is conducted after reaching the steady state,

25. Furukawa, T., and Matsumoto, K., to be published.

$$G_a(t) = \frac{\dot{\gamma}}{\gamma} \int_t^\infty G(t)\, dt \qquad\qquad (1.5.12)$$

1.6   The Yield Phenomenon

Although we have pointed out that many solid materials behave as elastic solids, this is true only for small deformations. Actually, there is a strain limit beyond which most materials either fracture or, in case of copper or other soft metals, undergo a continuing plastic deformation called the yield process. The criterion for yield to occur is the elastic (free) energy that an imperfect crystalline plane cannot endure. The stress-strain diagram involving yield phenomena, or plastic deformation, is shown in Figure 1.6.1. While plastic deformation continues, the recoverable strain energy remains in the deforming material, and upon the release of the external force, the elastic portion of the strain energy is recovered. When the critical strain energy level is reached in polycrystalline materials, the dislocations begin to migrate. According to McClintock and Argon,[26] the yield phenomenon is possible only if imperfections exist, and in perfect single crystals there is no conceivable mechanism for initiating and sustaining a yield phenomenon. The yield phenomenon is accompanied by slipping or twinning, which can occur most easily in the plane of the maximum shear stress. Even when a sample is pulled in tension, the yield occurs in the plane 45° from the direction of the pull. At the point at which the yield was initiated, the strain energy had reached the level at which the crystal plane could slip, which means that this energy for the shear yielding was *less* than the energy required for other possible ways of releasing energy, such as a fracture. As we will discuss later, a viscoelastic material can undergo a yield process if it is deformed sufficiently quickly and extensively.

The criterion for the yield can be set by the total shear energy. This is a form of energy that causes a shape change. The stress components for shape change are called *deviatoric*, as opposed to the *normal* stress

26. McClintock, F. A., and Argon, A. S., *Mechanical Behavior of Materials*, Addison-Wesley, Reading, MA, 1966.

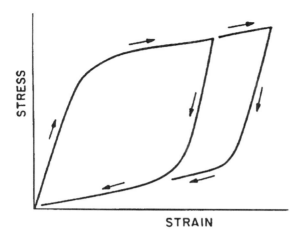

Figure 1.6.1   Stress-strain curves for the elastic behavior
followed by plastic behavior (Note 26).

components, which are for volume change. The sum of all deviatoric stresses
at one point is equal to the sum of the differences in the three orthogonal
principal stresses, σ_1, σ_2, σ_3. The critical total yield stress $\sigma*$ is given by the
equation:

$$\sigma* = \left\{ \tfrac{1}{2}[(\sigma_2 - \sigma_3)^2 + (\sigma_3 - \sigma_1)^2 + (\sigma_1 - \sigma_2)^2] \right\}^{1/2} \qquad (1.6.1)$$

Equation 1.6.1, which is credited to several authors, is often referred to as
the von Mises relation. Instead of the three orthogonal planes on which only
the principal stresses exist, we now take a genral case where the three planes
are in the x, y, and z directions. Equation 1.6.1 will now take on the form:

$$\sigma* = \left\{ \tfrac{1}{2}[(\sigma_y - \sigma_z)^2 + (\sigma_z - \sigma_x)^2 + (\sigma_x - \sigma_y)^2] + 3\sigma_{yz}^2 + 3\sigma_{zx}^2 + 3\sigma_{xy}^2 \right\}^{1/2} \quad (1.6.1')$$

and this $\sigma*$ is equal to $\sigma*$ in Equation 1.6.1, because either of them is really
the measure of the critical strain energy (a scalar quantity) at which the
plastic deformation starts. It can be shown from Equation 1.6.1´ that, when
there is only one shear stress component σ_{yz}, and all other σ_{ii}, σ_{ij} are 0, we
obtain the critical shear stress $\sigma_{yz}*$:

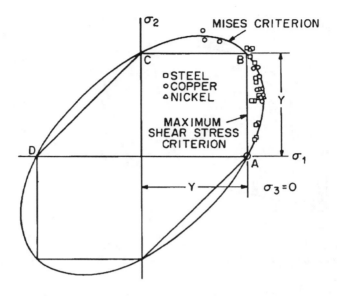

Figure 1.6.2   The von Mises criterion (constant deviatoric strain energy) versus the maximum shear stress criterion: for these metals, the former proves to be the better theory.

$$\sigma_{yz}{}^* = \frac{\sigma^*}{\sqrt{3}} \qquad (1.6.2)$$

For two-dimensional cases, such as in twisting a thin-walled cylinder, the von Mises stress is plotted as an ellipse in the 1-2 plane as shown in Figure 1.6.2. If a material is anisotropic, this ellipse will elongate in the direction of the increased strength, as shown in Figure 4.5.2 in Chapter 4 for the molten polymers.

As mentioned briefly above, the yield phenomenon can be observed in viscoelastic materials as well. When a viscoelastic material is deformed at a constant rate, the stress will eventually reach the terminal level that is equal to $G\dot{\gamma}\lambda$. In theory, then, when the strain rate $\dot{\gamma}$ is increased without limit, the terminal stress will become higher without limit, too. Eventually, however, the stress will reach the critical level at which some sort of structural breakdown takes place. For polymer solids, the intermolecular cooperative domain may break down, while for polymer melts the molecular entanglement may be forced to be broken. The maximum relaxation time for the polyisobutylene having a molecular weight of 10^6 is several hours at room temperature, but a sample of this polymer can be deformed at a rate of several strain units per second to induce the yield process at a strain of the order of 1. However, all polymer melts including this polyisobutylene exhibit linear viscoelastic behavior even at strain rates that far exceed the value of λ^{-1}, such as in the dynamic mechanical test to measure $G^*(\omega)$, as long as the stress amplitude is kept small so that the critical level of strain energy for the yield is never reached. The relaxation time of glassy polymers may be several hours to days or even longer, but they too can be brought to yield at strain rates which are too fast to allow them to relax. The limiting strain is several percent for the glassy polymers, rather than several hundred percent for the melt. However, even the glassy polymers exhibit linear viscoelastic behavior when the stress is substantially below the yield stress. Dynamic mechanical data and stress relaxation data support such notions. An example of linear viscoelastic data for the glassy polycarbonate is shown in Figure 1.6.3. The stress-strain-time superposition mentioned in Section 1.3 holds here, suggesting linear viscoelasticity. The slight deviation from linear viscoelasticity becomes more pronounced as the magnitude of stress is increased. As we shall discuss, this nonlinear behavior is primarily due to the combined effects of the distribution of multiple relaxation times and the plasticity in the limiting elastic strain energy state. The yield processes in metals have been identified with very specific molecular mechanisms, but no comparable clear molecular mechanisms have been demonstrated for polymers. The notion of defects in amorphous polymers is unclear, although such a concept has been invoked to explain the KWW equation for relaxation in the glassy state.

Even so, it is entirely reasonable to assume that there exists some strain energy limit similar to the von Mises elastic energy limit as the threshold of an intermolecular structural breakdown. A viscoelastic material will not reach this stress limit as long as the strain rate $\dot{\gamma}$ does not exceed the critical value

$$\dot{\gamma}^* = \frac{\sigma^*}{G\lambda} \tag{1.6.3}$$

because for $\dot{\gamma} < \dot{\gamma}^*$, the maximum stress attained will be the viscoelastic steady-state stress σ_{ss}, i.e.,

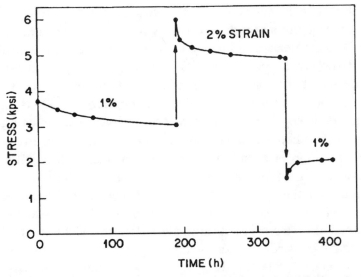

Figure 1.6.3   Results of a series of stress relaxation conducted on polycarbonate at 25 °C.

$$\sigma_{ss} = G\lambda\dot{\gamma} \qquad \text{for } \dot{\gamma} < \frac{\sigma^*}{G\lambda} \ (=\dot{\gamma}^*) \qquad (1.6.4a)$$

$$\sigma_{ss} = \sigma^* \text{ for } \dot{\gamma} > \frac{\sigma^*}{G\lambda} \qquad (1.6.4b)$$

Thus linear viscoelasticity prevails as long as σ^* is not reached. The stress reaches σ^* when $\dot{\gamma}$ exceeds the critical value $\dot{\gamma}^*$, which depends on the relaxation time λ. The molecular aspect of $\dot{\gamma}^*$ is really set by the microscopic elastic strain which reaches the limit $\gamma_e^* = \sigma^*/G$, which is yield strain. Thus $\gamma_e \equiv \dot{\gamma}^*/\lambda$. The condition set forth by Equations 1.6.4 a and b, which we call viscoplasticity, can be approximated by a single equation:

$$\sigma_{ss} = G\lambda\dot{\gamma}\left[1 - \exp\left(-\frac{\sigma^*}{G\lambda\dot{\gamma}}\right)\right] = \dot{\gamma}\int_0^{\sigma^*/G\dot{\gamma}} G\exp\left(-\frac{t}{\lambda}\right)dt \quad (1.6.5)$$

Real polymers exhibit multiple relaxation times, but if we assume that the yield strain is the same for all sizes of deforming domains, i.e., γ_e^* is the same for all modes of relaxation, then we have

$$\sigma_{ss} = \dot{\gamma}\sum_i G_i\lambda_i \left[1 - \exp\left(\frac{\gamma_e{}^*}{\lambda_i\dot{\gamma}}\right)\right] = \dot{\gamma}\int_0^{\gamma_e{}^*/\dot{\gamma}} G(t)\,dt \qquad (1.6.6)$$

Thus the nonlinear steady-state viscoplastic stress, $\sigma_{ss} = \sigma(t\to\infty)$ can be predicted from the *linear* viscoelastic spectrum. The experimentally observed yield stress σ_{ss} depends on the strain rate $\dot{\gamma}$ only because of the multiple relaxation times. For a single relaxation time, the yield stress is σ^* and does not depend on $\dot{\gamma}$.

After the yield stress has been reached and the macroscopic strain has exceeded the microscopic yield strain limit $\gamma_e{}^* = \sigma^*/G$, the initial structure is broken down and the material is now being deformed with the rate $\dot{\gamma}$. For ideal plasticity, the plastic stress is always σ^* regardless of the strain rate imposed. This can be visualized by a rod of a soft metal that can be twisted at any speed and still register the same torque. There is no "relaxation time," but the concept of an apparent relaxation time λ_a is introduced in the context of viscoelasticity, i.e.,

$$\lambda_a = \frac{\sigma_d{}^*}{G\dot{\gamma}} = \frac{\gamma_e{}^*}{\dot{\gamma}} \qquad (1.6.7)$$

Notably, λ_a is a function of $\dot{\gamma}$, which is an *experimental* variable. Here, the stress $\sigma_d{}^*$ might be called a dynamic yield stress, which may be less than the (static) structural yield stress that was discussed, since the dynamic friction coefficient is smaller than the static friction coefficient. For glassy polymers, $\gamma_e{}^*$ is in the order of 10^{-1}, as will be discussed in Chapter 3. An otherwise rigid polymer can behave as though rubbery (a short apparent relaxation time) when undergoing the yield process. For polymer melts, $\gamma_e{}^*$ is in the order of 1, as also discussed in another chapter. If $\gamma_e{}^*=1$, then from Equation 1.6.6 we obtain

$$\sigma_{ss} = \dot{\gamma}\int_0^{1/\dot{\gamma}} G(t)\,dt \qquad (1.6.8)$$

This equation is known as Gleisle's empirical rule,[27] from which the nonlinear viscoelastic steady flow stress can be predicted solely from the linear viscoelastic data.

A corollary to Gleisle's rule is the well-known Cox-Merz law.[28] Since

$$1 - \exp\left(-\frac{1}{\dot{\gamma}\lambda}\right) \approx \frac{1}{\left[1 + (\dot{\gamma}\lambda)^2\right]^{1/2}} \tag{1.6.9}$$

we can write

$$\sigma_{ss} = \dot{\gamma}\sum_{i}^{n}\frac{G\lambda_i}{\left[1 + (\dot{\gamma}\lambda_i)^2\right]^{1/2}} \tag{1.6.10}$$

the summation being the magnitude of the complex dynamic viscosity, and

$$\sigma_{ss} = \dot{\gamma}\,|\,\eta^*(\omega = \dot{\gamma})\,| \tag{1.6.11}$$

i.e., the nonlinear steady flow viscosity $\eta_{ss}(\dot{\gamma})$ is equal to the magnitude of the linear dynamic viscosity with the circular frequency set as the strain rate:

$$\eta_{ss}(\dot{\gamma}) = |\,\eta^*(\omega = \dot{\gamma})\,| \tag{1.6.12}$$

This equation is the Cox-Merz formula.

Now, instead of waiting to reach the steady state, we stop the deformation at some arbitrary strain γ_1 after time $t_1 = \gamma_1/\dot{\gamma}$ seconds. For the single relaxation model, the stress at this point is:

$$\sigma(t_1) = G\lambda\dot{\gamma}\left[1 - \exp\left(-\frac{t_1}{\lambda}\right)\right] \quad \text{for } \dot{\gamma} < \frac{\sigma^*}{G\lambda} \tag{1.6.13a}$$

$$\sigma(t_1) = \sigma^*\left[1 - \exp\left(-\frac{t_1}{\lambda}\right)\right] \quad \text{for } \dot{\gamma} > \frac{\sigma^*}{G\lambda} \tag{1.6.13b}$$

---

27. Gleisle, W. G., in *"Rheology,"* Vol. 2, Astarita, Marrucci, and Nicolais, Eds., Plenum, New York, 1980.
28. Cox, W. P., and Merz, E. H., *J. Polym. Sci.,* **28**, 619 (1958).

$$\sigma(t_1) = \int_0^{\gamma_1/\dot\gamma} G(t)\,dt \qquad (1.6.14)$$

and as we reasoned before, Equation 1.6.14 is true even for the multiple relaxation spectrum.

Often, a relaxation modulus is approximated by the power law:

$$G(t) = G_0 \left(\frac{t}{t_0}\right)^{-n} \qquad \text{for } t > t_0 \qquad (1.6.15)$$

$$G(t) = G_0 \qquad \text{for } t < t_0$$

From Equation 1.6.14, we obtain:

$$\sigma(\gamma_1) = G_0\gamma_1(\dot\gamma t_0)^n \gamma_1^n \qquad \text{if } t_1 > t_0 \qquad (1.6.16)$$

$$\sigma(\gamma_1) = G_0\gamma_1 \qquad \text{if } t_1 < t_0$$

From the above, we obtain for the secant modulus σ/γ at constant $\dot\gamma$:

$$\frac{\sigma}{\gamma} = G_0\gamma^n(\dot\gamma t_0)^n \qquad (1.6.17)$$

The logarithm of the secant modulus is predicted to be proportional to log γ with the slope of $-n$, when the relaxation modulus follows the power law, with the exponent $-n$. This behavior is observed in crystalline polymers, as shown below (Figure 5.3.6, Chapter 5).

2

Intermolecular Cooperativity

In the condensed state, polymer segments cannot relax without the cooperation of their intermolecular neighbors. The necessity for such cooperativity causes a large drop in entropy as the temperature is lowered. The glass transition occurs well above 0 K, and the size of a conformer affects the glass transition temperature. A new equation for the stretched exponential function is introduced based on the size distributions of cooperative domains.

2.1 A Molecular Model for Intermolecular Cooperativity[1]

When a force is applied over a polymer chain through the surrounding media, the molecular segments respond by readjusting themselves to relieve the stress. The momentarily raised free energy dissipates by a small amount every time a segment reorients to a new lower free energy state. The "stress" referred to here can also be in the form of an electrical potential acting on a polar segment. In polar polymers, the segmental dipoles react to the sudden imposition of an electric field by reorienting from the original random and isotropic orientational state to an orientation in the direction of the field. The new orientation cannot be achieved at once, however, because the rate at which the molecules can reorient is limited by their ability to undergo configurational changes.

The angular dependence of the potential energy for rotating the carbon-carbon bonds in butane has been investigated by Abe and Flory.[2] This is shown in Figure 2.1.1. The energy difference between the *gauche* and *trans* states is ca. 500 calories per mole, and the activation energy is ca. 3100 to 3500 calories per mole of bond. The relaxation time for the rotational

---

1. Matsuoka, S. and Quan, X., *Macromolecules,* **24**, 2770 (1991).
2. In *Macromolecules*, F. A. Bovey and F. H. Winslow, Eds., Academic Press, New York, 1979, p 247.

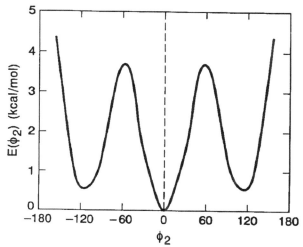

Figure 2.1.1   The energy of the angle of rotation in the inner carbon-carbon link in the butane molecule.

motion of the C-C bond between two methylene units is about 10^{-10} second at room temperature. In polymers the molecular segments undergo more complex motions involving triads as suggested by Helfand et al.[3] but the basic barrier is that of the C-C rotation. The barrier energy weakly increases with the size of the segments, as discussed below.

The smallest segmental unit of rotation (which we will call a conformer) is surrounded by other conformers in a solid or molten state. For a conformer to complete a rotational relaxation, its neighbors must also move *in cooperation.* The barrier for this process is intermolecular in nature. Under such restrictions a conformer can change its conformational state only if its close neighbors *cooperate* with it as if they were in a group of meshed gears. This is illustrated in Figure 2.1.1. A model incorporating meshed gears has been suggested by Adachi,[4] although his analysis is quite different from ours.

The effective domain size increases with the overall density. If

3. Helfand, E., Wasserman, Z. R., and Weber, T. A., *J. Chem. Phys.* **70**, 2016 (1979).

4. Adachi, K., *Macromolecules,* **23**, 1816 (1990).

equilibrium can be achieved at a low temperature limit we call T_0, every conformer becomes meshed with all others, the entire body of the polymer becomes one huge meshed domain, and the number of conformers per domain is infinite. This is the state of zero conformational entropy at temperature $T_0 \gg 0$ K. At the high temperature limit we call T^*, on the other hand, the conformers are sufficiently far apart that each can relax independently from the neighbors, and only the intramolecular barrier must be overcome. The number of conformers in each domain is 1. Between these two extreme temperatures, the size of a domain is specified by the number z of conformers in the domain. In the example in Figure 2.1.2, z is shown to be 6. For illustration purposes only, we first assume that each conformer can take three different conformations. At the high temperature limit T^*, where no cooperativity is at work among the conformers, six independent conformers are able to exhibit $W_z = 3^6$ conformational states. In the state illustrated, where six conformers are meshed together, however, for one conformer to change its conformation, all others must change also. Thus it makes no difference which conformer the observer disturbs, the result is always that every conformer in the domain of cooperativity must change its conformation. Thus a domain can take only the same number of states that one conformer can take, i.e., $W_z = 3$. We now generalize our example by calling the number of states a conformer can take c_1 instead of 3. Since the conformational probability depends on the populations of *gauche* and *trans* conformations, the value of c_1 is temperature dependent. c_1 is also species dependent, since some bond angles are prohibited in certain polymer chains. For 1 mole (of conformers) in which there are N_z domains consisting of z conformers, the conformational entropy S_c for 1 mole of conformers is

$$S_c = N_z k \ln c_1 \qquad (2.1.1)$$

where k is the Boltzmann constant. Because $z = N_A/N_z$, where N_A is Avogadro's number,

$$z = \frac{N_A k \ln c_1}{N_z k \ln c_1} = \frac{N_A k \ln c_1}{S_c} \qquad (2.1.2)$$

Thus the domain size z is inversely proportional to the conformational entropy. We now define s^* as the conformational entropy of one mole of conformers in chains that are not mutually restricted by each other, i.e., where each conformer relaxes independently:

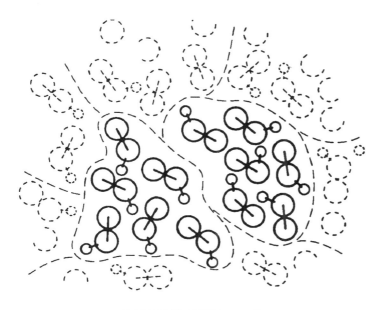

DOMAINS WITH $z = 6$

Figure 2.1.2   Model for intermolecular cooperativity wherein molecular segments in a domain can only relax together.

$$s^* = N_A k \ln c_1 \qquad (2.1.3)$$

Here s^* is the conformational entropy corresponding to that calculated by rotational isomeric state theory, and it, too, is temperature dependent. Thus, we obtain:

$$z = \frac{s^*}{S_c} \qquad (2.1.4)$$

At T^*, S_c and s^* are equal. Below T^*, as the temperature is decreased, the conformational entropy S_c (and enthalpy) will drop more rapidly than does s^* and will reach 0 at T_0, while s^* depends on the equilibrium concentration of various conformations and will reach 0 at 0 K. The comparison between the corresponding enthalpies is illustrated schematically in Figure 2.1.3. Curve A denotes the excess enthalpy h^* without meshing of the conformers, and it is approximately proportional to the concentration of higher energy configurations calculated from rotational isomeric statistics. According to the rotational isomeric model, the zero entropy temperature is 0 K. Curve B represents the conformational enthalpy H_c that incorporates the meshing or

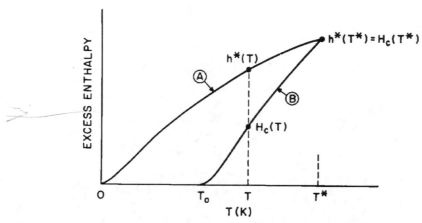

Figure 2.1.3   Excess enthalpy $h^*(T)$ without intermolecular cooperativity (curve A) and $H_c(T)$ with cooperativity (curve B). Curve A is obtained from the concentration of the high energy conformation(s) through calculation of the rotational isomeric states.

cooperativity concept, which raises the zero entropy temperature from 0 K to T_0. If we assume that curves A and B have the similar shape differing only in the temperature scale, curve B can be obtained by compressing curve A through a change in the temperature scale from $[0{\to}T^*]$ to $[T_0{\to}T^*]$, or $H_c = h^*[T^*(T - T_0)/(T^* - T_0)]$, and if we assume:

$$\left[\frac{\Delta c_p{}^*}{\Delta C_p}\right]_T \approx \frac{T^* - T_0}{T^*}$$

where $\Delta c_p{}^* = (\partial h^*/\partial T)_p$, we obtain the relationship:

$$\frac{H_c(T)/H_c(T^*)}{h^*(T)/h^*(T^*)} \approx \frac{(T - T_0)/(T^* - T_0)}{T/T^*} \tag{2.1.5}$$

and since

$$\frac{H_c}{h^*} \approx \frac{T\,S_c}{T\,s^*} \tag{2.1.6}$$

we obtain

$$\frac{S_c}{s^*} = \frac{T^*}{T^* - T_0}\frac{T - T_0}{T} = \frac{\Delta C_p}{\Delta c_p{}^*}\frac{(T - T_0)}{T} \tag{2.1.7}$$

The probability that z meshed conformers in a domain will relax *simultaneously* is the $1/z$-th power of the probability that one will relax, and the apparent activation energy must be z times the *intra*molecular activation energy for one conformer to relax. We define this energy barrier for one bond to relax as $\Delta\mu$, which is the free energy barrier shown in Figure 2.1.1. The relaxation time λ at T is related to the relaxation time λ^* at T^* by the formula:

$$\ln\frac{\lambda}{\lambda^*} = \frac{\Delta\mu}{k}\left(\frac{z}{T} - \frac{1}{T^*}\right) \tag{2.1.8}$$

but, from Equation 2.1.4,

$$\ln\frac{\lambda}{\lambda^*} = \frac{\Delta\mu}{k}\left(\frac{s^*}{TS_c} - \frac{1}{T^*}\right) \tag{2.1.9}$$

This equation is identical in form with the Adam-Gibbs equation,[5] although our S_c is largely intermolecular in nature and therefore is not limited to polymers. In fact we have shown that the dielectric relaxation of glucose is very similar in crucial aspects to that of polymers such as polyvinyl acetate. Kovacs has shown that thermodynamic recovery in glucose is similar to that of polyvinyl acetate.

Substituting Equation 2.1.7 into Equation 2.1.9, we obtain:

$$\ln\frac{\lambda}{\lambda^*} = \frac{\Delta\mu}{k}\frac{T^*-T_0}{T^*}\frac{1}{T-T_0} - \frac{\Delta\mu}{kT^*} \tag{2.1.10}$$

which is the Vogel-Fulcher equation,[6]

$$\ln\frac{\lambda}{\lambda^*} = \frac{\Delta\mu^*}{k}\frac{1}{T-T_0} - \frac{\Delta\mu^*}{k}\frac{1}{T^*-T_0} \tag{2.1.11}$$

where $\Delta\mu^* = \Delta\mu[(T^*-T_0)/T^*]$. In the equilibrium state, Equation 2.1.11 is completely equivalent to the Williams-Landel-Ferry (WLF) equation[7]:

---

5. Adam, G., and Gibbs, J. H., *J. Chem. Phys.* **43**, 139 (1965).
6. Fulcher, G. A., *J. Am. Ceram. Soc.* **8**, 339 (1925).
7. Williams, M. L., Landel, R. F., and Ferry, J. D., *J. Am. Chem. Soc.* **77**, 3701 (1955).

$$\log \frac{\lambda}{\lambda_{\text{ref}}} = - \frac{c_1(T - T_{\text{ref}})}{c_2 + T - T_{\text{ref}}} \tag{2.1.12}$$

where c_1 and c_2 are constants that depend on the choice of T_{ref}, and to the free volume equation by Doolittle[8]:

$$\ln \frac{\lambda}{\lambda_{\text{ref}}} = \frac{1}{\alpha_f(T - T_0)} - \frac{1}{\alpha_f(T_{\text{ref}} - T_0)} \tag{2.1.13}$$

However, an important difference exists between the Adam-Gibbs equation and the free volume equation. In the *non*equilibrium glassy state, the former correctly predicts the temperature dependence of the relaxation time , while the latter predicts temperature independence.[9]

Comparing Equations 2.1.11 and 2.1.13, it is immediately clear that $\Delta\mu^*/k$ should be numerically equal to $1/\alpha_f$, where α_f is the expansion coefficient of the Doolittle free volume fraction $f = V_f/V$; here V_f is the free volume $V - V_0$, and V_0 is the "occupied" volume, which is obtained by extrapolating the equilibrium liquidus line to T_0. The values of α_f are found experimentally to be nearly the same for many polymers, about 6×10^{-4} K^{-1}. This implies that $\Delta\mu^*$ should exhibit a "universal" value of about 3.3 kcal per mole of *conformer*. The experimental values of $\Delta\mu^*$ shown in Table 2.1 were calculated from the shift of viscoelastic relaxation spectra with temperature in the equilibrium state, most showing values close to 3 or 4 kcal. In fact $\Delta\mu^*$ is approximately equal to the *intra*molecular activation energy for the C–C bond rotation in butane. (For polymers with heteroatom backbones such as siloxanes and ethers below the dividing line in Table 2.1, $\Delta\mu^*$ is smaller, as are the bond rotation activation energies.) This implies that $\Delta\mu^*$ does not depend on the polymer species. However, $\Delta\mu$ varies with the chemical structure and, as will be shown, the relationship between $\Delta\mu$ of a given polymer and the universal value $\Delta\mu^*$ is described by the equation:

8. Doolittle, A. K., *J. Appl. Phys.* **22**, 1471 (1951).

9. Angell, C. A., and Sichina, W., *Annals N.Y. Acad. Sci.* **53** (1976); Hodge, I. M., *Macromolecules*, **16**, 898 (1983); Matsuoka, S., Fredrickson, G. H., and Johnson, G. E., *in Lecture Notes in Physics*, No. 277, *Molecular Dynamics and Relaxation Phenomena in Glasses*, T. Dorfmuller and G. Williams, Eds., Springer-Verlag, Berlin, 1987, p.187.

Table 2.1. Vogel-Fulcher Energy

Polymer	$\Delta\mu^*$ (kcal/mol)
Polyisobutylene	4.2
Polycarbonate	3.6
Polyvinyl acetate	3.4
Polystyrene	3.2
Poly-(α)-methyl styrene	3.1
Polymethyl acrylate	3.8
Polymethyl methacrylate	11.7
Hevea rubber	4.2
Poly-1,4-butadiene	3.1
Poly-1,2-butadiene	3.0
Styrene-butadiene copolymer	8.3
Polydimethyl siloxane	2.1
Polyoxymethylene	1.8
Polypropylene oxide	1.8

$$\Delta\mu = \Delta\mu^* \frac{T^*}{T^* - T_0} \tag{2.1.14}$$

Thus, the activation energy for the *intra*molecular relaxation of *one* C-C bond is greater with conformers that exhibit a higher T_0 and thus a higher T_g. As we shall discuss below, the differences in the packing densities among polymers of different conformer sizes affect the excess cohesive energy per mole of conformer.

It can be shown from thermodynamics that the specific heat related to the conformational entropy with cooperativity is

$$\Delta C_p = T\frac{dS_c}{dT} = T\left(\frac{\partial S_c}{\partial V}\right)_p \left(\frac{\partial V}{\partial T}\right)_p \tag{2.1.15}$$

where $\Delta C_p = C_{p,\text{liquid}} - C_{p,\text{glass}}$, hence,

$$T\left(\frac{\partial S_c}{\partial V}\right)_p = \frac{1}{V}\frac{\Delta C_p}{\Delta\alpha} \tag{2.1.16}$$

where the thermal expansion coefficient $\Delta\alpha = \alpha_{\text{liquid}} - \alpha_{\text{glass}}$. (Unless otherwise stated, all extensive quantities are per mole of conformers.) For convenience, we shall take T_g to be the temperature at which the characteristic relaxation time has a chosen value λ_g, even though we are aware that the glass transition temperature is not a thermodynamic temperature. The value of the relaxation time at $G(\lambda) = G_0/e$ for polysiobutylene is about 6 minutes at - 76 °C, according to Figure 1.4.1. The value of λ_g turns out to be one to ten minutes for $T_g = T_0 + 50$ °C, as will be discussed. This is similar to defining T_g to be the equilibrium temperature at which the shear viscosity has an arbitrary value (e.g., 10^{13} poise).

Now let us increase the volume at T_g from V_0 to V_g. The total increase in the enthalpy E_h is $T_g S_{cg}$ and

$$E_h = T_g S_{cg} = \frac{\Delta V_g}{V_g} \left(\frac{\Delta C_p}{\Delta \alpha} \right)_{T_g} \tag{2.1.17}$$

The E_h above has been designated as the "hole energy" by Kanig,[10] since it is the energy required to create the free volume fraction $f_g = \Delta V_g / V_g$ at T_g. The value of E_h (in calories per mole of repeat units) calculated from the experimental data for over 70 polymers shows, in Figure 2.1.4, a clear tendency to be greater for polymers with a higher T_g.[11]

Equation 2.1.17 should be, according to our model, on the basis of a mole of conformer. The hole energy E_h per mole of conformer is the cohesive energy per mole. However, this relationship should also hold between E_h per gram and ΔC_p per gram, since the volume ratio and the thermal expansion coefficients do not depend on the chosen amount of mass. The quantity $\Delta C_p / \Delta \alpha$ per gram is essentially independent of T_g, as shown in Figure 2.1.5. The value of E_h per gram decreases for greater M and the free volume fraction at T_g decreases with T_g.

In 1955 Bunn[12] published his observation that the molar heat of fusion for conformers of various sizes and shapes can be scaled with their molecular weights, drawing an analogy to Trouton's rule that the ratio of the heat of evaporation to the temperature of vaporization is nearly constant for liquids. Bunn's tabulated data show an apparent proportionality between the molar heat of fusion and the molecular weight with a proportionality

10. Kanig actually derives an equation with van der Waals volume in place of V_g in Equation 2.1.17 and introduces a correction that ends up essentially the same as Equation 2.1.17.

11. Kanig, G., *Kolloid-Z. u Z. Polym.* 233, 54 (1969); also, Wrasidlo, W., Thermal Analysis of Polymers, C: The Glass Transition, *Advances in Polymer Science;* No. 13, American Chemical Society, Washington, DC, 1974.

12. Bunn, C. W., *J. Polym. Sci.* 16, 323 (1955).

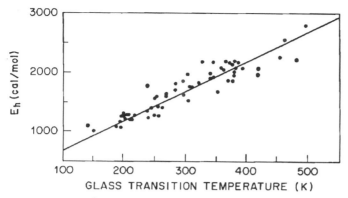

Figure 2.1.4   The hole energy[9] per mole of repeat unit is actually the molar cohesive energy per repeat unit, which is typically two conformers for vinyl polymers.

constant of ca. 50 cal/g for conformers which are *in the middle* of a chain rather than at the end. (Chain ends are at a higher energy level.) These values are shown in Table 2.2. However, Bunn finds the proportionality to be only an approximate relationship, and to be applicable to structures composed of a group of these conformers, a correction factor for the packing density must be taken into consideration. When segments are packed together, according to Bunn, the molecular volume is actually smaller than the sum of individual segments, and the cohesive energy is therefore greater than the sum. Corrected values for the molecular volume and the cohesive energy can be made following the equation:

$$E_1 - E_2 = 1.73 \frac{V_2 - V_1}{V_1} \tag{2.1.18}$$

for segmental species 1 and 2. This has been shown to hold for substances in which intermolecular forces are of the van der Waals type, regardless of whether there is a phase change from liquid to solid.[13]

---

13. This is exactly the correction factor Kanig introduced for the difference between the van der Waals volume and V_g. Thus the fractional free volume defined by V_f/V_g, rather than $V_f/V_{o,0K}$ should be regarded as the universal constant.

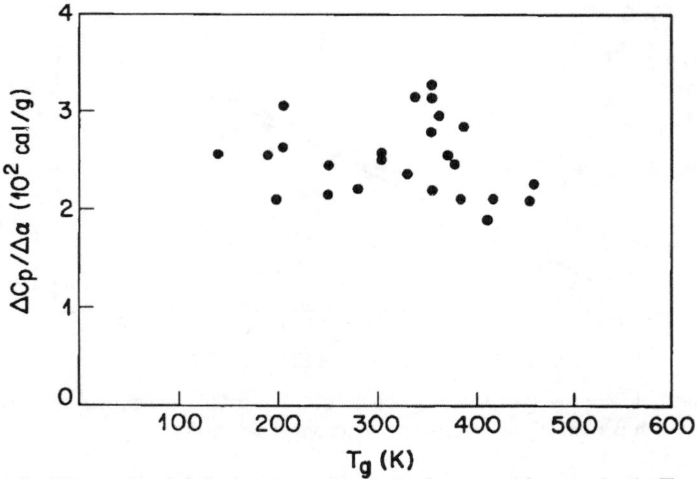

Figure 2.1.5 The ratio of ΔC_p (*per gram* instead of per *mole*) over $\Delta\alpha$ in Equation 2.1.17 vs. T_g. Unlike the hole energy, there is no trend indicative of a temperature dependence.

Table 2.2. Molar Heat and Volume of Fusion per Conformer

Conformer	E(cal/mol)	V(cm^3/mol)	M	E/M(cal/g)
-CH$_2$-	680	21.8	14	48
-C$_6$H$_4$-	3900	83.9	76	51
-CH=CH-	1700	32.0	26	65
-C(CH$_3$)=CH-	2400	53.8	40	60
-CH(CH$_3$)-	1360	42.8	28	49
-C(CH$_3$)$_2$-	1900	65.4	42	45
-CH(C$_6$H$_5$)-	4300	105.7	90	48
-CCl$_2$-	3100	53.4	77	40
-CHCl-	2360	37.6	45	52
-COO-	2900	28.9	44	66
-O-	1000	7.3	16	53
-CH$_3$	1700	27.8	15	113
-C$_6$H$_5$	5400	89.9	77	70
-Cl	2800	21.8	35.5	79
-COOH	5600	36.5	45	124
-OH	5800	14.9	17	341

We can apply Equation 2.1.18 to obtain a correction for the intermolecular energy when the molar volume is increased from V_1 to V_2 by increasing the molecular weight from M_0 to M:

$$E - E_0 \propto \frac{M - M_0}{M_0} \approx \ln M - \ln M_0 \qquad (2.1.19)$$

Thus the hole energy per mole increases with $\ln M$, whereas from simple additivity, E_h per mole might have been expected to be proportional to M. Thus E_h per *gram* decreases with the molecular weight and T_g, and so does ΔC_p per gram of polymer with higher T_g.

The $\ln M$ dependence of molar thermodynamic quantity can be explained with the concept of the free volume. Free volume is the effective volume over which the center of gravity of the conformers can be distributed wihtout change in the internal energy. The entropy increase associated with the free volume may be taken as the entropy of a perfect gas confined to a volume equal to the free volume, as the latter is the entropy of N_A points in a volume V. For 1 mole of conformer,

$$\Delta S = -k \ln (V - V_0) \qquad (2.1.19')$$

where V is the molar volume and V_0 is the molar occupied volume. The entropy increase associated with the free volume is really the hole energy divided by temperature, or $E_h/(T_g - T_0)$, but since $(T_g - T_0)$ is 50 °C for all polymers according to our definition for the iso-λ_g condition, this entropy is in fact proportional to the molar hole energy E_h per mole of conformer. The free volume $V - V_0$ scales with the molecular weight of the conformer M, and so does the excess entropy and enthalpy. The value of E_h per mole of conformer in Equation 2.1.17 increases with log molecular weight of the conformer, and E_h per gram scales with $(\ln M)/M$. The value of ΔC_p per gram is smaller for the higher T_g materials because it too follows this ratio, $(\ln M)/M$.

The conformational entropy S_{cg} at T_g in Equation 2.1.17 can be substituted with the entropy without cooperativity, s_g^*, using Equation 2.1.7 to obtain:

$$(T_g - T_0) s_g^* \frac{T^*}{T^* - T_0} = E_h = E_{h_0} + C(\ln M - \ln M_0) \qquad (2.1.20)$$

where E_{h_0} and M_0 refer to a hypothetical polymer with $T_0 = 0$ K. From the Vogel equation, $T_g - T_0$ must be a constant for various conformers to satisfy the iso-λ_g condition. The entropy s_g^* is for no meshing from the neighbors to

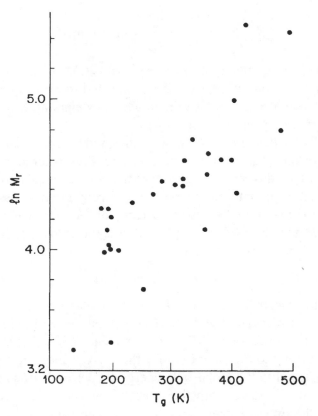

Figure 2.1.6   Log molecular weight of the repeat unit vs. T_g: A possible linear relationship exists if a proper choice for the conformer size is made instead of simply using the repeat unit as the segmental unit.

interfere. For that polymer with $M = M_0$ and $T_0 = 0$ K, $T_g s_g{}^* = E_{h_0}$. Thus Equation 2.1.20 states that among various species, the following relationship should hold:

$$(T^* - T_0)\ln M = C_3 = T^*\ln M_0 \qquad (2.1.21)$$

Figure 2.1.6 shows that T_g (i.e., $T_0 + 50$ °C) is higher for repeat units with greater molecular weight. Because a repeat unit may consist of one to several conformers, the scatter of the data points is not surprising. However, there is a trend suggesting the proportionality between the log molecular weight of repeat units vs T_g, i.e., E_h per mole $\propto \ln M$, i.e., $E_h \propto \ln M$. With our model, a repeat unit in a typical vinyl polymer consists of two conformers. If Equation 2.1.20 holds for the conformers, then Equation 2.1.21 should also hold and C_3 should be a universal constant. We find this to be true with $C_3 \approx 1750$ for many of the common vinyl polymers, when half of the monomer molecular weight is taken as M for the average size of the conformers. Examples are shown by polymers 1 through 14 in Table 2.3. The apparent proportionality between T_g and $\ln M$ of a conformer provides us with a further insight to thermodynamics of the entropy, enthalpy, and free volume, which depend on the size of conformer. Equation 2.1.17 can be transformed to an empirical formula:

$$E_h = C_4 \ln M \, S_{cg} = \frac{\Delta V_g}{V_g} \left[\frac{\Delta C_p}{\Delta \alpha} \right] \qquad (2.1.17a)$$

where C_4 is the proportionality constant $T_g/\ln M$. From the equation above, it is clear that for the same conformational entropy at T_g, the hole energy is $\ln M_2/\ln M_1$ times greater for material 2 than for material 1. This is equivalent to Bunn's formula in Equation 2.1.19. A similar argument may be applied to the fractional free volume at T_g, $\Delta V_g/V_g$ in Equation 2.1.17a above; since $[\Delta C_p/\Delta \alpha]$ per gram is constant, $\Delta C_p/\Delta \alpha]$ per mole is proportional to M, because $\Delta C_p \propto \ln M$ and $\Delta \alpha \propto (\ln M)/M$, and it is slightly dependent on the conformer size, $\propto (\ln M)/M$ and, the higher the T_g, the smaller the fractional free volume at its T_g. Thus, another general rule emerges on the dependence of thermodynamic quantities on conformer size:

$$\frac{E_h}{E_h{}^*} = \frac{\Delta C_p}{\Delta C_p{}^*} = \frac{\Delta \mu}{\Delta \mu^*} = \frac{\ln M}{\ln M_0} = \frac{T^*}{T^* - T_0} \qquad (2.1.22)$$

on a per *mole* basis, and only S_c per mole remains independent of the conformer size. On a per gram basis, it can be shown that:

$$\frac{\Delta C_p}{\Delta C_p{}^*} \text{ per gram} = \frac{\Delta \alpha}{\Delta \alpha^*} = \frac{f_g}{f_g{}^*} = \frac{\ln M}{\ln M_0} \frac{M_0}{M} \qquad (2.1.22')$$

and ΔC_p per gram decreases for a larger conformer with a higher T_g. Then f_g, the fractional free volume at T_g, is:

$$f_g = \frac{V_g - V_0}{V_g} = \frac{V_0}{V_g} \ln \frac{V_g}{V_0} \qquad (2.1.23)$$

A slight difference in the packing density V_0/V_g from one polymer to another will affect the quantity $\ln(V_g/V_0)$ strongly when $V_g \approx V_0$. From the discussion above, it is implied that vitrification occurs at a higher temperature for a larger conformer with a smaller value of f_g, but a larger molar free volume ($\sim \ln M$).

Because the Vogel-Fulcher and Doolittle equations can be equated, one obtains $\Delta\mu/k = 1/\alpha_f$, where α_f is the thermal expansion coefficient of the Doolittle free volume fraction. As will be shown in Chapter 3, for polyvinyl acetate, we obtain $k/\Delta\mu^* \approx 5.7 \times 10^{-4}$, from which $k/\Delta\mu \approx 3.8 \times 10^{-4}$ is obtained. This value is exactly that of $\Delta\alpha = 3.85 \times 10^{-4}$![14] It can further be shown that the free volume fraction at T^* is about 0.5, or at this high termperature limit two conformers share the vacancy the size of one conformer, while at a lower temperature (but still in the equilibrium state), the free volume with the size of one conformer is shared by z conformers. Here are some typical values for the reader's interest: with values such as $\Delta C_p/\Delta\alpha = 200$ cal/g, $\Delta V/V = 0.025$, $\Delta\alpha = 5 \times 10^{-4}$, $\Delta C_p = 0.1$ cal/g °C, $M = 52$, and $T_g = 100$ °C, we obtain $S_{cg} = 0.70$ eu/mol, and $E_h = TS = 260$ cal/mol. This leads to $s^* = 2.6$ and $c_1 = 3.8$ instead of 3. Thus our excess enthalpy at T_g is not the same as Kanig's cohesive energy, although it is closely related and one can be calculated from the other. They are both proportional to $\ln M$.

In Table 2.3 below, the following items are listed: the polymer name, the average conformer size (the molecular weight of the repeat unit / the number of conformers per repeat unit), the experimental value of T_g mostly by differential calorimetry), $T^* - T_0$ by assuming $T^* = 500$ °C and $T_0 = T_g - 50$ °C, and $\ln M$ and C_3 calculated from Equation 2.1.21.

The universal value 1750 for C_3 translates to M_0 of 9.6 (or two-thirds the size of a methylene unit) for the previously mentioned hypothetical polymer with T_0 of 0 K, in which the domain size remains 1 down to 0 K with no intermolecular meshing. In the following exercise of estimating the number of conformers per repeat unit in polymers, one should keep in mind that the local relaxation of interest is essentially the "unkinking" of segments

---

14. The Ferry parameter, $B = \Delta\alpha/\alpha_f$, thus has its meaning in $B = \Delta\mu/\Delta\mu^* = T^*/(T^*-T_0)$.

in the main chain backbone, the process characterized by the internal viscosity.[15] Note that we arrive at the conclusion that the glass transition temperature of linear polyethylene (polymer 1) is the γ transition temperature. The β transition in polyethylene, according to the same rule, would involve three carbons as two conformers. For polyvinyl chloride (PVC) (polymer 10) with strong dipoles, C_3 is substantially smaller, but a density correction to M will result in $C_3 \approx 1750$. Two notable exceptions to the simple rule of two conformers per repeat unit are polymers 6 (polyisobutylene) and 8 (*cis*-polyisoprene). In both cases, the most suitable conformer size for the correct T_0 values is 16 or 17, which is a size only slightly larger than a methylene unit; i.e., each methyl unit is a conformer. It is most likely that the methyl group participates in the configurational changes in these two polymers. If each methyl group is counted as one conformer, there are four conformers per monomer unit in polyisobutylene, and also in cis-polyisoprene.

The universality of the value of C_3 has also been tested with a number of other polymers, and some additional guidelines for defining conformer size have been determined. For vinylidene cyanide copolymerized with various vinyl monomers, shown as polymers 15 through 21 in Table 2.3 (data obtained through the courtesy of Dr. I. Seo of Mitsubishi Petrochemical Company) again the value of ca. 1750 (or slightly less because of the dipoles) is obtained when each *monomer* is considered as one conformer. The strong dipole-to-dipole interaction within the co-mer unit of these piezoelectric copolymers results in the large bulky conformers with high T_g's. For the four linear polyethers 22 through 25, the rule can be applied successfully, though the value of C_3 is slightly lower than 1700, this time because the ether bond with a smaller $\Delta\mu*$ is in the chain. If the conformer of the -O- unit is scaled as 0.7 of the -C- unit, $C_3 = 1750$ is obtained. For polyvinyl ethers 26 through 30, again the value of C_3 is uniform but less than 1700 if the -O- conformer is counted as 1. If it is counted as 0.7, however, the approximate value of 1750 is obtained. On the other hand, when a side branch of an aliphatic chain is attached, T_g goes *down* with each additional -C- in the branch. This is because each -C- unit on the branch participates in

---

15. As opposed to the external viscosity, which involves irreversible slippage of molecules or molecular segments.

Table 2.3. Conformer Size and T_g

	Aliphatic Polymers					
	Polymer	M	T_g	T^*-T_0	$\ln M$	C_3
1	Polyethylene (linear)	14/1	-110	660	2.64	1742
2	Polyethylene (branch)	41/2	-30	580	3.02	1751
3	1,4-Poly(butadiene)	54/3	-55	605	2.85	1750
4	1,2-Poly(butadiene)	54/2	20	530	3.30	1749
5	Polypropylene	42/2	-30	580	3.04	1765
6	Polyisobutylene	56/3.5	-74	624	2.77	1728
7	Gutta percha	68/3	-10	560	3.12	1748
8	*cis*-Polyisoprene	68/4	-69	619	2.83	1753
9	Poly(4-methyl pentene)	85/3	29	521	3.34	1742
10	Polyvinyl chloride	62/2	90	460	3.43	1577
11	Polystyrene	108/2	100	450	3.93	1769
12	Poly(α methyl styrene)	119/1	180	370	4.78	1768
13	Poly(trifluoro-chloroethylene)	118/3	79	471	3.67	1728
14	Polyvinyl acetate	86/3	29	521	3.36	1748
15	VDCN-vinyl acetate	164/2	179	371	4.41	1636
16	VDCN-vinyl formate	150/2	152	398	4.32	1718
17	VDCN-vinyl propionate	178/2	176	374	4.49	1678
18	VDCN-vinyl benzoate	225/2	186	364	4.72	1719
19	VDCN-methyl methacrylate	178/2	145	405	4.49	1818
20	VCDN-vinyl acetyl chloride	199/2	167	383	4.60	1761
21	VDCN-vinyl pivallate	206/2	171	379	4.63	1757
22	Polyoxymethylene	30/2	-73	623	2.71	1687
23	Polyoxyethylene	44/3	-67	617	2.69	1657
24	Polyokypropylene	58/4	-75	625	2.67	1671
25	Polyoxybutylene	72/5	-88	638	2.67	1701
26	Polyvinylmethyl ether	58/3	-22	572	2.96	1694
27	Polyvinylethyl ether	72/4	-33	583	2.89	1685
28	Polyvinylisopropyl ether	86/4	-12	562	3.07	1724
29	Polyvinylbutyl ether	100/6	-56	606	2.81	1704
30	Polyvinylhexyl ether	128/8	-74	624	2.77	1730
31	Polymethyl methacrylate	100/2	105	445	3.91	1741
32	Isotactic Polymethyle methacrylate	100/3	46	504	3.51	1767
33	PethylMA	114/3	65	485	3.64	1764
34	Polypropyl methacrylate	128/4	35	515	3.47	1784
35	Polymethyl acrylate	86/4	9	541	3.07	1660
36	Poly(*t*-butyl acrylate	132/5	31	519	3.27	1698

Note: VCDN stands for vinylidene cyanide.

Table 2.3. Conformer Size and T_g (Continued)

Aromatic Polymers

	Polymer	M	T_g	T^*-T_0	$\ln M$	C_3
37	Polyphenylene sulfide	108/2	110	440	3.99	1755
38	Polyphenylene oxide	92/2	90	460	3.83	1761
39	Polyethylene terephthalate	182/5	64	486	3.59	1746
40	Polycarbonate	254/3	147	403	4.44	1788
41	Polyethyer etherketone	288/3	158	392	4.56	1790
42	Polysulfone	444/4	187	363	4.71	
43	Polyether imide	596/4	200	350	5.00	1750
44	Polyimdie (PMDA)	207/1	222	328	5.33	1749
45	Polyether sulfone	232/1	225	325	5.45	1770
46	Poly(tri-methyl phenylene ether)	172/1	210	340	5.15	1750
47	Kevlar	242/1	235	315	5.49	1729
48	B+F	315/2.5	187	363	4.84	1755
49	C+F	376/2	210	340	5.24	1780
50	A+D	358/2.5	195	355	4.96	1762
51	B+D	420/1.5	243	307	5.63	1730
52	C+D	480x3	310	240	7.29	1750
53	A+E	434/5	148	402	4.46	1794
54	B+E	496/4.5	172	378	4.70	1778
55	C+E	540/3.5	205	345	5.04	1730
56	A+F	254/3	147	403	4.44	1788

For the copolymers from 48 to 56,
A: bisphenol A
B: bisphenol AP
C: fluorene
D: terephthalate + isophthalate 50/50
E: 2,2´ - biphenyl carboxylate
F: carboxylate

the relaxation process (polymers 6 and 8) and thus is considered to be a conformer in the conformational change. When this rule is applied to methacrylates 31, 33, and 34, C_3 of about 1750 is obtained. For isotactic polymethyl methacrylate (PMMA: 32), three conformers instead of two conformers had to be assumed, possibly because a cooperative conformational change with the ester group is needed in the more densely packed isotactic polymer system. For the two acrylates 35 and 36, the greater number of conformers also reflects the importance of the conformational changes within the ester groups when the α-methyl group in the methacrylate is removed.

In aromatic polymers, we find that a para phenylene group alone cannot

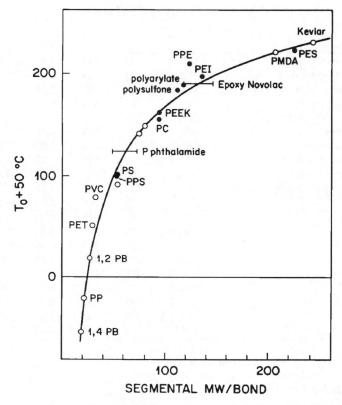

Figure 2.1.7 T_g vs. the "conformer size" as determined following the rule described in connection with Table 2.3. The theoretical curve from Equation 2.1.21 is plotted. This plot is useful in estimating the conformer size when T_g is known, providing insight into the relevant intramolecular motion for segmental relaxation.

be counted as one conformer. A *p*-phenylene unit can rotate about its own longitudinal axis without disturbing the immediate neighbors on either side. Such a rotational mode does not contribute toward the relaxation of an applied stress, since it does not help unkink twisted segments. The rotation of the same phenylene group about a bond once removed, however, would be accompanied by a change in the shape of the local structure. Thus, if an ether or a carbonyl group is in the adjacent position in the main chain, it should be included as part of the conformer, i.e., a phenyl-O- or a phenyl-C:O- group should be counted as one conformer, and this leads to C_3 of 1750, as shown by the examples, polymers 37 through 46 in Table 2.3. If one follows this rule, a bisphenol A with -O- on both sides should be considered to be two conformers. Thus the repeat unit of bisphenol A polycarbonate consists of three conformers. The case of Kevlar is an exceptional one. It can be shown with molecular models that the whole repeat unit can be rotated without a change of conformation, the feature analogous to that of the rotating *p*-phenylene group, so the whole unit is counted as one conformer.

A group of high temperature aromatic copolymers prepared by T. Tanaka of Unitika Ltd. have also been examined (polymers 47 through 56 in Table 2.3). The chemical structures of the basic groups are described below Table 2.3. The copolymers in Table 2.3 are polyarylates combining (A) bisphenol A, (B) bisphenol AP, or (C) fluorene with (D) a 50/50 mix of terephthalate and isophthalate, (E) 2,2'-biphenylcarboxylate, or (F) carboxylate. The numbers of conformers are (A) 2, (B) 1, (C) 1, (D) 0.5, (E) 3, (F) 1, for which again C_3 of ca. 1750 is obtained. The curious number of 0.5 assigned to the D group is perhaps because the terephthalate half does not participate in the conformational change independently, while the isophthalate half will. We have no proof at this point: we know only that either of homopolymers alone crystallizes, while the 50/50 mixtures do not. The conformer size is thus a convenient form of quantifying the rigidity of a chain, and the activation energy for the *intra*molecular bond rotation depends on the conformer size because of the molar volume of packing, through the relation $\Delta\mu = \Delta\mu^* \ln M / \ln 9.6$. Equation 2.1.21 with $C_3 = 1750$ is plotted in Figure 2.1.7, together with the points corresponding to various polymers, some of which are included in Table 2.3. The data point for polyphenylene ether (PPE) moves onto the curve if it is considered to be a 50/50 mixture of head-to-head and head-to-tail.

Finally, we summarize the useful features of this model by showing the so-called transition map for polycarbonate and polyethylene terephthalate (Figure 2.1.8). A transition map is a plot of the frequency for the maximum rate of relaxation versus $1/T$ K.

There is a question whether the shortest relaxation time λ^* in Equation 2.1.11 should in fact be a universal value. We propose this to be so. We say that f^* or $(2\pi\lambda^*)^{-1}$ is the frequency above which the term "relaxation" has lost its meaning, because the rate of relaxation is in the order of the frequency of libration. For the high temperature limit T^* to be universal, and it seems so from the near universality of the constant C_3 in Table 2.3, λ^*

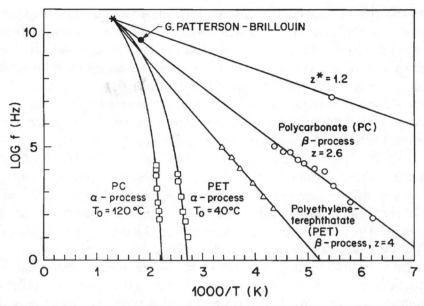

Figure 2.1.8   The transition map: log frequency at which the dielectric loss maximum is observed vs. $1/T$ K, for polycarbonate and polyethylene terephthalate. The asterisk depicts the relaxation time at T^*, which is common to all polymers with different glass transition temperatures.

should be also. All conformers are similar in librational frequency and λ^* should be the same. An alternative to this argument would be to introduce λ_0^* the relaxation time at T^* for the conformer with T_0 of 0 K, as the universal value. If this is taken to be the case, then all λ^*'s would be different, with higher T_g materials exhibiting a greater λ^*, and the β transition curve would intercept the α transition curve at lower frequency than at λ^*. All curves, however, including the β transition, seem to meet at $T^* = 500$ °C, $\log \lambda^* = -11.4$ (seconds).[16] The limiting relaxation time λ^* of ca.

16. With exception of the β mecahnisms that involve side groups rather than the conformers in the main chain (e.g., the β transition in polymethyl methacrylate).

3×10^{-12} second corresponds to the range of the dielectric relaxation time for heptane extrapolated to T^*,[17] and near the rotational vibrational frequency at a C-C bond. Thus, we assume that the corresponding frequency $\log f^* \approx 10.5$ (Hz) is the upper limit at which a relaxation process is observable for any polymer. Similarly, $T^* = 500$ °C is the upper limit of temperature for T_0. As was mentioned earlier, λ_g of 6 minutes is obtained for $\Delta\mu^*$ of 3.5 kcal and $T_g = T_0 + 50$ °C. From Equations 2.1.14 and 2.1.11, the following equation is obtained:

$$\Delta\mu \frac{s^*}{S_c} = \Delta\mu z = \Delta\mu \frac{T^* - T_0}{T^*} \frac{T}{T - T_0} \qquad (2.1.24)$$

from which the domain size z (which depends on the temperature) can be estimated. The slope of the α-process curves in Figure 2.1.7 divided by the gas constant is not equal to $\Delta\mu z$, because z changes with T. The derivative of Equation 2.1.11´ with respect to $1/T$ is $\Delta\mu T^2/k(T - T_0)^2$, which is usually a large value in the range of 200 kcal near T_g. The apparent activation energy in the glassy state where z is constant, a more reasonable value of ca. 40 kcal/mol is obtained. Since $\Delta\mu \approx 4$ to 6 kcal/mol (of conformer), the domain size z_g at T_g is typically ca. 7 to 10 conformers. Generally, a sudden decrease in the slope of the shift factor is observed when the entropy S_c is frozen and z is fixed, as the liquid departs from the equilibrium state and enters the nonequilibrium glassy state.

The β relaxation process is a constant activation energy process, and the value of the activation energy is progressively smaller if the transition occurs at a lower temperature. The process can be considered to be the relaxation of molecular segments trapped but able to continue local rotations even after the rest are vitrified. The apparent activation energy is a few times greater than $\Delta\mu^*$, which leads to the speculation that a chain is "pinned" at various parts and intramolecular cooperativity is needed for this relaxation process. To permit relaxation below T_g, the number of conformers in the β process must be equal to or smaller than the domain size for the α process at the

---

17. Fröhlich, H., *Theory of Dielectrics*, Oxford Press University Press, London, 1958, p. 124.

glass transition. Otherwise the motion corresponding to the β transition will be included as part of the α transition, and no separate β transition will be observed.

Most polymer molecules are made of conformers of different sizes. Among these, the largest conformer becomes pinned by the neighbor during the glass transition, while the smaller conformers are able to relax through *intra*molecular cooperative motions. Since the largest conformer occurs once per repeat unit, the number of conformers cooperating intramolecularly in the β relaxation is typically the number of conformers in one repeat unit. For polycarbonate, the size of a unit of relaxation for the β process is between 2 and 3 conformers, whereas for polyethylene terephthalate (PET) the size is 4 or 5 conformers. These values correspond to the number of conformers per repeat unit in the α transition (see Table 2.3, the column for M). This suggests that it is much easier to pin a particular conformer within a repeat unit, thus making one repeat unit a typical size for the simultaneous intramolecular cooperative unit in β relaxation. The larger number for PET is related to many C-C links, each acting as a conformer within the repeat unit. When β relaxation involves the conformers in the main chain as these examples do, the β process merges with the α process at T^*, and the molecular weight of the repeat unit divided by these numbers agrees with the molecular weight of the respective conformers used for calculation in Equation 2.1.21.

The activation energy, T_β, and the number of conformers in the repeat unit are closely tied together and if one of these factors is known, the other two can be calculated. Thus even though polycarbonate has a higher T_g than polyethylene terephthalate, its β temperature is lower. This feature should be useful for designing a polymer molecule with a high T_g but a low T_β which has perhaps better low temperature fracture properties.[18] If a side group is responsible for the β relaxation as in PMMA, the β process will merge with the α process at a substantially lower temperature than T^*,[19] and the two

---

18. Some high T_g polymers exhibit low T_β but can be brittle. Because some conformers are extremely large, only a small number of them can participate in the β transition with low loss dispersion.

19. McCrum, N. G., Read, B. E., and Williams, G., *Anelastic and Dielectric Effects in Polymeric Solids,* John Wiley and Sons, New York, 1967, p255.

curves will not appear to be tangentially touching each other. A high energy state of the chain end in a short chain will bring the effective transition temperature down, and the whole β curve is shifted to the left in a transition map. One point shown on the straight line labeled $z^* = 1.2$ in Figure 2.1.8 corresponds to the frequency and the temperature of the methyl group rotation in the polyethylene molecule, which we think is a good example of the unhindered conformer, i.e., z is always 1. This line then is the limit of the shortest relaxation time for the glass transition of polymers and olefins of all kinds. T_0 for this conformer turns out to be ca. 6 K.

The method of analysis for the structural dependence of T_g utilized here has been based on conformer size as the fundamental variable. We have pointed out that the Vogel activation energy $\Delta\mu^*$ increases with $\ln M$, where M is the molecular weight of the conformer. The popular notion of chain stiffness might be invoked as a factor that translates to a higher T_g. However, we hope to have clarified that a higher intermolecular potential energy barrier against bond rotation does not translate directly to a higher T_g.

2.2 Distribution of Relaxation Times near the Glass Transition

2.2.1 Stage 1: Relaxation of Conformers

A "master" curve for the relaxation modulus of an amorphous polymer in the equilibrium state was shown in Figure 1.4.1 on page 16. The wide range of the relaxation spectrum is divided into three stages, stage 1 being the comparatively fast-relaxing stage observed at low temperatures, stage 2 the transition zone between the solidlike stage 1, and the much slower stage 3 observed in a typical melt.

We will discuss only stage 1. This stage is observed in the solidlike state where the characteristic relaxation time λ_c is in the order of minutes. (A benchmark can be set at λ_c of 1 hour at $T_g - 5\,°C$ with $G(10\ \text{minutes})$ of 10^9 dynes/cm^2.)

Our cooperative domain model has dealt up to this point with a single relaxation time associated with the characteristic domain size. However, the possibility of a variation in domain size must exist. At a given temperature T, the cooperative domains with size z will exhibit a relaxation time λ following the equation:

$$\ln\left(\frac{\lambda}{\lambda_c}\right) = \frac{\Delta\mu}{kT}(z - z_c) \qquad (2.2.1)$$

where the subscript c refers to the characteristic (maximum or "cutoff") size. The maximum size z_c and the corresponding relaxation time are uniquely determined by the pressure and temperature.

To estimate the distribution of relaxation times, we seek to find the distribution of domain sizes. We assume that a mole of conformers contains a certain amount of free volume which, at equilibrium, depends uniquely on temperature and pressure. In the foregoing discussion, we had tacitly assumed that the free volume was distributed uniformly among all domains of a uniform size z_c; i.e., each domain contained the free volume fraction, which was the same as the overall fraction, hence a single relaxation time. We further suggested in the paragraph following Equation 2.1.23, that the free volume with size of one conformer existed per domain on average. We now attempt to extend this model to the case of free volume that is not distributed uniformly, while the same overall level of free volume is maintained. One of the basic assumptions of the free volume theory for liquids is that the liquid molecules are able to move their center of mass without having to pay a penalty in internal energy. The "holes" are assumed to be redistributed at the same free energy level. Let us now consider N_c domains, each of which consists of z_c conformers, to contain the free volume v_f cm³. The subscript c refers to the critical or cutoff size. This means that $\rho v_f/z_c M$ is the fractional free volume, where M is the molecular weight of one conformer. The total free volume is $N_c v_f = (N_A/z_c)v_f$ cm³. (N_A is Avogadro's number.) We now change the distribution by exchanging one "hole" of size v_f in one domain with one conformer in an adjacent domain, and repeat this procedure between every pair among the originally uniform sized domains. Now half the total number of domains contains two "holes" and one less conformer, and the other half has no holes but one extra conformer. However, the total mass, the total free volume and, most important, the total internal energy, all remain unchanged. There are now $N_c/2$ domains containing $z_c - 1$ conformers. Proceeding in this way further to come to a redistribution of free volume into N_z domains containing z conformers and $z_c - z$ holes and the rest with no free volume at all, we obtain for the number of domains with $z_c - z$ holes:

$$N_z = \frac{N_c}{z_c - z + 1} \qquad (2.2.2)$$

Since N_c is equal to N_A/z_c, we obtain:

$$N_z = \frac{N_A}{z_c(z_c - z + 1)} \qquad (2.2.3)$$

for the number of domains of size z, when *the equilibrium domain size is* z_c.

According to the formula above, there are substantial numbers of very small domains with a very short relaxation time, even where the "main" relaxation time is, say, in the order of minutes. For example, when $z_c = 6$ at $T = 400$ K, there are 20% as many (by number) domains with the size of only one conformer with the relaxation time of 7×10^{-9} second, and the weight fraction of 3%.

The relaxation of the domains of size z occurs around $t = \lambda_c$, or their own characteristic relaxation time, where $\ln(\lambda_z/\lambda_c) = (\Delta\mu/kT)(z - z_c)$, and the intensity of relaxation time is proportional to the population of the domain,

$$N_z = \frac{G(\ln\lambda_z - \Delta\ln\lambda)\text{-}G(\ln\lambda_z + \Delta\ln\lambda)}{G(\ln\lambda_z)} = -\Delta\ln G(\ln\lambda_z)$$

$$= \frac{1}{z_c}\left[\frac{1}{z_c - (z - \Delta z)} - \frac{1}{z_c - (z + \Delta z)}\right] \qquad (2.2.4)$$

where we set Δz as $\frac{1}{2}$, or half the conformer. We now integrate all $\Delta\ln G$'s starting from $z = 1$ to $z = z$,

$$N_1 + N_2 + .. N_z = \ln G(0) - \ln G(\ln\lambda_z)$$

$$= \frac{1}{z_c}\left[\frac{1}{z_c\text{-}1} - \frac{1}{z_c - z + 1}\right] \qquad (2.2.5)$$

Now we let parameter ς be such that $\ln(t/\lambda_c) = -\Delta\mu(z_c - \varsigma + 1)/kT$ or $\ln(t/\lambda_c{}') = -\Delta\mu(z_c - \varsigma)/kT$. Then we obtain:

$$\ln G(t) = \ln G(0) + \frac{1}{z_c}\frac{\Delta\mu}{kT}\left[\frac{1}{\ln(t/\lambda_c{}')}\right] \qquad (2.2.6)$$

where $G(0)$ corresponds to the modulus for which all domains, i.e., $(z \geq 1)$, are unrelaxed. The new term λ_c' is the longest limit for the spectrum. The equation above applies only when $z < z_c$ and $t < \lambda_c$. Before t approaches λ_c, the most slowly relaxing units begin to relax, and this is the terminal relaxation *for this mechanism* of relaxation. The model predicts a single relaxation time λ_c' beyond this time. Polymers actually enter stage 2 at this point and follow the power law with the exponent of approximately $-\frac{1}{2}$. This will be discussed in the next section briefly and in Chapter 4 in more detail, since this stage is called the "transition zone."

Equation 2.2.6 above is a new formula for the relaxation function. We now compare this formula with the well-known Kohlrausch-Williams-Watts (KWW) equation,[20] since the stage 1 relaxation process is frequently approximated by this equation:

$$\ln G\left(\frac{t}{\lambda_c}\right) = \ln G(0) - \left(\frac{t}{\lambda_c}\right)^{\beta} \tag{2.2.7}$$

The KWW formula has the convenient feature that its characteristic relaxation time corresponds to the dielectric loss maximum frequency as well as the time at which the relaxation modulus has decreased to $1/e$ of the initial value. It turns out, however, that, while the KWW formula is very good when t or ω^{-1} is near λ_c, it is poor at extremely short times such as 5 decades shorter than λ_c. This is illustrated by comparing the dashed line in Figure 2.2.1 against the dielectric loss data points.

Our equation, Equation 2.2.6, may be transformed to a form that is convenient for comparing with the KWW formula:

$$\ln G\left(\frac{t}{\lambda_c'}\right) = \ln G(0) + \frac{\beta}{\ln(t/\lambda_c')} \tag{2.2.6'}$$

where

---

20. Williams, G., Watts, D. C., *Trans. Faraday Soc.* **66**, 80 (1970)

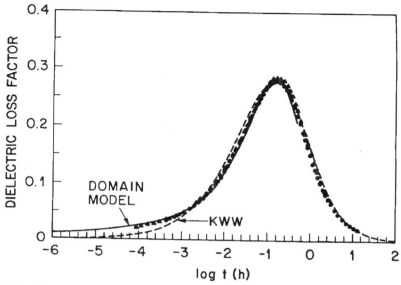

Figure 2.2.1 Dielectric loss vs. log time (= -log circular frequency). Data by G. E. Johnson (private communication). The dotted line is calculated from the KWW equation (Equation 2.2.7) using $\beta = 0.6$ and $\lambda_c = 0.3$; the solid line is from the domain model (Equation 2.2.6), with $\lambda_c = 0.6$. Our model implies the right half of the loss peak to be Gaussian with a single relaxation time.

$$\beta = \frac{\Delta\mu^*(T - T_0)}{kT^2} \qquad (2.2.6'')$$

is an independently determined parameter. Its value is 0.54 at $T_g = 373$ K, while for the same polymer at $T = 423$ K, it is 0.84, and the distribution is definitely narrower at 50 K above T_g. If this is true, then the time-temperature superposition principle is only approximately true, and the Vogel equation applies only to the characteristic relaxation time. The loss peak of the dielectric relaxation has been observed to be narrower at elevated temperatures even in the equilibrium state.[21]

---

21. Matsuoka, S., Williams, G., Johnson, G. E., Anderson, E. W., and Furukawa, T., *Macromolecules,* **18**, 2652 (1985).

The relaxation spectrum $H(\ln\lambda)$ is approximately:[22]

$$H(\ln\lambda) \approx -\frac{dG(t)}{d\ln t}\Big|_{t=\lambda} \tag{2.2.8}$$

The loss factor for the domain model was calculated from the spectrum derived from Equation 2.2.6 and is included in Figure 2.2.1 as the solid line. The fit with our equation is better than with the KWW equation at the high frequency (short time) end, reflecting the feature of our model that the abundance of the smaller domains is responsible for the persistent tail of the stretched exponential function at the high frequency limit, which even the KWW equation underpredicts. It is important to note that, even near the glass-forming temperature range, domains of one conformer persist. Kanaya et al.,[23] in their inelastic neutron-scattering study on *cis*-polybutadiene, found a mode of local motions with a characteristic time of 5×10^{-11} seconds with an activation energy of 2.5 kcal/mol in the temperature range from 40 °C to 100 °C. This is very close to the limit of relaxation noted by the asterisk in Figure 2.1.8. Also, Sumpter et al.,[24] in their molecular simulation, have seen defects migration in crystalline polymers with speeds in the order of picoseconds.

Even though Equation 2.2.6 appears to be very different from the KWW equation, these relations can be made to nearly coincide by the suitable choice of constants. Figure 2.2.2 is such an example. In this case, the choice of $\Delta\mu/z_c kT = 0.5$ ($\Delta\mu$ = 3 kcal, T = 300 K, z_c = 10) for Equation 2.2.6 (curve A) yields the slope of $-\frac{1}{2}$ at $t = \lambda_c/e$. The slope for the KWW formula (curve B) is $-\beta$ at $t = \lambda_c$. The greater slope of our model at short times is, again, an important improvement over the KWW equation in predicting the creep and relaxation behavior of polymers in the glassy state for $t \ll \lambda_c$, where the KWW equation typically underestimates the intensity of relaxation. If these "stretched" exponential functions are in fact a reflection of the distribution of the size of cooperative domains, this may be

---

22. At the terminal region it is a single relaxation process where this approximation is obviously not applicable.

23. Kanaya, T., Kaji, K., and Inoue, K., *Macromolecules*, **24**, 1826 (1991).

24. Sumpter, B. G., Noid, D. W., and Wunderlich, B., *J. Chem. Phys.* **93**, 6875 (1990).

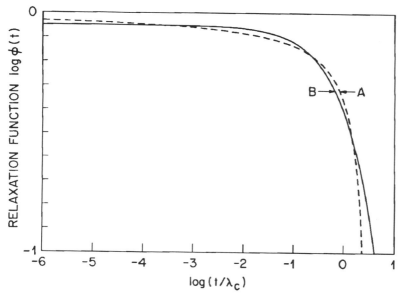

Figure 2.2.2   Comparison of the relaxation functions, the KWW equation (curve B) with β = 0.5 and λ_c = 0.3, and Equation 2.2.6 with $\Delta\mu$ = 3 kcal/mol, T = 300 K, z_c = 10, and $\lambda_c c$ = 0.6. (curve A).   *I thought $\Delta\mu = 4$ too6 (p 63)*

the reason for the apparent success of the universal scheme created by Ngai and coworkers,[25] which makes a connection between the KWW exponent β and the value of the apparent activation energy.

Both the KWW equation and our Equation 2.2.6 cut off fairly abruptly beyond $t \geq \lambda_c$, whereas the experimental viscoelastic relaxation modulus continues into stage 2 (the "transition zone") for many more decades, as a result of the so-called *external* viscosity, rather than the *internal* viscosity with which we have been concerned here. The behavior that is identified with the external viscosity is unique to polymers because it depends on the molecular weight, whereas the stage 1 behavior we have discussed involves only the local segmental relaxation observed by dielectric, volumetric, thermodynamic, and viscoelastic measurement. The values of the dielectric and viscoelastic λ_c for the stage 1 are nearly the same.

25. Ngai, K.; Rendall, R. W.; Rajagopal, A. K.; and Teiler, S. *Ann. N. Y. Acad. Sci.*, **484**, 150 (1986)

So far we have discussed only for the *equilibrium* state above T_g. In the *non-equilibrium* state, the spectrum broadens at lower temperatures. The broadening occurs because the relaxation times of the larger domains exhibit a greater temperature coefficient than those of smaller domains. This has been observed in both viscoelastic[26] and dielectric[27] relaxation. We can use the KWW formula (which is good in the range $t \approx \lambda_c$) to predict this broadening quantitatively. The slope of a plot of $\log G(t)$ vs. $\log t$ such as shown in Figure 2.2.3 is $-\beta(t/\lambda_c)^\beta$ according to the KWW formula. We now let $\ln t_0$ be equal to $\ln \lambda_c - \Delta\mu z_c/kT$, which remains constant *for a given thermal history*. At $t = \lambda_c$, $\log G(t) = \log G(0) - \log e$, or $\ln G(t) = \ln G(0) - 1$, and the slope is exactly $-\beta$. We define the time t_0 as shown in Figure 2.2.3, such that

$$\frac{1}{\beta} = \ln \lambda_c - \ln t_0 \tag{2.2.9}$$

Now, we change the temperature from $T_A = 90\ °C$ to $T_B = 57\ °C$ in Figure 2.2.3 without changing the domain size distribution so that z_c remains unchanged. The characteristic relaxation time changes from λ_A to λ_B, and

$$\frac{1}{\beta_B} = \ln \lambda_B - \ln t_0 = \ln \lambda_A + \frac{\Delta\mu}{k} z_c \left[\frac{1}{T_B} - \frac{1}{T_A} \right] - \ln t_0 \tag{2.2.10}$$

Thus,

$$\frac{1}{\beta_B} - \frac{1}{\beta_A} = \ln \lambda_A - \ln \lambda_B = \frac{\Delta\mu^*}{k} \frac{T_f}{T_f - T_0} \left[\frac{1}{T_B} - \frac{1}{T_A} \right] \tag{2.2.11}$$

One condition required for these equations is that the thermal history be the same for comparing the temperature dependence, because both t_0 and z_c depend on physical aging. The two curves in Figure 2.2.3 are not exactly for

---

26. Matsuoka, S., Bair, H. E., Bearder, S. S., Kern, H. E., and Ryan, J. T., *Polym. Eng. Sci.* **18**, 1073 (1978).

27. Mashimo, S., Nozaki, R., Yagihara, S., and Takeishi, S., *J. Chem. Phys.* **77**(12), 6259 (1982).

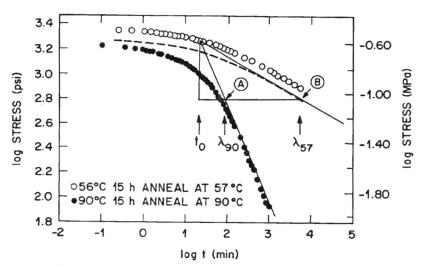

Figure 2.2.3   In the glassy state the relaxation spectrum broadens with a drop in temperature. This is *not* a result of a simultaneous physical aging process. The broadening indicates the multiple values of apparent activation energy that depend on the sizes of cooperative domains.

the same physical aging, but the values of t_0 are close enough to allow the assumptions to stand.

When the polymer is quenched from the initial equilibrium state at T_f to a new glassy state at temperature $T < T_f$, the nonequilibrium glassy state is specified by the fictive temperature T_f. The relaxation time has changed from the initial value λ_{cf} to the new λ_c, while z_c remains unchanged. The broadening of the spectrum is given by the decrease in β from β_f by the formula:

$$\frac{1}{\beta} - \frac{1}{\beta_f} = \ln \lambda_c - \ln \lambda_{cf} = \frac{\Delta \mu^*}{k(T_f - T_0)} \left[\frac{T_f}{T} - 1 \right] \qquad (2.2.12)$$

which pertains to the *non*equilibrium states only. The fictive temperature T_f is typically 5 to 10 °C below the experimental T_g. The value of β is smaller and the spectrum broader in the glassy state as described by Equation 2.2.12.

2.2.2 Stage 2: The "Transition" Zone

Stage 2 relaxation, known as the "transition zone" of the relaxation spectrum, is discussed in detail in Chapter 4; we briefly explore here the possible application of the methodology used with the domain model. Clearly, there is a fundamental difference in the molecular mechanisms for stage 1 and stage 2. Stage 1 is associated with the *internal* viscosity, which resists the local unkinking of segments under the stress, while stage 2 is associated with the *external* viscosity, which resists the tendency of chains to slip past their neighbors. According to deGennes,[28] the ratio of the internal stress σ_{in} to the external stress σ_{ex} is

$$\frac{\sigma_{in}}{\sigma_{ex}} = \frac{\varsigma_{in}}{\varsigma_{ex}} \frac{1}{X^2} \tag{2.2.13}$$

where X is the number of conformers slipping; ς_{in} is the friction coefficient for conformational relaxation $\propto \exp(z_c \Delta\mu / kT)$, while ς_{ex} is the frictional coefficient per bond proportional to $\exp(X \Delta\mu_e / kT)$. Here, $\Delta\mu_e$ stands for the activation energy needed for one segment to slip past others surrounding it, whereas $\Delta\mu$ is for the activation energy required for the rotation of one conformer as defined earlier. The detailed form of Equation 2.2.13 is specific for the Rouse model (see Chapter 4, Section 4.3, and note 7). If we assume that $\Delta\mu$ and $\Delta\mu_e$ are approximately equal (we will discuss on this point subsequently), then stage 2 takes over where stage 1 leaves off, i.e., when $X \geq z_c$.

Recent studies on dielectric relaxation by Adachi, Imanishi and Kotaka,[29] and by Boese and Kremer,[30] reveal a clear distinction between stage 1 and stage 2. Stage 1 is observed in polymers with the dipoles perpendicular to the chain direction, signifying the local segmental reorientation. Stage 2, on the other hand, is observed in polymers with

28. deGennes, P.-G., *Scaling Concepts in Polymer Physics,* Cornell University Press, Ithaca, NY, 1985, p. 171.

29. Adachi, k.; Imanishi, Y; and Kotaka, T.; *J. Chem. Soc., Faraday Trans. 1.,* **85**(5),1065 (1989)

30. Boese, D.; and Kremer, F.; *Macromol.,* **23**, 829 (1990)

dipoles that are parallel to the chain, signifying a large order reorientation in the scale of a chain. These authors were able to distinguish the two mechanisms taking place in polyisoprene, in which the perpendicular and parallel components of the dipoles are about equal in magnitude. They observed the parallel components, which respond to the dielectric field with the relaxation time which depends on the molecular weight, as observed in stage 2 of viscoelastic relaxation. Other supporting evidence for this view of the two stages is found in Osaki's rheo-optical data on polystyrene[31] which showed that the stress optical coefficient in stage 1 is typically the opposite in sign and 20 times smaller in magnitude than the stress optical coefficient in stage 2, signifying distinctly different molecular mechanisms for the two stages of relaxation. The opposite sign is a consequence of the phenyl group in a branch position, but the large difference in the magnitude of the optical coefficient is due to the large difference in the unrelaxed moduli for the two processes.

Stage 2 in the log-log plot of the master relaxation modulus shown in Figure 1.4.1 includes a substantial straight-line portion with a slope of -0.6, and it is consistent with the well-known Rouse model, which predicts a power law with the exponent of -0.5. The equation for the power law can be written in the form:

$$G(t) = \frac{G_0}{e} \left(\frac{t}{\lambda} \right)^{-n} \tag{2.2.14}$$

where e is the natural logarithm base, and $n \simeq 0.6$ when in equilibrium. On the other hand, stage 1, which follows the Kohlrausch-Williams-Watts (KWW) equation, shown earlier by Equation 1.4.2:

$$G(t) = G_0 \exp\left[-\left(\frac{t}{\lambda} \right)^{\beta} \right] \tag{2.2.15}$$

where β is often found to be approximately 0.5, can be joined with Equation 2.2.14 at $t = \lambda$ and, moreover, such λ is in fact equal to λ_c. The master

31. Osaki, K., paper presented at International Conference on Relaxation Phenomena, Crete, June 1990.

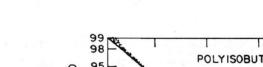

Figure 2.2.4   The stage 2 viscoelastic relaxation plotted on the probability paper. The straight line represents the normal probability distribution of the sizes of strands of chains participating in the relaxation process. The center of the distribution is roughly Kuhn's strand length and the molecular weight is 1000.

viscoelastic relaxation curve can be represented by the composite of two equations, Equation 2.2.15 when $t < \lambda_c$, and Equation 2.2.14 when $t > \lambda_c$, with the value of the power $n = \beta$. The value of β in equilibrium liquids is typically nearly 0.5. The smaller values are observed in the nonequilibrium glassy state at lower temperatures, according to Equation 2.2.13, which we derived from the Adam-Gibbs equation.

Catsiff and Tobolsky[32] made the interesting observation that the logarithmic relaxation modulus in the "transition zone" fits the normal distribution curve when the abscissa is in logarithm of time, i.e.,

$$\log G\,(t) = \tfrac{1}{2}(\log G_0 + \log G_r)$$
$$+ \tfrac{1}{2}(\log G_0 - \log G_r)\,\mathrm{erf}\left[\frac{h\log t}{\lambda}\right] \qquad (2.2.16)$$

where h is a parameter for the width of the distribution and G_r is the rubbery

32. Catsiff, E., and Tobolsky, A. V., *J. Colloid Sci.*, **10**, 375 (1955).

modulus of the "plateau zone." The notation "erf" denotes the Gaussian error function. The data fit the normal distribution extremely well over the most of the transition zone, as shown in Figure 2.2.4 except for the very short time end, which is well within stage 1. These authors proposed this formula as a parametric empirical formula, without suggesting physical reasons. This equation does, significantly, combine the two equations above in one, except for the extremely short times for which our own Equation 2.2.6 is a better choice than the KWW equation.

Polymers exhibit a spectrum of multiple relaxation times because a polymer chain can undergo various modes of relaxation. Here, we are not considering polydispersity, nor the entanglement effects above the critical molecular weight. The longest relaxation time corresponds to the relaxation of a whole chain. The shorter relaxation modes involve the harmonics for parts of the molecule, which we will call "strands." The "weight" of each mode is a measure of the population of the strand of that particular size. The probability that the length of a strand falls between X_1 and X_2 is given by the formula:

$$P = \int_{X_1}^{X_2} \frac{1}{\Delta X \sqrt{2\pi}} \exp\left[- \frac{(X - X_M)^2}{2\Delta X^2} \right] dX \qquad (2.2.17)$$

where a Gaussian distribution is assumed. ΔX is the standard deviation (rms value), and X_M is the mean of distribution. This probability P corresponds to the number of strands whose length falls between X_1 and X_2. Or, alternatively, if we let $X = \log \lambda$, it is the weighting function for the relaxation time λ. For the latter case, the incremental modulus between time t_1 and t_2 is a measure of the population of a mode(s) whose relaxation time falls between t_1 and t_2 (this is why the relaxation spectrum $H(\ln \lambda) = -/ dG/d\ln t$ as noted in Equation 1.5.3), but we must normalize by dividing the increment by the modulus itself:

$$P = \frac{G_2 - G_1}{G_1} = \ln G_2 - \ln G_1 \qquad (2.2.18)$$

as shown earlier in deriving Equation 2.2.4. From Equations 2.2.17 and 2.2.18, we obtain:

$$\log G = \tfrac{1}{2}(\log G_0 + \log G_r)$$

$$+ \tfrac{1}{2}(\log G_0 - \log G_r)\frac{h}{\sqrt{\pi}}\int_{X_M}^{X} \exp\Big[-[h(x-X_M)]^2\Big]dx \qquad (2.2.19)$$

We now assign $\log t$ for the variable X:

$$\log G = \tfrac{1}{2}(\log G_0 + \log G_r) + \tfrac{1}{2}(\log G_0 - \log G_r)$$

$$\frac{h}{\sqrt{\pi}}\int_{\log \lambda_M}^{\log t} \exp\Big[-\Big[h\log \frac{t}{\lambda_M}\Big]^2\Big]d\log t \qquad (2.2.20)$$

where λ_M is the relaxation time for the mean size strands. The standard deviation in $\log t$ is found, in Figure 2.2.4, by first taking $\log t = -9.3$ for the 50% relaxed point and $\log t = -7.2$ for the 16% unrelaxed point, then taking the difference in those values of $\log t$, and it is found to be 2.1 $[h = 1/(2.1\sqrt{2})]$.

To summarize the discussion of this section, the distribution of relaxation times in the transition zone or stage 2 fits a normal distribution for the population of the strands that could be identified with the characteristic relaxation modes. The mean of such a distribution corresponds to the shear modulus of ca. 3×10^7 dynes/cm^2. This corresponds to the molecular weight of 1000 according to the formula $G = \rho RT/M$, or 20 conformers if the average molecular weight is 50. The very nature of the normal distribution with the standard deviation in $\log t$ of 2 gives rise to the slope of about -0.5 for the log-log plot of the modulus vs. time. We explore molecular reason for this in Chapter 4. The lower limit of the strand size may be $M = 30$ for which the shear modulus of 10^9 dynes/cm^2 is obtained, whereas the upper limit of 3.4×10^4 is obtained for the modulus of 10^6 dynes/cm^2, which is in the range of forming the entanglement.

SUMMARY

The features of the cooperative domain model and its implications are summarized as follows:

1. A model for the glass transition has been proposed that incorporates restrictions on individual segments from relaxing independently of

their *inter*molecular neighbors. A domain of cooperativity is defined as a group of segments that must undergo relaxation simultaneously. The model has been used to explain several universal aspects of relaxation phenomena in polymers.

2. The origin of the distribution of relaxation times in "solids" is the size distribution of the cooperatively relaxing domains. The Adam-Gibbs formula is a natural consequence of the temperature dependence of the domain size.

3. The KWW equation is a simple and convenient formula that approximates the dielectric relaxation near λ_c but not where $t \ll \lambda_c$. Our model leads to Equation 2.2.6, which exhibits a better fit to the data. The parameter β depends slightly on temperature (Equation 2.2.6´´) even in the equilibrium state.

4. The distribution of relaxation times broadens markedly in the nonequilibrium glassy state as the temperature is lowered from T_g because the activation energies are different for different domain sizes (Equation 2.2.12).

5. The larger the conformer size, the greater the molar specific heat ΔC_p and T_g, which is proportional to log molecular weight. The specific heat per mass, therefore, decreases for the high T_g polymers with the larger conformer sizes.

6. The upper limit temperature of cooperativity can be extrapolated to 500 °C and 10^{-12} second. The lower limit of the conformer size can be extrapolated to the molecular weight of 9.6.

7. Using those parameters, T_g can be accurately predicted for many polymers from their chemical structure.

8. The β transition is the *intra*molecular cooperative relaxation between the conformers that are pinned by their neighbors at the glass transition. Since the same conformer within a repeat unit is most likely to be pinned, the size of cooperative segments in β relaxation is often equal to that of a repeat unit.

3

The Glassy State

When the thermodynamic state is changing and the rate of change depends on the thermodynamic state, the "apparent" time constant is not a constant at all. The solution of a differential equation describing physical aging is an exponential integral, and the "apparent time constant" turns out to be about 30 times the segmental relaxation time, which is continuously changing.

3.1 Isothermal Contraction/Expansion in the Nonequilibrium State

The unrelaxed state under stress is by definition not in equilibrium, meaning that the material will eventually return to the equilibrium state. Up to this point, however, we have been concerned with a relatively small perturbation such that the time dependence of the volume, entropy, and enthalpy changes were not considered. In this Chapter, we are concerned with the effect of the changing volume, and other variables on the conformational relaxation as a coupled phenomenon.[1] When the temperature drops suddenly to a point near the glass transition temperature, the structural change in response to the temperature drop is slow compared to the time for the temperature to equilibrate. The volume will continue to decrease after the temperature has equilibrated. We now define δ as the deviation in volume from the equilibrium value at the new temperature T after the quenching, i.e.,

$$\delta = \frac{V(t) - V_\infty}{V_\infty} \tag{3.1.1}$$

where V_∞ is the specific volume at equilibrium at T and $V(t)$ is the specific volume at time t. The rate of the volume recovery toward the equilibrium value is described by the equation:

---

1. Ngai has used the terminology "coupled" relaxation process for many classes of relaxation processes characterized by stretched exponential relaxation and large energy of activation.

$$-\frac{d\delta}{dt} = \frac{\delta}{\lambda_{eff}}$$

(3.1.2)

where λ_{eff}, the effective volume recovery time, is affected not only by temperature and pressure but also by entropy, volume, etc., and is a function of δ and is continuously shifting with time until it reaches equilibrium. Kovacs, Stratton, and Ferry[2] who compared the volume recovery process with dynamic mechanical relaxation, concluded that the temperature dependence of λ_{eff} is quite different from that of the viscoelastic relaxation spectrum.

In addition to this nonlinear aspect of Equation 3.1.2, it is necessary to account for the multiplicity of relaxation times:

$$-\frac{d\delta}{dt} = \sum_i \frac{G_i \delta_i}{\lambda_i}$$

(3.1.3)

where each λ_i is a function of time or, more precisely, a function of δ_i and T, and G_i is the weighting factor for the ith relaxation mechanism. The total perturbation is a weighted sum of δ_i's:

$$\delta = \frac{\Sigma G_i \delta_i}{\Sigma G_i}$$

(3.1.4)

To find a suitable distribution function, let us consider a case where the temperature is suddenly dropped from $T(0)$ to T by quenching the sample. If the temperature change is sufficiently small, the perturbation δ_i is so small that the relaxation time λ_i remains essentially constant, the process is considered to be linear, and the rate of decay of $\delta(t)$ reflects the distribution of relaxation times. In this regime, the perturbation from the opposite side in the change of temperature (i.e., a sudden heating) should exhibit the same distribution of relaxation times, and the two curves of $\delta(t)$ vs. $\log t$ should appear as mirror images of each other. Such a curve, it was found, can be approximated by a stretched exponential function such as the KWW formula. The value of the KWW parameter β was found to be about 0.5, and since

---

2. Kovacs, A. J., Stratton, R., and Ferry, J. D., *J. Phys. Chem.* **67**, 152 (1963).

this is a familiar expression for describing the molecular relaxation, it has come to be widely accepted as the applicable form of function for the thermodynamic recovery function.[3] Sasabe and Moynihan[4] were the first to formulate the kinetics of thermodynamic recovery processes using the KWW equation,

$$\delta = \delta_0 \exp\left[-\left(\int_0^t \frac{dt}{\lambda_{\text{eff}}} \right)^\beta \right] \tag{3.1.5}$$

and δ is considered to be proportional to the difference between the temperature of vitrification T_f (the fictive temperature) and the temperature T. The relaxation time λ_{eff} depends on T_f as well as T, since it depends on the structure (*e.g.*, the cooperative domain size). Instead of adopting a Vogel-Fulcher type of formulation, however, Sasabe and Moynihan chose an Arrhenius form, originally introduced by Narayanaswamy[5]:

$$\ln\lambda(T_f, T) \propto \frac{H}{k}\left[\frac{x}{T} + \frac{1-x}{T_f} \right] \tag{3.1.6}$$

which partitions the contributions from the structural factor T_f and the thermal factor T with an empirical parameter x, and the formula obviously converges to the Arrhenius equation at equilibrium. Aside from the fact that an extremely large value for the activation energy H must be introduced, and that the value of λ_{eff} does not shed any light on a possible connection to the segmental relaxation time λ_c, the Narayanaswamy equation is not a good empirical approximation for fitting the volumetric data precisely. This is illustrated in Figure 3.1.1, where the parameter x must be changed progressively for different temperatures, and the value of H cannot be maintained constant if a good fit is desired. Clearly a new approach is desirable. One of the serious corrections required in the foregoing approach

---

3. The term "recovery" is used instead of "relaxation" to denote a recovery from a perturbed thermodynamic *non*equilibrium state back toward the equilibrium state.
4. Sasabe, H., and Moynihan, C. T., *J. Polym. Sci. Phys. Ed.* **16**, 1177 (1978).
5. Narayanaswamy, O. S., *J. Am. Ceram. Soc.* **54**, 491 (1971).

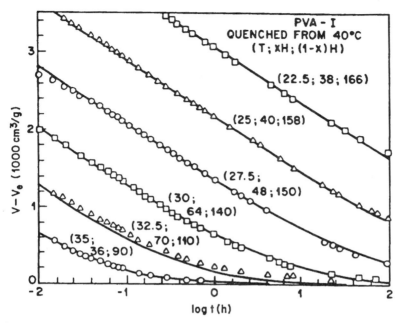

Figure 3.1.1 Isothermal volume contraction data by Kovacs, to which an attempt was made to fit Narayanaswamy's (Equation 3.1.6). A good fit was possible only after the parameter x equation bad been varied for different temperatures. T, since it depends on the structure (*e.g.*, the cooperative not necessarily 1, either.

is that λ_{eff} in Equation 3.1.2 is more strongly dependent on time t than δ is. In such a case, the assumed functional form of λ_{eff} is crucial to the successful fit to data. We will start with the characteristic relaxation time λ_c and show how it may shift as the volume changes in the nonequilibrium regime. If we assume that the viscoelastic modulus follows the KWW formula, λ_c is equal to the time required for the modulus to decay to $1/e$ of the initial value. Since the KWW formula underestimates the short time (high frequency) side of the spectrum, $1/10$ instead of $1/e$ might be a better choice, as were discussed in Section 2.1. According to the model presented in Chapter 2, λ_c is greater than the characteristic dielectric relaxation time λ_c by the amount $\Delta \log \lambda \approx 1$, and it is the relaxation time of the largest domain. In the equilibrium state, λ_c is given by the Vogel-Fulcher formula, Equation 2.1.11:

$$\ln \frac{\lambda_c}{\lambda^*} = \frac{\Delta\mu^*}{k} \frac{1}{T - T_0} - \frac{\Delta\mu^*}{k} \frac{1}{T^* - T_0} \qquad (2.1.11)$$

It is recalled that the Vogel-Fulcher formula was derived from the Adam-Gibbs formula,

$$\ln \frac{\lambda_c}{\lambda^*} = \frac{\Delta\mu}{k} \left[\frac{s^*}{TS_c} - \frac{1}{T^*} \right] \qquad (2.1.9)$$

by substituting the following expression for the equilibrium entropy:

$$\frac{S_c}{s^*} = \frac{T^*}{T^* - T_0} \frac{T - T_0}{T} \qquad (2.1.7)$$

and for the $\Delta\mu$:

$$\Delta\mu^* = \Delta\mu \frac{T^* - T_0}{T^*} \qquad (2.1.14)$$

It is also recalled that Doolittle's free volume formula:

$$\ln \frac{\lambda_c}{\lambda_{\text{ref}}} = \frac{1}{\alpha_f(T - T_0)} - \frac{1}{\alpha_f(T_{\text{ref}} - T_0)} \qquad (2.1.13)$$

where the subscript "ref" refers to a reference temperature T_{ref}, is equivalent to the Vogel-Fulcher formula 2.1.11 above, by making $\Delta\mu^*/k = 1/\alpha_f = 1/\Delta\alpha$.[6] The fractional free volume $f = V_f/V$ is connected to the activation energy $\Delta\mu^*$ for the conformational relaxation of one conformer of molecular weight M_0 (~ 9.6) by the formula:

$$\frac{1}{f} = \frac{\Delta\mu}{kT} \frac{s^*}{S_c} = \frac{\Delta\mu^*}{k(T - T_0)} \qquad (3.1.7)$$

We now extend all those formulas above to the nonequilibrium state. The glassy state is the state whose structure at some elevated temperature T_f was frozen during quenching to below the glass transition temperature. The structure that was at equilibrium at the old temperature was brought down

---

6. The reason for this identity was discussed in Section 2.1.

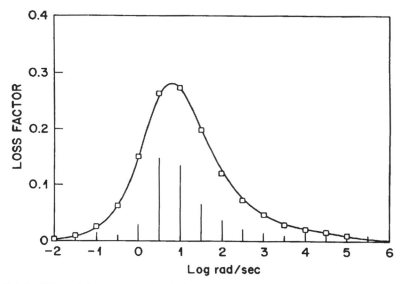

Figure 3.1.2 Dirac deltas are obtained that reproduce the loss factor data as shown. The abscissa could be called "log frequency in hertz at 45 °C" or "- log *t* in hours at 35 °C" to make the graph quantitative for polyvinyl acetate for Kovacs' kinetic data on volume change in the glassy state. The high frequency side of the spectrum is in good agreement with the domain model, Equation 2.2.6, rather than the KWW equation. *What about low freq side ?*

intact to the new temperature T, and the entropy is retained unchanged. (The temperature equalization is assumed to take place at a much faster rate, since it is carried out by the elastic wave.) The temperature before quenching is invoked to describe the structure, and it is called the fictive temperature, T_f. Equation 2.1.7 for the entropy is modified accordingly:

$$\frac{S_c}{s^*} = \frac{T^*}{T^* - T_0} \frac{T_f - T_0}{T_f} \tag{3.1.8}$$

and the Vogel-Fulcher formula, Equation 2.1.11, is:

$$\ln \frac{\lambda_c}{\lambda^*} = \frac{\Delta\mu^*}{kT} \frac{T_f}{T_f - T_0} - \frac{\Delta\mu^*}{k(T^* - T_0)} \tag{3.1.9}$$

and both Equations 3.1.8 and 3.1.9 revert to the original equilibrium formulas when T_f is substituted for T. Similarly, the fractional free volume at

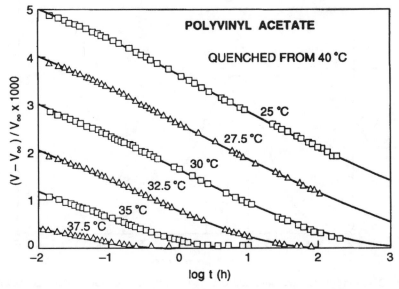

Figure 3.1.3   The dielectric spectrum shown in Figure 3.1.2 was utilized with Equation 3.1.11 to predict Kovacs' data. The following values were used: $\Delta^* m$ = 3.9 kcal, T_0 = -14.5 °C, log λ_g = -1.7 (hour) at T_g = 35 °C, $\Delta\alpha$ = 3.85 × 10^{-4} °C. Note that the 35 °C curve extends by the straight line to log $t \sim 0.5$ (hour), whereas the loss peak in Figure 3.1.2 is at log λ_c of -1 (hour). The difference of 1.5 decades is approximately equal to log f_e, as discussed in the text.

the moment of quenching is determined by the entropy and, therefore, f is different from the value before. The fractional free volume in the nonequilibrium state is:

$$f = \frac{k}{\Delta\mu^*}(T_f - T_0)\frac{T}{T_f} \tag{3.1.10}$$

and, since $\Delta\mu^* / kT = \Delta\alpha^*$,[7]

---

7. The asterisk refers to the conformer with molecular weight of M_0 and T_0 of 0 K.

$$f = \Delta\alpha^*(T_f - T_0)\frac{T}{T_f} \tag{3.1.11}$$

This equation is consistent with the previously derived relationship between the conformational entropy S_c and the free volume fraction, as stated with Equation 2.1.17, which we now rewrite for the nonequilibrium case:

$$TS_c = f\frac{\Delta C_p}{\Delta\alpha} = f\frac{\Delta c_p{}^*}{\Delta\alpha^*} \tag{3.1.12}$$

and

$$f = \Delta\alpha^*\frac{TS_c}{\Delta c_p{}^*} = \Delta\alpha^*(T_f - T_0)\frac{T}{T_f}\frac{s^*}{\Delta c_p{}^*} \tag{3.1.13}$$

and, since $T^*s^*/\Delta C_p{}^*T^* = 1$ as we discussed in Section 2.1, Equation 3.1.13 is the same as Equation 3.1.11.

Relaxation time depends on entropy and free volume, while the rate of change for both is controlled by the changing relaxation time; the relaxation process is coupled with thermodynamic change. Meanwhile, the characteristic relaxation time λ_c increases as the entropy is decreased. The effective time constant λ_{eff} for this recovery process is expected to be related to the segmental relaxation time λ_c, but we know from Kovacs' study that they are not identical (Ref. 8)

The Adam-Gibbs formula, with the new definition (Equation 3.1.9) that allows for both equilibrium and nonequilibrium states, can be written for the relaxation time λ_c with respect to the fractional free volume,

$$\lambda_c = \lambda_r\exp\left[\frac{1}{f} - \frac{1}{f_r}\right] \tag{3.1.14}$$

where the subscript r refers to some reference state of the observer's choosing.

To formulate how this λ_c changes with time, we first take a simpler case of $T < T_0$. We call this a simpler case because, compared to the case of $T > T_0$, the condition $T < T_0$ implies that as $t \to \infty$, $f \to 0$, $z \to \infty$, $\lambda_c \to \infty$, and $d\lambda_c/dt \to 0$. In contrast, for $T > T_0$, the physical aging ends as $f \to f_e$ and the mathematics becomes more complicated. (All Kovacs' data are in this latter category.)

If $T < T_0$, the rate of change in λ_c is obtained by differentiating

Equation 3.1.14 with respect to time t:

$$\frac{d\lambda_c}{dt} = \lambda_c \frac{d(1/f)}{dt} = -\frac{\lambda_c}{f^2} \frac{df}{dt} \tag{3.1.15}$$

As we shall show below, the condition:

$$\frac{d\lambda_c}{dt} = f \tag{3.1.16}$$

will satisfy both Equations 3.1.14 and 3.1.15. From Equation 3.1.16,

$$\lambda_c \frac{d(1/f)}{dt} = f$$

or

$$\frac{\lambda_c}{f} d\frac{1}{f} = dt \tag{3.1.17}$$

and letting $x = 1/f$, and $A = \lambda_r \exp(-1/f_r)$,

$$\int_{1/f_r}^{1/f} \frac{\lambda_c}{f} d\frac{1}{f} = \int_{x_r}^{x} xAe^x dx = \int_{t_r}^{t} dt \tag{3.1.18}$$

where $f = f_r$ when $t = t_r$. Integrating the equation above by parts, we obtain:

$$\left[xAe^x - Ae^x \right]_{x_r}^{x} = \int_{t_r}^{t} dt \tag{3.1.19}$$

and we can write:

$$\frac{\lambda_c}{f} - \lambda_c = t \tag{3.1.20}$$

To check this equation, it needs to be shown that

$$\frac{d}{dt}\left[\frac{\lambda_c}{f} - \lambda_c \right] = 1 \tag{3.1.21}$$

by simply calculating each term:

$$\frac{1}{f^2}\left[\frac{d\lambda_c}{dt}f - \frac{df}{dt}\lambda_c\right] - \frac{d\lambda_c}{dt}$$

$$= \frac{1}{f}\frac{d\lambda_c}{dt} + \frac{d\ln\lambda_c}{dt}\lambda_c - \frac{d\lambda_c}{dt} = 1 + f - f = 1 \qquad (3.1.22)$$

Also, from Equation 3.1.15, we obtain

and 3.1.2

$$-\frac{1}{f}\frac{df}{dt} = \frac{f^2}{\lambda_c} = \frac{1}{\lambda_{eff}} \approx \frac{f}{t} \qquad (3.1.23)$$

The effective time constant λ_{eff} is for the case where $T < T_0$ and $f_e = 0$, but λ_{eff} changes rapidly with time t. The meaning of the term "time constant" breaks down in this case, since it IS equal to $t/f!$ Thus, the time constant for the volume recovery is:

$$\lambda_{eff} = \frac{\lambda_c}{f^2} = \frac{t}{f} \qquad (3.1.24)$$

where λ_c is about $1/30$ ($\approx f$) of the elapsed aging time according to Equation 3.1.20.[8] Also, we obtain:

$$\frac{d\ln\lambda_c}{d\ln t} = \frac{t}{\lambda_c}\frac{d\lambda_c}{dt} = \left(\frac{1}{f} - 1\right)f = 1 - f \qquad (3.1.25)$$

This is the so-called μ factor, and it is nearly 1 when $f \ll 1$. λ_c will stay constant as long as the ratio λ_c/t is greater than the current value of f. In this time regime, no aging will proceed and μ is zero. This is true in the temperature regime $T \ll T_g$, or in the time regime represented by $t \ll f\lambda_c$. At the other extreme, at a temperature near T_g, as f approaches the equilibrium value, the rate of aging slows down and eventually comes to a virtual halt. In this regime μ becomes zero again. Between these two extreme conditions, the steady state value for μ is nearly 1.

When $T > T_0$, as $t \to \infty$, $f \to f_e$, and the perturbation $\delta = f - f_e$ replaces f in Equation 3.1.21, and for the rate equation we have:

---

8. If we assume that $\lambda_{eff} = \lambda_c$, on the other hand, we have $\lambda = t/f$; i.e., the relaxation time is more than an order of magnitude greater than the aging time, and the stress will not be able to relax!

$$-\frac{1}{\delta}\frac{\mathrm{d}\delta}{\mathrm{d}t} = \frac{1}{\lambda_{\text{eff}}} \approx \frac{f^2}{\delta t} \approx \frac{f^2}{\lambda_c} \tag{3.1.26}$$

The first two terms are identical to Equation 3.1.2. $\mathrm{d}\lambda_c/\mathrm{d}t$ will reach 0 when $f \to f_e$, but it can be negative if $f < f_e$. Thus Equation 3.1.16 is not always true if $T > T_0$. However, if we replace f with δ in it, i.e.,

$$\frac{\mathrm{d}\lambda_c}{\mathrm{d}t} = \delta \tag{3.1.27}$$

we find that Equation 3.1.24 holds without modification. Equation 3.1.16 is in fact a special case of Equation 3.1.25 when f_e is 0, i.e., $T < T_0$. There is no simple relationship between λ_c and t (such as Equation 3.1.20 found for $T < T_0$). However, when $f > f_e$, the following equation is approximately true until $f \approx f_e$:

$$\frac{\lambda_c}{\delta} - \lambda_c \approx t \tag{3.1.28}$$

Until the value of f approaches very close to the final f_e, we can use the results obtained for $T < T_0$, i.e., Equations 3.1.16 through 3.1.25. During physical aging at a temperature near T_g, the shift of the relaxation time is obtained by Equation 3.1.28; i.e., the relaxation time is proportional to the aging time and is about $\delta/(1-\delta)$ or 1/20 to 1/40 of the aging time. This feature is experimentally supported, as discussed in a later chapter for PVC and polystyrene. For example, for polystyrene at 90 °C, for aging times of 1, 15, and 150 hours, λ_c values are 2, 30, and 300 minutes, respectively, as shown below in Figure 3.2.3.

We are now ready to compare Kovacs' dilatometric data on polyvinyl acetate with our dielectric data. The dielectric loss factor for this polymer is shown in Figure 3.1.2. From the shift of the loss peak with temperature, we have obtained the following Vogel-Fulcher parameters: $\Delta\mu^* = 3.6$ kcal/mol, $T_0 = 14.5$ °C, and $\lambda_c = 12$ minutes at 35 °C. When the temperature is suddenly changed from $T(0)$ to T, the fractional free volume does NOT remain constant, following Equation 3.1.11:

$$f_r = \Delta\alpha^*(T(0) - T_0)\frac{T}{T(0)} \tag{3.1.29}$$

The complex nature of the fractional free volume in the nonequilibrium state makes necessary two important corrections on δ_r and λ_r. One is that the

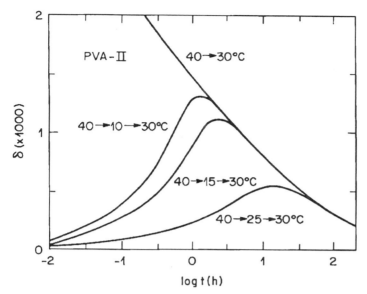

Figure 3.1.4 The memory effect data were calculated from the Adam-Gibbs formula, the differential equation above (3.1.3), and the dielectric spectrum shown in Figure 3.1.2. As indicated in the text, the calculated values of hours spent at the respective minimum temperatures agree well with the experimental values.

initial value of δ ($= f - f_e$) is smaller when quenched isentropically from above than when heated from below T by the same increment in temperature, ΔT. The volume $\delta = (V(t) - V_\infty)/V_\infty$ must be modified accordingly:

$$\delta_r = \Delta\alpha^*(T(0) - T_0)\frac{T}{T(0)} - \Delta\alpha^*(T - T_0)\frac{T}{T} \qquad (3.1.30)$$

The other correction is made necessary because the same value of f in equilibrium and in nonequilibrium states results in different values of λ_c's. This is the origin of the extra Arrhenius term needed for shifting between the same value of f at two different temperatures -- a well-known fact among the researchers who have analyzed Kovacs' data in detail.[9] Because

9. Matsuoka, S, Fredrickson, G. H., Williams, G., and Johnson, G. E., in *Lecture Notes in Physics*, No. 277, *Molecular Dynamics and Relaxation Phenomena in Glasses*, Th. Dorfmüller, and G. Williams, Eds., Springer-Verlag, Berlin, 1987, p. 188.

everything is made in reference to λ_r and not to λ_e, this correction becomes very important. When quenched from the equilibrium at T_g to the new T, the initial f_r is in the nonequilibrium state such that

$$\frac{1}{f_r} = \frac{1}{f_{T,S_g}} = \frac{1}{f_{T_g,S_g}} + \Delta\frac{1}{f} \tag{3.1.31}$$

where f_{T_g,S_g} is the equilibrium quantity, and

$$\Delta\frac{1}{f} = \frac{\Delta\mu^*}{k}\frac{s^*}{S_g}\left(\frac{1}{T} - \frac{1}{T_g}\right) \tag{3.1.32}$$

At the same time, the shift of f downward by Δf requires a shift in the time scale, since the plot of $\ln(1/f)$ vs. $\ln t$ is nearly a straight line with a slope of unity until f approaches f_e. The correction in the time scale is needed by the same amount as for the correction made for $\log\lambda_r$. Thus, the total correction for the nonequilibrium f, in reference to the equilibrium state at T_g is made:

$$\Delta\ln\lambda_c = 2\Delta\frac{1}{f} = 2\frac{\Delta\mu^*}{k}\frac{T_g}{T_g - T_0}\left(\frac{1}{T} - \frac{1}{T_g}\right) \tag{3.1.33}$$

This correction amounts to the Arrhenius term with ca. 40 kcal/mol in addition to the Adam-Gibbs term, as we noted in our earlier paper, although we were not able to explain it at that time.

With all these equations shown above, and applying the distribution of λ_i's around the characteristic[10] relaxation time ($\log\lambda_c$ = -1.7 in hours at 35 °C), Kovacs' data[11] for the isothermal contractions of polyvinyl acetate have been reproduced with accuracy in Figure 3.1.3. The $\Delta\alpha$ values of 3.85×10^{-4} °C has been used for the calculation of $(V - V_\infty/V_\infty)$, but this value is exactly the reciprocal of $\Delta\mu/k = \Delta\mu^*T^*/(T^* - T_0)/k$ with $\Delta\mu$ of 3900 cal mol (of conformers), T^* = 500 °C, T_0 = - 14.5 °C. The value of λ_c is nearly 1/30 of the ongoing aging time t, since the equilibrium values of $\log\lambda_c$

---

10. λ_c was taken from the experimental dielectric relaxation spectrum as shown in Figure 3.1.2.

11. Kovacs, A. J., *Fortschr. Hochpolym. Forsch.* **3**, 394 (1963).

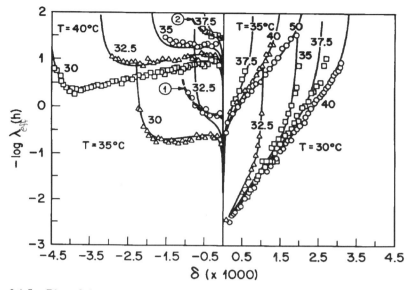

Figure 3.1.5 Plot of the overall rate of total volume change vs. perturbation. Numbers on curves denote the initial temperature at which the sample was at equilibrium before it was plunged to the temperature T °C. Curve 1 was calculated by changing the initial temperature to 33 °C and the final T to 35.5 °C, whereas for curve 2, only the final temperature was changed, to 40.5 °C. We have found that the longer time end of the spectrum must be excluded to give a good fit, implying that this is a stage 1 relaxation process. These curves were reproduced by the computer program in Chaper 7 (Section 7.2).

calculated from the dielectric and volumetric data are 2.63, 1.36, 0.22, -0.79, -1.70, and -2.53 in hours at 25, 27.5, 30, 32.5, 35, and 37.5 °C, respectively. The values of log t extended by the straight lines to $\delta = 0$ are almost 2 decades longer (i.e., 5.5, 4.1, 2.5, 1.3, 0.2, -0.8), and this corresponds to $\approx \log f_e$

It might be speculated that the coupled phenomena due to the changing thermodynamic state during aging constitute the sole reason for the stretched exponential function for the volume recovery curves. This is not true, however, because the form of the relaxation function is stretched partly because of the multiple relaxation times. This is evidenced from Kovacs' "memory effect" data.

The memory effect experiment was carried out by Kovacs in the following manner: first the sample was quenched from 40 °C to the low temperature of 10, 15, or 25 °C, where it was held for the precise period of time needed to ensure that the subsequent transfer to the bath held at 30 °C would result in the volume at exactly the equilibrium value. What happens after this last step is well known: the specific volume does not stay at this equilibrium value; instead, it expands for a time and then comes back to the equilibrium value (see Figure 3.1.4). The amplitude of this volumetric excursion is greater if the initial drop in temperature is greater. This phenomenon is explained only by the intrinsic distribution of relaxation times. We prefer to place physical meaning further by relating it to the distribution of domain sizes. During the initial quench from 40 °C to, say, 10 °C, the smaller domains with shorter relaxation times densify faster than the larger domains with longer relaxation times. When the sample is suddenly transferred to 30 °C bath, the smaller domains are denser than the overall density while the larger domains are less dense. Now in the bath at 30 °C, the smaller domains are too dense so they begin expanding, while the larger domains are continue to densify. The average specific volume will first expand and then finally contract toward the equilibrium value. Thus the last portion of the memory effect data coincides with that of a straight quenching from 40 °C to 30 °C. This has an important implication in engineering applications in that annealing a glassy polymer without ever reaching the equilibrium state can be approximated by the same formula as that for isothermal aging after the quenching.

Kovacs also has published the data for the overall rate of volume change vs. the perturbation $\delta(t)$, shown in Figure 3.1.5. Figure 3.1.4 is one of the best known and the most challenging collections of data for model builders. Because relaxation time depends on structure, it is longer at a smaller volume and vice versa at a given temperature. The plot of δ vs. $\log t$ during isothermal experiments following sudden cooling (contraction) and a sudden heating (expansion) are shown in Figure 3.1.6. It is noted that when the temperature jump is small, the curves from above and from below the equilibrium line are nearly symmetrical, meaning a linear differential equation in which λ is practically independent of changes in δ. Each of the Dirac deltas in the relaxation spectrum will change while δ is changing, and so will the dielectric shift factor, $\log \lambda / \lambda_{\infty}$. We can develop the relationship between the ith relaxation time λ_i and the elapsed time t in the following manner. First we define $x_i = 1 - T_0/T_{f_i}$, and it can be shown that $dx_i/dt = T_0/T_{f_i}\lambda_i$. Assuming the relationship (Equation 3.1.28):

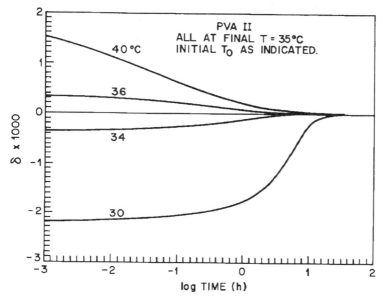

Figure 3.1.6   Isothermal recovery curves calculated from Equations 3.1.3, 3.1.4, and 3.1.6. When the temperature "jump" is small, the curves are nearly symmetrical against the abscissa (cf, linear viscoelasticity), but when it is large, the nonlinear aspect is evident.

$$\delta_i \approx \frac{\lambda_i}{t} = \frac{\Delta\mu}{kT}\frac{1}{x_i} \qquad (3.1.34)$$

Differentiating with respect to t, we obtain

$$\frac{d\lambda_i}{dt} = \frac{\Delta\mu}{kT}\frac{1}{x_i} + \frac{\Delta\mu}{kT}t\left(-\frac{1}{x_i}\frac{dx_i}{dt}\right) = \frac{\Delta\mu}{kT}\frac{1}{x_i} + \frac{T_0}{T_{f_i}} \qquad (3.1.35)$$

Now, the first term is ca. 40 to 50, while the second term is always less than 1. Hence we can make the approximation:

$$\frac{d\lambda_i}{dt} \sim \frac{\Delta\mu}{kT}\frac{1}{x_i} = \frac{\lambda_i}{t} \qquad \text{hence} \qquad \frac{d\ln\lambda_i}{d\ln t} \sim 1 \qquad (3.1.36)$$

meaning that the slope of $\log\lambda$ vs. $\log t$ should be 1. Thus each relaxation time λ_i grows proportionally to the elapsed time, and the shape of the spectrum remains the same during isothermal aging.

Figure 3.1.7 shows this to be true with respect to dielectric relaxation time while thermodynamic recovery (aging) is taking place. The shift factor

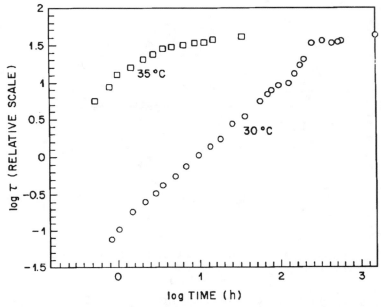

Figure 3.1.7 The dielectric shift factor was traced during isothermal aging to show that the shift factor is approximately proportional to the elapsed time of aging, and the value of μ is nearly 1. Note that the 35 °C curve reaches the equilibrium state at $\log t$ of about 0.5 (hour), in agreement with the results in Figure 3.1.3.

should *never* be confused with the overall rate of the change in perturbation δ, if the latter is a sum result of multiple relaxation times, i.e.,

$$-\frac{d\ln\delta}{d\ln t} \neq \frac{1}{\lambda_{\text{eff}}} \tag{3.1.37}$$

The multiple relaxation times λ_i with multiple domain sizes z_i suggests the existence of multiple values for the apparent activation energy $\Delta\mu z_i$. The distribution of relaxation times will become more widely spread initially when the temperature is decreased while in the nonequilibrium state. This is reflected in the change in the slope of the plot of $\log G(t)$ vs. $\log t$ for glassy polymers at different temperatures, as discussed later.

It has been pointed out that the Adam-Gibbs equation depicting the cooperative relaxation and the Doolittle equation incorporating the free volume concept both reduce to the identical form in the equilibrium state, i.e., the Vogel equation. However, their predictions are different in the nonequilibrium state. The Adam-Gibbs equation becomes an Arrhenius

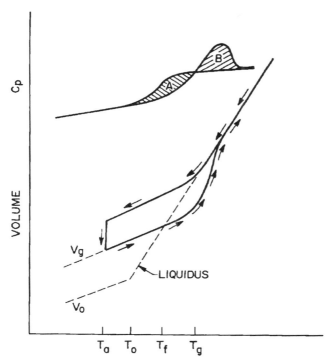

Figure 3.2.1 Schematic diagram of specific volume vs. temperature. The polymer is at equilibrium at high temperature but, when cooled, eventually deviates away from the equilibrium liquidus line. When held at annealing temperature T_a it decreases to V_g. The point at which this glassy volume intersects the (dashed) liquidus line is the fictive temperature T_f. When this glassy state is heated, it overshoots the liquidus line. T_g is sometimes defined as the temperature at which the slope is the greatest or at which the derivative of the slope changes the sign (the point of inflection). Either way, T_g is higher than the fictive temperature. The specific heat shown here is proportional to the thermal expansion coefficient, which is the normalized derivative of the volume with respect to temperature.

equation if the entropy is "frozen" at T_f, with the apparent activation energy being equal to $\Delta\mu T_f/(T_f - T_0)$ and the typical value ranging from 30 to 40 kcal/mol. Doolittle's free volume formula, on the other hand, suggests that the temperature effect is entirely due to the change in free volume, so that the relaxation time of the glassy state is predicted to be independent of temperature. i.e.,

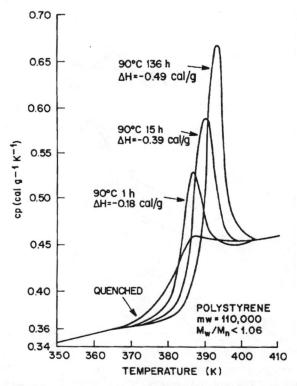

Figure 3.2.2   Specific heat vs. temperature for polystyrene with various thermal histories [Bair, H. E., Johnson, G. E., Anderson, E. W., and Matsuoka, S., *Polym. Eng. and Sci.* **21**(14), 930 (1981)].

$$\ln \lambda \propto \frac{1}{\alpha_f(T_f - T_0)} \qquad (3.1.38)$$

This is clearly wrong and in disagreement with experimental data, but

$$\ln \lambda_c \propto \frac{1}{\alpha_f{}^*(T_f - T_0)} \frac{T_f}{T} \qquad (3.1.39)$$

is correct, where

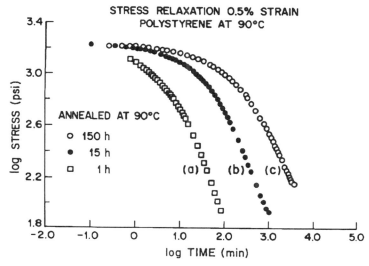

Figure 3.2.3   The shift of stress relaxation curves with physical aging. A definitive relationship exists between the time spent for physical aging and the relaxation time, namely, that the ratio of the characteristic relaxation time to the aging time is the deviation δ, i.e., 1/20 to 1/30, until equilibrium is approached.

$$\frac{\Delta\mu^*}{k} = \frac{1}{\Delta\alpha_f^*} \tag{3.1.40}$$

and

$$\alpha_f = \Delta\alpha = \frac{T^* - T_0}{T^*}\alpha_f^* \tag{3.1.41}$$

which we have shown to be correct for polyvinyl acetate.

In summary, the cooperative relaxation model works well both for the equilibrium and nonequilibrium states, if a proper formulation is made for the appearance of relaxation among λ, z, δ, S_c, and T_f. It suggests that the conformational entropy involved in local molecular arrangements, rather than the longer range molecular conformations that give rise to rubberlike elasticity, may perhaps serve as the criterion for relaxation phenomena. The concept of intermolecular cooperativity has tied together the phenomena of dielectric and viscoelastic relaxation with the physical aging process.

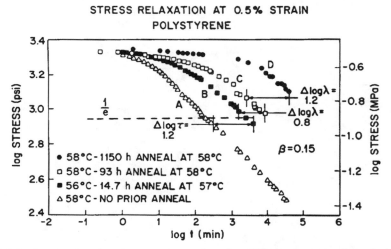

STRESS RELAXATION AT 0.5% STRAIN
POLYSTYRENE

Figure 3.2.4   Stress relaxation curves commencing after different periods of physical aging at 58 °C. The broadening of the spectrum is the most important feature of the nonequilibrium glassy state. The prediction of the temperature dependence of the KWW parameter β is shown by Equation 3.2.3.

3.2 Linear Viscoelastic Relaxation in the Glassy State

A typical glassy state is not in the equilibrium state, although after aging for a long time near T_g the volume can reach the equilibrium liquidus line. If the temperature is subsequently decreased, however, the equilibrium glassy state will move on to a new nonequilibrium state, followed by the physical aging process. The glassy nonequilibrium volume is usually above the liquidus line, an exceptional case being that, when the glassy state is heated rapidly toward the temperature $T \approx T_f$, the volume expansion lags the heating rate and the volume is found temporarily below the liquidus line, as shown in Figure 3.2.1. When the glass transition temperature is determined by this type of temperature ramping method, the value of T_g is higher than T_f of the glassy state. The difference between T_g and T_f becomes greater if the glassy state is extensively aged, as the former increases and the latter decreases. This increase in the apparent T_g with aging can be explained by noting that the relaxation time of the extensively aged glassy state is greater because its domain size is greater and the response to the temperature rise takes a longer time. Because the enthalpy of the glassy state decreases with

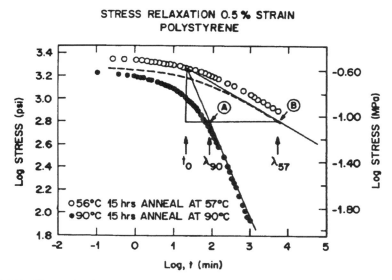

Figure 3.2.5 Change in the relaxation spectrum of polystyrene in the nonequilibrium glassy state. The change arises because the large domains exhibit a greater increase in relaxation time when the temperature is decreased. If the sample is allowed to age until equilibrium is reached, the shape of the distribution will approach that of the equilibrium state.

aging, the plot of specific heat ΔC_p vs. temperature exhibits a greater peak, as illustrated in Figure 3.2.2. In analyzing the viscoelastic relaxation process for the non-equilibrium glassy state, it is important to remember that the thermodynamic state continues to change while the relaxation measurement is conducted. If the rate of the thermodynamic aging process were equal to or faster than the rate of stress decay, we would not have observed stress relaxation in the glassy state. We pointed out in Section 3.1, however, that the relaxation time λ_c is an order of magnitude shorter than the aging time, and that the relaxation time shifts nearly proportionally ($\lambda_c \approx \delta t$) with the time spent for the thermodynamic recovery (aging), as illustrated in Figure 3.1.5. The same sort of behavior is observed in the viscoelastic relaxation of polystyrene at 90 °C, as shown in Figure 3.2.3. The three curves for the relaxation experiments are identical except for the aging time. The samples were aged for 1, 15, and 150 hours, respectively, before the sudden imposition of strain at time t_0, which is set as 0 time for the relaxation measurement. The three samples exhibited relaxation times nearly a decade apart, (i.e., 2, 30, and 300 minutes, respectively), supporting Equation 3.1.26. The linear viscoelastic relaxation process should be observable only when the aging rate is much slower than the relaxation rate. The KWW parameter β for these curves is about 0.4, which is slightly less than the value of $\beta \sim 0.5$ for the equilibrium state near T_g, suggesting a slightly broadened relaxation spectrum when in the nonequilibrium state. The broadening occurs when the temperature is decreased in the nonequilibrium condition, as a result of the difference in the activation energies of the domains of different sizes. For the domain of size z_i, ($z_i < z_c$), its relaxation time λ_i shifts by a lesser amount than the characteristic relaxation time λ_c:

$$\ln \frac{\lambda_i}{\lambda_c} = \frac{\Delta\mu}{kT} (z_i - z_c) \tag{3.2.1}$$

That is, the apparent activation energy is proportional to the domain size.

The tendency for the relaxation spectrum of the nonequilibrium glassy state to broaden at lower temperatures is more clearly demonstrated in Figure 3.2.4 for the same polystyrene at 58 °C.

The value of β is now found to be 0.15. In addition, the straight portion of the curve, depicting the power law, now shows a comparably smaller slope, maintaining the relaxations as follows:

$$G(t) = \frac{G_0}{e} \left(\frac{t}{\lambda_c} \right)^{-\beta} \qquad \text{for } t > \lambda_c \tag{3.2.2}$$

where the same KWW β is used. The discussion of the temperature dependence of β in Section 2.2 is amplified in Figure 3.2.5, which compares two curves for polystrene having undergone the same aging period at two temperatures. (The value of G_0 declines at the elevated temperature, accompanying the decrease in the density and the bulk modulus, and the increase in C_v, but we will not discuss this aspect at this point.) The KWW and the power law curves join at $t = \lambda_c$, where $G(t) = G_0/e$, and the slope $-\beta(t/\lambda)^\beta$ at this point is equal to $-\beta$. The right triangle drawn in Figure 3.2.5 with the altitude $\log e = 0.43$ and the base $\beta \log e$ has a slope of $1/\beta$, and the apex is located at $\log \lambda - \beta \log e$ as shown. The apex of the two right triangles meets at the same point for a reason that is explained by invoking the domain model later in this section. Thus, when the temperature is changed from T_g at equilibrium to new T where it will remain in the nonequilibrium state for a substantial time, we obtain:

$$\frac{1}{\beta} = \frac{1}{\beta_g} + \ln\lambda - \ln\lambda_g \qquad (3.2.3)$$

and we obtain:

$$\frac{1}{\beta} = \frac{1}{\beta_g} + \frac{\Delta\mu}{k}z_c\left(\frac{1}{T} - \frac{1}{T_g}\right) \qquad (3.2.4)$$

or

$$\frac{1}{\beta} = \frac{1}{\beta_g} + \frac{\Delta\mu}{k}\frac{T_f}{T_f - T_0}\left(\frac{1}{T} - \frac{1}{T_g}\right) \qquad (3.2.5)$$

Here, we used T_f rather than T_g to characterize z_c. The fictive temperature T_f is equal to T_g only if the glassy state has been quenched from the equilibrium state at T_g and no further aging has taken place, but this is in general not the case.

Struik[12] has generated a large quantity of creep data which show basically the same features we have shown with the stress relaxation data. There are, however, some differences between the creep and relaxation data, and these differences are important relative to the relaxation process on the molecular scale. In the stress relaxation experiment, the free energy is raised initially, and its decay with time is measured while no further work is added. The relaxation modulus is a measure of the unrelaxed energy still remaining in the sample. In contrast, with the creep experiment, the stress is first built up and then maintained constant, and to do so, work is continuously supplied. The recoverable strain energy is maintained constant throughout the creep experiment. The ratio of creep stress to creep strain (the creep modulus) is not the same as the relaxation modulus, because creep strain includes the irreversible macroscopic strain. In Section 1.3 (Figure 1.3.4) we demonstrated that the creep modulus (i.e., the stress vs. the creep strain) is ahead of the relaxation modulus, and that the creep modulus appears as though the spectrum is broader than the relaxation spectrum obtained from

---

12. Struik, L. C. E., "Physical Aging in Amorphous Polymers and Other Materials," TNO Central Laboratorium Communications No. 565 Delft, 1977.

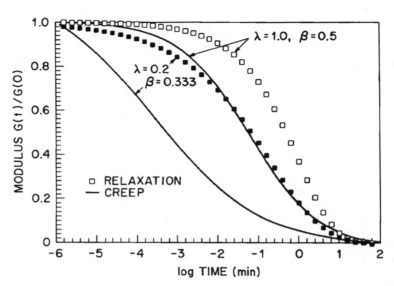

Figure 3.2.6   Comparison of creep and relaxation moduli. The linear viscoelastic relaxation modulus and creep compliance are not reciprocals of each other, but they must satisfy the condition stated in Equation 1.3.9. The creep modulus is more widely spread then the relaxation modulus is, and the creep retardation time is shorter than the relaxation time.

the stress relaxation experiment. Figure 3.2.6 compares the creep modulus with the relaxation modulus for two "materials" with different sets of λ and β for the KWW formula. The creep modulus of the material with larger values of λ and β nearly can be superimposed over the relaxation modulus of the other, having smaller values of λ and β. For example, the relaxation modulus with β of 0.5 can be matched with the creep modulus with β of 0.33 which, as we shall see, will become the Andrade-type power law with the exponent of 1/3 in the longer time regime.[13] The creep data in the KWW time regime of Stage 1 can be approximated by the reciprocal of a KWW equation:

13. Plazek has shown Andrade creep behavior in many glassy polymers. Also, Andrade, E. N. da C, *Phil. Mag.* **17**, 497, 698 (1934); *Proc. R. Soc.* **A215**, 36 (1952).

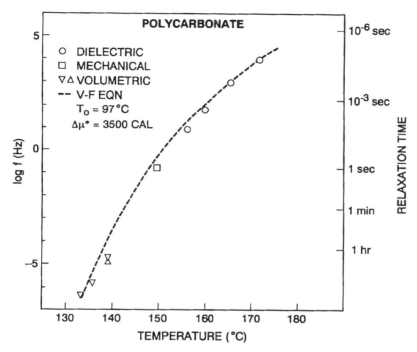

Figure 3.2.7 The characteristic frequency corresponding to λ, for polycarbonate: circle, from the dielectric loss peak; squares, from the in-phase modulus dropping to 1/10 in the temperature scan; triangle, from dilatometric aging data (obtained by Randy Duran, University of Florida, Gainesville) extrapolating to $\delta = 0$.

$$\gamma(t) = \frac{\sigma_0}{G_0} \exp\left(\frac{t}{\lambda'}\right)^{\beta'} \qquad (3.2.6)$$

as Struik has done, but β' for creep tends to be smaller than β obtained from the stress relaxation data. Dynamic mechanical data and dielectric data, inasmuch as they reflect the unstressed state as the ground state and the stressed state without large strains, are consistent with the stress relaxation data but not with the creep data. The characteristic λ_c is a parameter that is nearly the reciprocal of the circular frequency for the maximum in the dielectric loss factor. According to the KWW formula, it is also approximately the same as the time at which the linear viscoelastic relaxation modulus has decayed to $1/e$ of the initial value; actually, however, $1/10$ should be the better value, since the KWW formula fails to account for very short time relaxation. The value of λ_c from dynamic mechanical data should be determined from the in-phase modulus $G'(\omega)$, i.e., the reciprocal of the circular frequency at which $G'(\omega)$ is $1/10$ of $G'(\infty)$. The relaxation time obtained from the temperature sweep at one frequency is thus a better value than the frequency for the maximum $G''(\omega)$, since the latter will be an average of stage 1 and stage 2 (the transition zone). The KWW parameter for the creep β' being different from the relaxation β, the corresponding λ_c' is shorter than the λ_c obtained from either the relaxation or the dynamic data. This difference will increase when the values of β and β' are smaller (or the distribution broader). Figure 3.2.7 shows the three kinds of characteristic relaxation time related to stage 1 relaxation above for polycarbonate. The dilatometric relaxation time was obtained by extrapolating the isothermal volume decrease curve approaching the equilibrium volume. The time ($\log t$) that is extrapolated to $\delta = 0$ by a straight line is about 1.5 decades ($\approx \log f$) greater than $\log \lambda_c$. This method works because because, according to Equation 3.1.28, $\log \lambda_c \approx \log t + \log \delta$ and, as shown schematically in Figure 3.2.8, the slope of the two curves are nearly equal when $\delta \approx f$ but become progressively different as the equilibrium state is approached. When $T < T_0$, the two curves are always parallel, because the rate constant is solely a function of f.

Up to this point, the discussion has centered around the KWW formula, which is a phenomenological formula with two empirical parameters. We will now shift to the formula based on the cooperative domain model, to understand why the mathematical manipulations of those parameters work so well empirically. The linear viscoelastic relaxation modulus for stage 1 for the segmental conformational relaxation process in the thermodynamic equilibrium state is described by Equation 2.2.6 discussed earlier:

$$\ln G(t) = \ln G(0) + \frac{1}{z_c} \frac{\Delta \mu}{kT} \left[\frac{1}{\ln(t/\lambda_c)} \right] \qquad (2.2.6)$$

where $t < \lambda_c$. The maximum (cutoff) relaxation time λ_c for the maximum domain size z_c represents the last resistance barrier of the kind before the strain energy decays to zero, unless another mechanism for relaxation intervenes. For polymers, there is another mechanism and that is the external viscosity for chain slipping, as opposed to the internal viscosity for

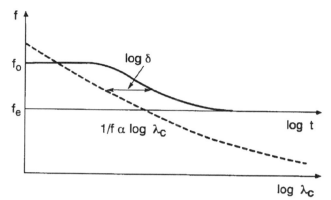

Figure 3.2.8   Schematic diagram of the volume vs. log t curve compared to volume vs. log λ. As the equilibrium is approached, the two curves diverge. λ can be conveniently picked from the volumetric isotherm by the approximate method: see Equation 3.1.28.

chain unkinking of stage 1. As a result, the stress does not decay precipitously beyond this point, but enters stage 2, to be discussed in the sections that follow. For glucose, a nonpolymer, the dielectric spectrum is similar in shape to that of polyvinyl acetate, but the glassy glucose does not exhibit the viscoelastic relaxation beyond λ_c.

Since $z_c = T_f/(T_f - T_0)$,

$$\ln G(t) = \ln G(0) + \frac{\Delta\mu}{kT} \frac{T_f - T_0}{T_f} \left[\frac{1}{\ln(t/\lambda_c)} \right] \tag{2.2.6a}$$

When in equilibrium, $T_f = T$, and we obtain:

$$\ln G(t) = \ln G(0) + \frac{\Delta\mu}{kT} \frac{T - T_0}{T} \left[\frac{1}{\ln(t/\lambda_c)} \right] \tag{3.2.7}$$

The slope for log $G(t)$ vs. log t from Equation 3.2.7 is equal to $\Delta\mu(T - T_0)/kT^2$ when $t/\lambda \approx 0.1$. The slope for log $G(t)$ vs. log t from the KWW formula is β when $t/\lambda_c \approx 1$. These two formulas are found to approximate each other closely if a slightly smaller value of λ is chosen for the KWW formula and, in so doing, the following approximation can be established between the parameters in the two formulas:

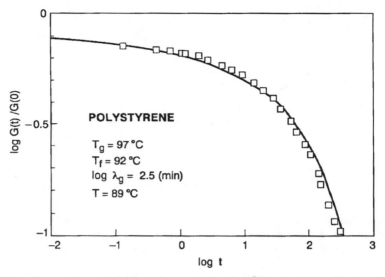

Figure 3.2.9   Comparison of the experimental data from Figure 3.2.3 with the theoretical curve for a polymer with T_g = 97 °C, T_f = 92 °C, log λ =2.5 (minutes). T_f depends on the extent of the physical aging.

$$\beta = \frac{\Delta\mu}{kT} \frac{T - T_0}{T} \tag{3.2.8}$$

Specifically, for the glassy state that has been aged at T_g to reach equilibrium, the value of β_g is obtained:

$$\beta_g = \frac{\Delta\mu}{kT_g} \frac{T_g - T_0}{T_g} \tag{3.2.8a}$$

Thus the empirical KWW parameter β_g in the *equilibrium* state depends on the glass transition temperature (T_0 + 50 °C) and is proportional to T^{-2}. For a value of $\Delta\mu^*$ of 3.5 kcal/mol of conformer, β_g at T_g ranges from 0.3 for high T_g polymers to 0.6 for low T_g polymers. For a given material with a specific value of T_g, β increases with T. Especially in the nonequilibrium state, however, β decreases markedly with the temperature drop.

Equation 3.2.7 is compared to the experimental relaxation modulus data for polystyrene near T_g in Figure 3.2.9. At 90 °C, the "shape" of the relaxation curve is nearly the same as those in the equilibrium state. Both the

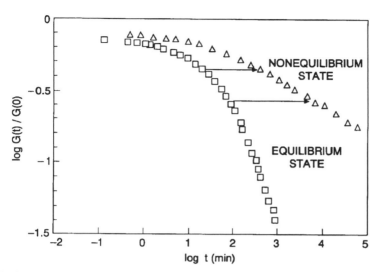

Figure 3.2.10 Schematic diagram for the temperature shift from the equilibrium condition at 90 °C to a nonequilibrium condition at 56 °C where the fictive temperature is initially equal to 90 °C.

KWW and the domain model formulas fit the data well, although we demonstrated in Figure 2.2.1 that the domain model can show a better fit in the extremely short time range. This feature becomes quite important when we discuss relaxation in glassy states well below T_g. For example, the domain model predicts creep and relaxation in very high T_g materials such as polyimides at room temperature, while the KWW equation predicts no relaxation.

In the nonequilibrium glassy state, the apparent activation energy is proportional to the domain size, i.e., $\Delta\mu z_i/k$ for the domains of size z_i. In Section 2.2 we derived the distribution of domain sizes and based the derivation of the relaxation function on such a distribution. The relaxation modulus at $t = \lambda_i$ depends on the domain size z_i such that

$$\ln G(\lambda_i) - \ln G(\lambda_c) = \frac{1}{z_c}\frac{\Delta\mu}{kT}\left[\frac{1}{\ln(\lambda_i/\lambda_c)}\right] \qquad (3.2.4)$$

When the temperature is changed from the equilibrium condition at T_g to a non-equilibrium condition at new T, the relaxation time will shift from the original $\lambda_{c,g}$ to the new $\lambda_{c,T}$ following the formula:

$$\ln\lambda_{c,T} = \ln\lambda_{c,g} + \frac{1}{\beta_T} - \frac{1}{\beta_g} \tag{3.2.10}$$

for $z = z_c$. For $z_i < z_c$, the change in λ_i will be by a lesser amount:

$$\ln\lambda_{i,T} = \ln\lambda_{i,g} + \left(\frac{1}{\beta_T} - \frac{1}{\beta_g}\right)\frac{\ln G(0) - \ln G(\lambda_{i,g})}{\ln G(0) - \ln G(\lambda_{c,g})} \tag{3.2.11}$$

Here we have scaled the temperature shift by shifting in the vertical direction with $\Delta \ln G$. This scaling is valid only if the fictive temperatures for the two states are equal, in this case $T_f = T_g$. Only in such a case do the straight lines tangential to the two curves merge at $\ln G(0)$, as in the example cited for polystyrene at 90 °C and 56 °C in Figure 3.2.10. In general, the shift from the corresponding states, one in equilibrium and the other in the nonequilibrium state, should be compared for the common fictive temperature, i.e., the equilibrium state at $T = T_f$, where

$$\beta_f = \frac{\Delta\mu}{kT_f}\frac{T_f - T_0}{T_f} \tag{3.2.12}$$

Then, shift from that equilibrium state to the nonequilibrium state at T without changing T_f, and

$$\frac{1}{\beta_T} = \frac{1}{\beta_f} + \frac{\Delta\mu}{k}\frac{T_f}{T_f - T_0}\left[\frac{1}{T} - \frac{1}{T_f}\right] \tag{3.2.13}$$

and from Equation 3.2.11, to scale $\ln G(t)$ at T from $\ln G(t)$ at T_f,

$$\ln t_T = \ln t_f + \left[\frac{1}{\beta_T} - \frac{1}{\beta_f}\right]\frac{\ln G(0) - \ln G(t_f)}{\ln G(0) - \ln G(\lambda_c)} \tag{3.2.14}$$

to be shifted horizontally along the log t axis. There is also a temperature dependence of the unrelaxed modulus $G(0)$, as discussed in Section 3.3 on the yield mechanism. This will necessitate a shift of $\ln G(t)$ in the vertical direction as well. Taking both the horizontal and vertical shifts, in Figure 3.2.11, the relaxation modulus curves have been calculated for a polymer with T_g of 147 °C, λ_g of 1 hour, and T_f of 142, at 20, 60, 100, and 120 °C, and compared to the creep modulus data for polycarbonate. A computer program for this parametric methodology in Chapter 7. The stress

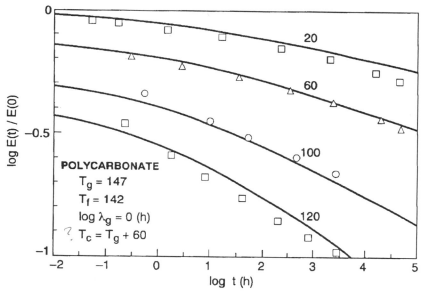

Figure 3.2.11   Relaxation modulus calculated from Equation 3.2.14 for the nonequilibrium glassy state for a polymer with T_g = 147 °C at temperatures 20, 60, 100, and 120 °C; T_f = 142 °C was assumed. Note that the curves are almost straight, indicating power-law-like behavior, because of the severely stretched scaling in the log *t* axis at low temperature. The KWW formula would be horizontal and flat in these temperature ranges. The experimental moduli for polycarbonate are shown as points for comparison.

relaxation data for polycarbonate begin to exhibit nonlinear characteristics above 3% strain. Although this phenomena has been analyzed frequently by invoking the Bernstein-Kearsley-Zappas (BKZ) theory, we attribute it result partly to the viscoplastic effect and partly to the finite time needed to reach the initial strain. Both these effects are discussed in detail in later sections.

3.3   Plasticity and Nonlinear Viscoelasticity in the Glassy State

3.3.1   The Magnitude of Relaxation Time in Glassy Polymers

Now we review some of the fundamental equations introduced earlier and present an example of a polymer with T_g in the range of 100 to 150 °C. T_g is a time-dependent quantity, and its observed value depends on the rate of heating or, in case of dynamic measurement, on the frequency. One definition would be to choose the "isorelaxation time" $T_g = T_0 + 50$ °C. The characteristic relaxation time at this temperature is approximately 10 seconds, $\log \lambda_c = -2.5$ (hours), and the characteristic frequency f_{max} for the loss maximum is about 1 Hz. (See, for example, Figure 3.2.7).

The change in the relaxation time during the shift from the equilibrium state at T_g to the nonequilibrium state at T without the entropy change (constant T_f) will be, from Equation 3.1.7:

$$\Delta \ln \lambda_c = \frac{\Delta \mu^*}{k} \frac{T_g}{T_g - T_0} \left[\frac{1}{T} - \frac{1}{T_g} \right] \tag{3.3.1}$$

where $T_f = T_g$ was assumed, because T_f of the glassy state at T is equal to the temperature from which it has been quenched, i.e., T_g. Some convenient values to remember are: apparent activation energy, of 28 kcal/mol, $\Delta \log \lambda_c = 1.7$ decades for every 5 °C change; and λ_c of 1 hour at 7 °C below T_g.

The Doolittle fractional free volume at this T_g is obtained from the equation:

$$f_g = \frac{k}{\Delta \mu^*} (T_g - T_0) \tag{3.3.2}$$

and f_g of 0.0286 for $\Delta \mu^* = 3.5$ kcal/mol is obtained. The real fractional free volume is obtained with Equation 2.1.22 or 2.1.23a by multiplying the Doolittle free volume by $T^*/(T^* - T_0)$, or ca. 0.05 at T_g. The value of β at T_g is obtained from our domain model, Equation 3.2.8:

$$\beta = \frac{\Delta \mu^*}{kT_g} \frac{T_g - T_0}{T_g} \tag{3.3.3}$$

with $\beta = 0.547$ for $T_g = 400$ K.

For nonequilibrium glass, the relaxation curve in the time range $t \ll \lambda_{c,T}$, where $T \ll T_g$, can be approximated by the power law: $\log[G(t)/G(0)] = -n \log t + C$, and the slope $-n$ is obtained by differentiating Equation 3.2.7 with respect to $\log(t/\lambda_c)$ to obtain:

$$-n = -\frac{\beta}{[\log(t/\lambda_c)]^2} \tag{3.3.4}$$

from which one obtains the value 0.022 for n at 100 °C below T_g, since $(\lambda_{c,T}/\lambda_{c,g})$ is about 10^5, and $\beta/\log(10^5) = 0.0219$.

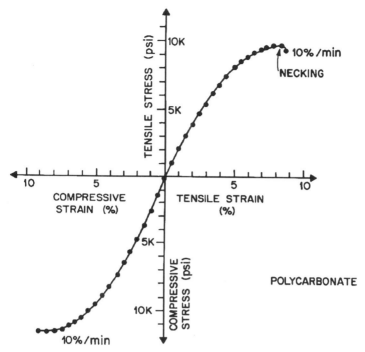

Figure 3.3.1   Stress-strain curves in tension and uniaxial compression for polycarbonate at 23 °C. The two curves are almost exact replicas of each other, and this result opposes the free volume theory for the nonlinear viscoelastic behavior of polymer glasses.

All these numbers are closely supported by the corresponding experimental data, and the formulas above can be used as the foundation for predicting the engineering properties of glassy polymers in later sections.

3.3.2 The Free Volume Hypothesis

The experimental yield stress in polymer solids depends on the rate of strain. It increases as the temperature is lowered or as the hydrostatic pressure is raised. The viscoelasticity is nonlinear well below the yield stress. These observations can give the impression that the yield phenomenon in polymers is fundamentally different from that in metals that follow the plasticity criteria, and that it might be a special and unique nonlinear viscoelastic effect. This nonlinear viscoelasticity, it might further be speculated, may be a result of strain-induced reduction in relaxation time and/or in elastic rigidity. If relaxation time were shortened with increase in strain, the stress eventually would reach a maximum when $\lambda(\gamma) = 1/\dot{\gamma}$. The strain-induced increase in free volume has been invoked to explain this kind of nonlinear behavior. Most glassy materials dilate under the tensile stress by the amount

$$\frac{\Delta V}{V} \approx \varepsilon(1 - 2\nu) \tag{3.3.6}$$

where ε is the tensile strain and ν is the Poisson ratio. The volume increase above is immediately substituted into the free volume equation for the relaxation time, i.e.,

$$\ln \frac{\lambda}{\lambda_0} = \frac{1}{f_0 + \varepsilon(1 - 2\nu)} - \frac{1}{f_0} \tag{3.3.7}$$

to obtain the shift factor. With typical values of $f_0 = 0.025$, and $\nu = 0.375$, a strain of 10% will result in a shift of 8 decades, a convincingly reasonable magnitude. The tensile strain argument does not, however, hold up against the empirical fact that yield can be induced under uniaxial compression. In fact, the tensile and compressive stress-strain curves are almost exact replicas of each other, as discussed subsequently for polycarbonate in Figure 3.3.1. Instead of strain-induced dilation, one might also argue that a deformation is accompanied by an increase in the conformational entropy, which results in a shift in relaxation time:

$$\ln \frac{\lambda}{\lambda_0} = \frac{\Delta\mu}{kT} \left[\frac{s^*}{S_c(\gamma)} - \frac{s^*}{S_c(\gamma = 0)} \right] \tag{3.3.8}$$

This equation will obtain the same amount of strain-induced shift factor as obtained by Equation 3.3.3, if the entropy increase is linked with the volume. In that sense this is another form of free volume model. Later in this chapter, however, we show how entropy can increase with strain and how it is linked to apparently nonlinear behavior.

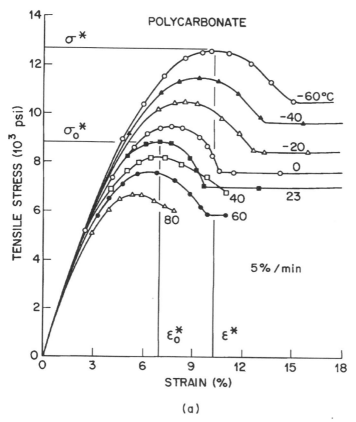

Figure 3.3.2   Stress-strain data for polycarbonate (a) at various temperatures and (b) under different strain rates. The "shape" of the curves remains unaffected by the change in temperature, and a straight line drawn through the yield stress points will pass through the origin. This feature essentially supports the form of Equation 3.3.9.

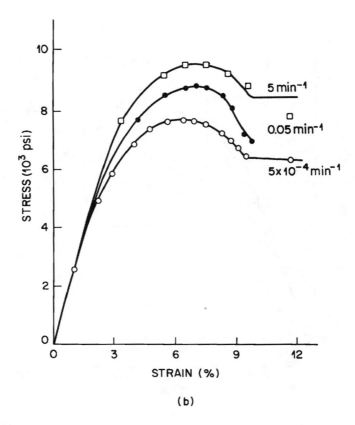

(b)

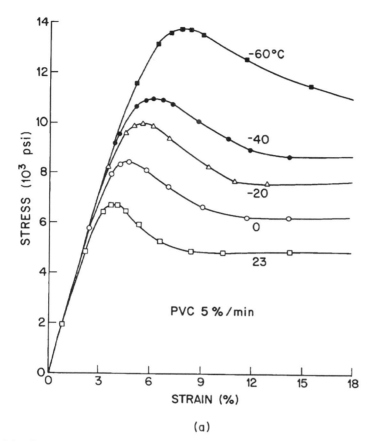

(a)

Figure 3.3.3   Stress-strain data for polyvinyl chloride (a) at various temperatures and (b) under different strains ratios. The comments for Figure 3.3.2 apply.

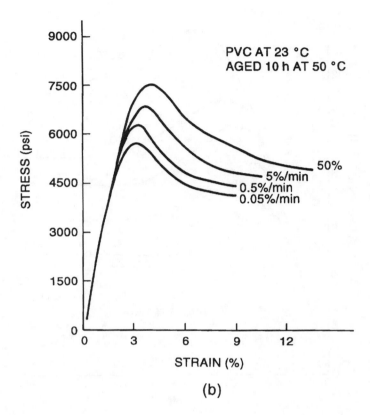

(b)

3.3.3 Plasticity and Yield Phenomena

Another possible mechanism for nonlinear viscoelasticity is reduction in elastic rigidity at increased deformation. Such a hypothesis is formulated into a relaxation modulus as a product of a purely strain-dependent component $f(\gamma)$ and a purely time dependent component $g(t)$, i.e.,

$$G(\gamma,t) = f(\gamma) g(t) \qquad (3.3.9)$$

$$E(\varepsilon,t) = f(\varepsilon) g(t)$$

and, if one chooses for $f(\gamma)$ a strongly decreasing function in γ, such as

$$f(\gamma) = \exp(-c\gamma) \qquad (3.3.10)$$

or

$$f(\varepsilon) = \exp(-c\varepsilon)$$

the stress undergo a maximum. Equation 3.3.9 predicts that the stress-time plot under constant $\dot{\gamma}$ (or $\dot{\varepsilon}$ in tension) will shift only vertically as λ is increased (i.e., as the temperature is decreased). The stress-strain plot at constant $\dot{\gamma}$ will accordingly shift both vertically and horizontally with the increasing $\dot{\gamma}$ or decreasing T, such that the same "shape" of the stress-strain curve is always maintained. This is supported by the data for polycarbonate and PVC shown in Figures 3.3.2 and 3.3.3, respectively. If $g(t)$ can be approximated by a power law, then in either of these figures, a straight line should be drawn through the maximum stress points *and* the origin. This turns out to be only approximately correct, since the exponent of the creep function is smaller than that of the relaxation function, as we pointed out with respect to the difference in the KWW parameter β for the creep ($\sim$ 1/3) and for the relaxation ($\sim$ 1/2). This is explained in detail when we discuss the scaling law for stress-strain curves.

Equation 3.3.10 is also supported by data, such as shown in Figure 3.3.4, with the constant C_5 being about 10. This number will prove to be key evidence in support of the viscoplasticity theory for the yield phenomenon in the glassy polymers.

Thus the nonlinear viscoelastic model of Equation 3.3.9 is in good agreement with data, but it is difficult to attach physical significance to the form of the equations, and there is no independent verification that the strain-softening of the *elastic* component actually occurs. If the strain

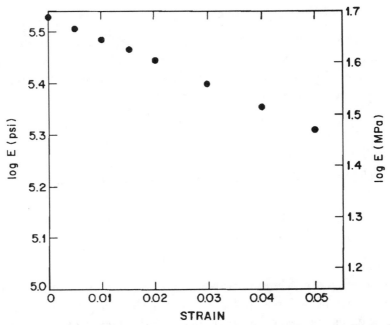

Figure 3.3.4   The secant modulus, the stress-strain ratio, in the logarithmic scale, vs. the strain, in the linear scale. The straight line supports Equation 3.3.10.

function $f(\gamma)$ is an elastic coefficient, then it is conservative and should be independent of history; i.e., the same value should be obtained either from the higher strain or the lower strain. This is difficult to test, because all the test data contain the relaxation component $g(t)$. However, in certain aspects the viscoplasticity model can explain both $f(\gamma)$ and the history dependence of it, which the nonlinear elasticity model cannot.

The physics involved in von Mises' plasticity theory is easy to understand. It invokes the maximum strain energy as the yield criterion. It does not, however, relate to the time or the rate of deformation. If the time and temperature dependence of the yield stress can be incorporated, then such a "modified" von Mises theory would be able to provide better insight to the structure-property relationship in polymers undergoing yield.

Recognizing that the experimentally observed yield stress depends on the deformation rate, we shall first consider an upper limit for the yield stress. This limit is the true yield stress that can occur in the absence of the conformational (unkinking) relaxation process. It can be described as the yield stress for the glassy state in equilibrium at T_0, which is attainable only at $t \to \infty$. Or, it can be described as the yield stress observed at the infinite strain rate (but isothermally!) so no viscoelastic relaxation can occur. This stress will be defined as $\sigma_\infty{}^*$. This is the von Mises stress, i.e.,

$$\sigma_\infty{}^* = \left[\frac{1}{2} \sum_{i,j} (\sigma_{ii} - \sigma_{jj})^2 \right] \qquad (3.3.11)$$

as shown in Equation 1.6.1. When there is only one shear stress component $\sigma_{23}{}^*$ and all other σ_{ii} and σ_{ij} are 0, as in Equation 1.6.2, we obtain

$$\sigma_\infty{}^* = \sqrt{3}\, \sigma_{23}{}^* \qquad (3.3.12)$$

or, in uniaxial tension (or compression), $\sigma_{11}{}^*$,

$$\sigma_\infty{}^* = \sigma_{11}{}^* \qquad (3.3.13)$$

Thus, between the maximum tensile yield stress $\sigma_{11}{}^*$ and the maximum shear yield stress $\sigma_{23}{}^*$, there is a relationship:

$$\sigma_{11}{}^* = \sqrt{3}\, \sigma_{23}{}^* \qquad (3.3.14)$$

The tensile elastic modulus E and the shear elastic modulus G are related by the equation:

$$E = 2(1+\nu)G \qquad (3.3.15)$$

where ν is the Poisson ratio. This will lead to the relationship between the maximum tensile yield strain $\varepsilon_{11}{}^*$ and the maximum shear yield strain $\gamma_{23}{}^*$:

$$\frac{1+\nu}{\sqrt{3}} \varepsilon_{11}{}^* = \frac{\gamma_{23}{}^*}{2} \qquad (3.3.16)$$

All these formulas are based on the condition that the free (strain) energy at the yield point is constant regardless of how the stress plane is chosen. This is self-evident from the scalar nature of energy. The free (strain) energy, expressed by the von Mises $\sigma_\infty{}^*$, is a material parameter.

Struik[14] has calculated the maximum yield stress by taking a derivative

---

14. Struik, L. C. E., *J. Noncryst. Mater.*, **131-133**, 395 (1991), *special Issue on relaxation phenomena in complex systems* .

of the intermolecular cohesive energy with respect to the molecular separation and setting the maximum value as σ_∞*. He finds a rather simple but useful rule that the tensile yield stress is 1/30 of the tensile modulus. It means that the tensile yield strain in the absence of viscoelastic relaxation is only 3%. (For shear, the ratio would be 1:17, and the strain would be 5% instead, according to Equations 3.3.14, 3.3.15, and 3.3.16.) By assuming a tensile modulus of 10^6 psi or 7×10^{10} dynes/cm^2 for a polymer glass, E over 30 will give σ_∞* $\approx 2.3 \times 10^9$ dynes/cm^2 or 30 kpsi. The free energy for the deformation is 3.5×10^7 ergs/cm^3 or 0.8 cal/g, assuming the density of 1 g/cm^3. This amount of energy is in the order of the enthalpy decrease caused by the physical aging. For example, for polystyrene aged at 90 °C shown in Figure 3.2.2, ΔH is -0.18 cal/g after 1 hour, -0.39 cal/g after 15 hours, and -0.49 cal/g after 150 hours. The mechanical deformation will raise the energy and the enthalpy until the critical level is reached, at which time the structure will break up and the entropy will increase as in fusion. The yield process will raise the enthalpy and entropy, wiping out the effect of physical aging. We conducted an experiment[15] for measuring changes in temperature while polymers were deformed in tension or in shear in a thermally well insulated condition and found that the temperature dropped by about 1 °C up to the yield, after which the temperature began to rise. This consistently reproducible result will be discussed in detail after we have presented the viscoplasticity theory. Since C_p of the polymer is about 0.5 cal/g °C, (see Figure 3.2.2), we have calculated an enthalpy rise of 0.5 cal/g, which is again of a convincing order of magnitude.

The temperature dependence of the experimental yield stress σ* (as opposed to the theoretical and limiting yield stress σ_∞) can be evaluated by setting the free energy:

$$\frac{1}{2} \frac{\sigma^{*2}}{E} = \Delta H^\dagger - T \Delta S^\dagger \tag{3.3.16a}$$

where $\Delta H^\dagger$ is the enthalpy increase involved in the yield and $\Delta S^\dagger$ is the entropy increase. $\Delta H^\dagger$ is 0.8 cal/g or 3.5×10^7 ergs/cm^3. $\Delta H^\dagger - T \Delta S^\dagger$ is

15. Matsuoka, S, and Bair, H. E., *Polym. Eng. and Sci.* 18, 1073 (1978).

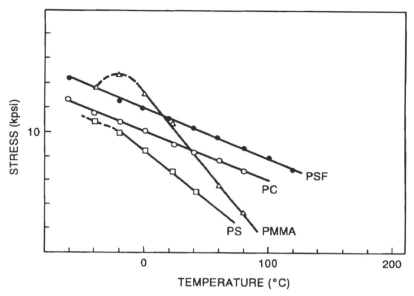

Figure 3.3.5 The temperature dependence of the yield stress can be calculated by equating the von Mises energy for the yield to the Gibbs free energy as in Equation 3.3.16a. The same temperature dependence is observed for the unrelaxed modulus, and from this the vertical shift factor is calculated. The dashed lines indicate premature brittle fracture.

zero at some high temperature T_c, which extrapolates to $\sigma^* = 0$. For polymers that exhibit a stress overshoot at yield[16] (e.g., polycarbonate, polysulfone, polyvinyl chloride) T_c is 20 to 50 °C higher than the respective T_g. For those that exhibit little or no overshoot (e.g., polystyrene, PMMA, T_c is about equal to T_g. For polycarbonate, $\Delta S^\dagger$ is 1.6×10^{-3} eu/g, while for polystyrene it is 2.1×10^{-3} eu/g. Using the relationship that the tensile σ^*/E is about 1/30, we obtain from Equation 3.3.16a above:

---

16. The stress overshoot phenomenon, which is not to be confused with the necking phenomenon, is discussed later.

$$\sigma^* = 2 \times 10^9 \left(1 - \frac{T}{T_c} \right) \tag{3.3.16b}$$

Similarly, the unrelaxed shear modulus at T is

$$G_0 = 2.2 \times 10^9 \left(1 - \frac{T}{T_c} \right) \tag{3.3.16c}$$

assuming the Poisson ratio to be 0.375. Thus, $\log(1 - T/T_c)$ should be used as the vertical shift factor for the $\log G(t)$ vs. $\log t$ plot as shown earlier (Figure 3.2.11). The temperature dependence of the yield stress is shown in Figure 3.3.5.

If the foregoing amount of enthalpy change is compared to the heat of fusion which, as shown in Table 2.2, Section 2.1, typically is about 50 cal/g for a conformer in the chain, the energy required for the yield to occur is very small ($\sim$2%), perhaps suggesting that it is a very localized phenomenon, reminiscent of the death-birth cycle of dislocations involved in the yield process of polycrystalline metals.

The limiting maximum stress $\sigma_\infty{}^*$ is the critical stress that a material of a given structure can bear. If the material is capable of relieving the stress through conformational relaxation, it may do so while it can. If it is deformed too fast, however, the stress could reach $\sigma_\infty{}^*$ and the ideal plastic deformation would ensue. This is the basis of the model that is about to be described here.

As a start, we take a single relaxation time (Maxwell) body. The stress under a constant strain rate $\dot{\gamma}$ is

$$\sigma = \dot{\gamma} G \lambda \left[1 - \exp\left(-\frac{\gamma}{\dot{\gamma}\lambda} \right) \right] \tag{3.3.17}$$

and the steady state stress is obtained as $t \rightarrow \infty$,

$$\sigma_{ss} = \lim_{\gamma \to \infty} \sigma = \dot{\gamma} G \lambda \tag{3.3.18}$$

When the rate of strain is increased, the higher level of stress is realized at steady state until $\sigma_\infty{}^*$ is reached. Further increase in the deformation rate will not serve to raise the level of the steady state stress, which will stay at $\sigma_\infty{}^*$ thereafter. This simple model thus behaves as a linear viscoelastic body until the critical stress is reached, and the stress never exceeds that stress by increasing either $\dot{\gamma}$ or λ. The critical strain rate $\dot{\gamma}*$ is $1/\lambda$, below which there is linear viscoelasticity and above which plasticity prevails. A set of two conditions will describe the steady state stress σ_{ss}:

$$\sigma_{ss} = \dot{\gamma}G\lambda \qquad \text{for } \dot{\gamma} \leq \dot{\gamma}* = 1/\lambda \qquad (3.3.19)$$
$$\sigma_{ss} = \sigma_{\infty}* = \dot{\gamma}*G\lambda \qquad \text{for } \dot{\gamma} > \dot{\gamma}*$$

As shown in Section 1.6, these two conditions can be met approximately by one equation:

$$\sigma_{ss} = \dot{\gamma}G\lambda\left[1 - \exp\left(-\frac{\sigma_{\infty}*}{\dot{\gamma}G\lambda}\right)\right] = \dot{\gamma}G\lambda\left[1 - \exp\left(-\frac{\gamma*}{\dot{\gamma}\lambda}\right)\right] \qquad (3.3.20)$$

where $\gamma*$ is the physical meaning of the maximum elastic strain before the yield phenomenon occurs and is equal to $\sigma_{\infty}*/G$. Because $G(t) = G_0 \exp(-t/\lambda)$, we now obtain the apparent (rate-dependent) yield stress $\sigma*$:

$$\sigma* = \sigma_{ss} = \dot{\gamma}\int_0^{\gamma*/\dot{\gamma}} G(t)\, dt \qquad (3.3.21)$$

For the polymer glass, $\gamma*$ is less than 0.1. When $\gamma* = 1$, as in the polymer melt (see Chapter 4), we have instead the formula known as Gleisle's empirical formula.[17] Significantly, with Equation 3.3.21, it becomes possible to predict the nonlinear viscoelastic steady state stress solely from the linear viscoelastic relaxation modulus. Though the equation above was derived for a single relaxation time body, it applies to the generalized Maxwell model:

$$G(t) = \sum_i G_i \exp\left(-\frac{t}{\lambda_i}\right) \qquad (3.3.22)$$

because the integration is carried out termwise and summed. Thus Equation 3.3.21 is applicable to any polymer having any form of linear viscoelastic

17. Gleisle, W. G., in "*Rheology*", Vol. 2, Astarita, Marrucci, and Nicolais, Eds., Plenum, New York, 1980.

relaxation spectrum. The temperature dependence of $G(t)$ is accounted for by the change in G_0 or the "vertical shift factor," which follows Equation 3.3.16c.

We now have shown how the apparent yield stress σ^* depends on the rate of strain $\dot{\gamma}$. The yield stress was calculated as the final stress at $t\rightarrow\infty$. When there are n sets of Dirac deltas (G_i, λ_i) to describe the relaxation spectrum, only those Dirac deltas with relaxation times λ_i that exceed $1/\dot{\gamma}$ will reach the weighted yield stress $G_i\sigma_\infty^*/\Sigma G_i$, while others with λ_i's that are shorter than $1/\dot{\gamma}$ will never reach their weighted maximum stress levels but will stop at their viscoelastic steady state stress levels. If all had been able to reach their respective weighted yield stress levels, the total would have been equal to σ_∞^*. The slower the strain rate $\dot{\gamma}$, the more Dirac deltas will fail to reach the weighted maximum stress, and the sum of all, σ^*, will be smaller. By the same token, the yield stress σ^* will be greater if all λ_i's have been shifted toward higher values because the temperature or hydrostatic pressure added has been decreased.

Thus, the two theories, entailing plasticity and nonlinear viscoelasticity, which at first seemed to be opposed to each other, can blend in and are not necessarily mutually exclusive. However, plasticity combined with the linear viscoelasticity has more physics and fewer totally empirical formulas that happen to fit data. With this modified plasticity theory, we have demonstrated that the tensile, shear, and uniaxially compressive yield stresses and strains can be related. By including viscoelasticity as the characteristic behavior under low strain energy conditions, we have shown how the yield stress will depend on the rate of strain, since it can be predicted by knowing only the linear viscoelastic relaxation spectrum. The temperature and pressure effects, as well as the effect of aging, can also be predicted. This model will be called the viscoplasticity model. We shall later demonstrate that it can be applied to melt rheology.

3.3.4 Viscoplasticity and Nonlinear Viscoelasticity

In the preceding section, we were concerned with the yield condition only, which is a "final" stress condition as $t\rightarrow\infty$. In this section we examine the state that precedes the steady state, and consider how the phenomenology of nonlinear viscoelasticity, as discussed earlier, can be explained by the viscoplasticity model derived for the yield stress in the condition well below σ^*.

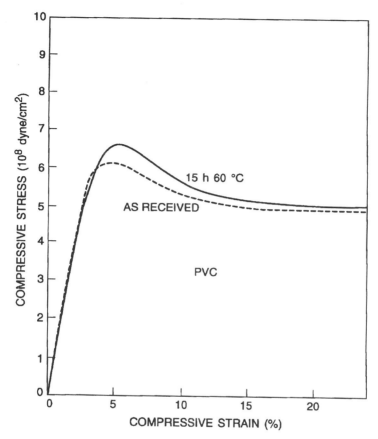

Figure 3.3.6   Yield stress under uniaxial compression for polyvinyl chloride. Even polystyrene will exhibit similar ductile behavior under compression.

We consider the n Maxwell elements to represent a distribution of relaxation times by domain size, and the stress and strain that the ith element undergoes under the constant strain rate $\dot{\gamma}$. As we noted in the preceding section, the strain rate must be fast enough for the stress to reach the yield stress $\sigma_i^* = G_i\gamma_e^*$, where γ_e^* is the von Mises yield strain and is equal to the yield stress at the infinite strain rate divided by the unrelaxed modulus, i.e., $\sigma_\infty^*/G(t = 0)$. When the strain rate is slow, (i.e., $\dot{\gamma}\lambda_i < \gamma_e^*$), the yield stress is never reached, and the final steady state stress is that of the linear viscoelasticity, $G_i\lambda_i\dot{\gamma}$. If the material exhibits no stress overshoot in the yield stress, then $\gamma_e* = \dot{\gamma}\lambda_i$ and the steady state stress is equal to the yield stress, σ_i*. When overshoot is observed, $\gamma_e* < \dot{\gamma}\lambda_i$, and beyond the yield when the structure is broken up, a new smaller value of λ_i emerges, which is equal to $\gamma_e*/\dot{\gamma}$. Most glassy polymers exhibit overshoot, which is not to be confused with the apparent stress matximum due to a reduced cross-sectional area by necking. Stress overshoot is observed in uniaxial compression where no necking is present, as shown in Figure 3.3.6. For most polymers, the yield strain is smaller than $\dot{\gamma}\lambda_i$. Thus there are two categories of strain rates, one that is greater than γ_e/λ_i and the other smaller. Within each of those two categories, there also are different categories of behavior depending on the magnitude of strain. Those cases are summarized as follows:

1. For $\dot{\gamma} < \gamma_e*/\lambda_i$ and $G_i\lambda_i\dot{\gamma} < \sigma_i*$, linear viscoelasticity:

$$\sigma_i = G_i\lambda_i\dot{\gamma}\left[1 - \exp\left(-\frac{\gamma}{\dot{\gamma}\lambda_i}\right)\right]$$

for all values of γ,

2. For $\dot{\gamma} < \gamma_e/\lambda_i$ but σ_i* is reached before the linear viscoelastic steady state stress can be reached, i.e., $\sigma_i* < G_i\lambda_i\dot{\gamma}$,

(a) $\sigma_i = G_i\lambda_i\dot{\gamma}\left[1 - \exp\left(-\frac{\gamma}{\dot{\gamma}\lambda_i}\right)\right]$ when $\gamma < \gamma_e*$ and

(b) $\sigma_i = \sigma_i* = G_i\gamma_e*$ when $\gamma > \gamma_e*$.

3. For $\dot{\gamma} > \gamma_e/\lambda_i$ it is always true that $G_i\lambda_i\dot{\gamma} > \sigma_i*$.

(a) $\sigma_i = G_i\lambda_i\dot{\gamma}\left[1 - \exp\left(-\frac{\gamma}{\dot{\gamma}\lambda_i}\right)\right]$ when $\gamma < \gamma_e*$, but

(b) $\sigma_i = \sigma_i* = G_i\gamma_e*$ when $\gamma > \gamma_e*$.

From the above, one can conclude that strain magnitude is a crucial factor in determining whether the linear viscoelastic or plastic path is followed. Regardless of transient or steady state conditions, it depends on whether $\gamma < \gamma_e*$ or $\gamma > \gamma_e*$. Such behavior is approximated by a single equation:

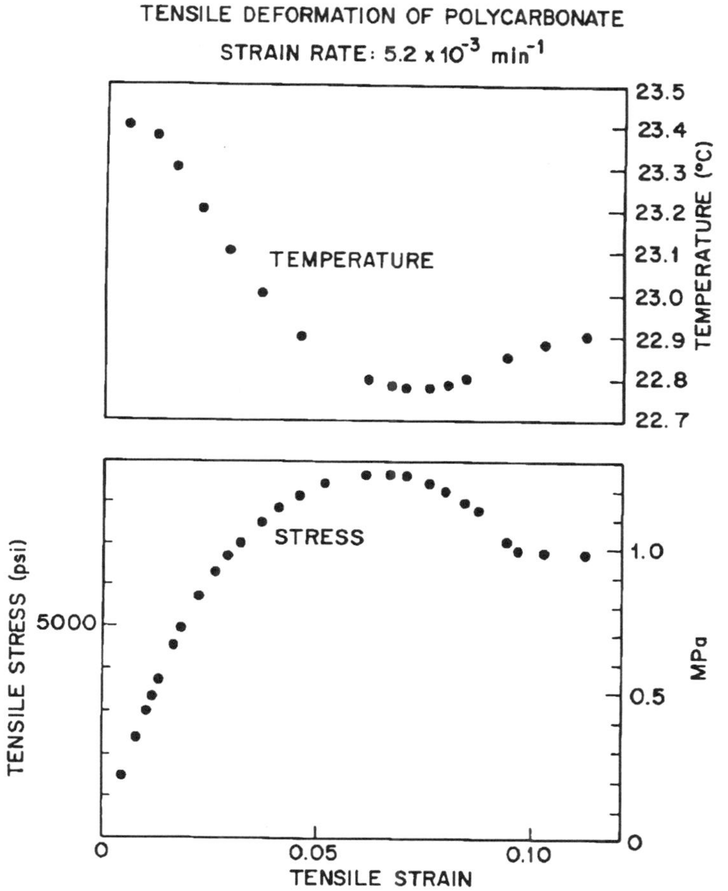

TENSILE DEFORMATION OF POLYCARBONATE
STRAIN RATE: 5.2×10^{-3} min^{-1}

Figure 3.3.7   Temperature drop observed during tensile deformation in a thermally insulated polycarbonate specimen. The stress-strain curve is shown for comparison.

$$\sigma_i = G_i \gamma_e^* \left[1 - \exp\left(- \frac{\gamma}{\gamma_e^*} \right) \right] \qquad (3.3.23a)$$

The exponential term can be expanded into a polynomial, and when γ is in the order of γ_e^*, it is approximately:

$$\sigma_i = G_i \gamma \exp\left(- \frac{\gamma}{2\gamma_e^*} \right) \qquad (3.3.23b)$$

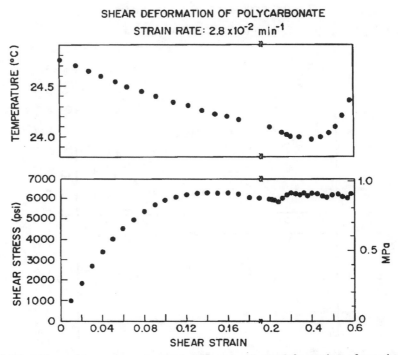

Figure 3.3.8   Temperature drop observed during the shear deformation of a twisted rod polycarbonate specimen. The shear test result is another piece of evidence against the free volume theory for yield phenomena.

This formula is true even at a very fast strain rate, and thus it is the vertical shift factor $f(\gamma)$. The relaxation modulus, for example, is expressed as the product of the stress multiplier above and the linear viscoelastic function:

$$
\frac{\sigma(t)}{\gamma}\ \bigg|_{\gamma} = \frac{\dot{\gamma}}{\gamma}\sum_{i=1}^{r} G_i \lambda_i \left[1 - \exp\left(\frac{\gamma}{\dot{\gamma}\lambda_i}\right)\right]
$$

$$
+ \frac{1}{\gamma}\sum_{r}^{n} G_i \gamma_e^* = \exp\left(-\frac{\gamma}{2\gamma_e^*}\right) G(t) \tag{3.3.24}
$$

and for other viscoplastic equations, the linear term $G(t)$ is substituted by a suitable linear viscoelastic function. For the case of a constant rate of strain, the stress undergoes through a maximum, and the above equation predicts the behavior quantitatively well.

This equation is a nonlinear viscoelastic function which has been derived from the viscoplasticity. However, the prediction of the stress-strain relationship requires only the linear viscoelastic data. For example, even though $G(0)$ changes with γ because of the structural change, Equation 3.3.24 is still valid. According to this model, the stress in the i-th element reaches the critical level in the order of the decreasing λ_i starting from the element with the longest λ_i. In physical terms, each element represents the domain of a given size, and G_i is their population. The plastic deformation begins first with the largest domains, and on with the smaller ones in that order. If the deformation rate is small enough, then the small domains will be able to relax as a linear viscoelastic body without breaking up the structure into smaller sizes. Before reaching the critical stress level, the stress increase is accompanied by the energy increase without an increase in entropy, i.e., the enthalpy increases. Upon reaching the critical strain energy, the domain structure is broken up, and the entropy increases and heat is absorbed. If the test specimen is thermally insulated, every time when each domain size undergoes the yield process the temperature should drop. This in fact is observed in tension as well as in shear, as shown in Figures 3.3.7 and 3.3.8. The temperature plot is practically a mirror image of the stress plot. Every incremental increase in entropy is a result of a conversion of the strain energy into heat via a microscopic and partial "melting." The relative population that has undergone this process is:

$$\frac{E_0 - E}{E_0} = \ln\frac{E_0}{E} = 1 - \frac{E_0}{\sigma_\infty^*} \tag{3.3.25}$$

where E_0 is the unrelaxed modulus, E is the modulus, and σ_∞^* is the stress for breaking up the structure or the yield stress at 0 K. This is the origin of the vertical shift factor $E \propto \exp(-c\varepsilon)$ discussed earlier as a totally empirical expression. For polycarbonate, values of $\sigma_\infty^* = 21,000$ psi and $E_0(23$ °C$) = 330,000$ psi in Equation 3.3.25 will give $c = 15.7$; for the common log of E, c is 6.8. This is supported by the vertical shift factor for polycarbonate relaxation modulus, shown in Figure 3.3.9. If the shift were calculated on the basis of the change in the relaxation times via free volume or entropy change, shift along would not be enough and the vertical shift still would be needed. The vertical shift factor for the relaxation modulus thus found is approximately equal to the slope of the logarithm of the secant modulus (stress vs. strain) under the constant deformation rate, shown earlier in Figure 3.3.4. This is an important point for the vertical shift factor as the

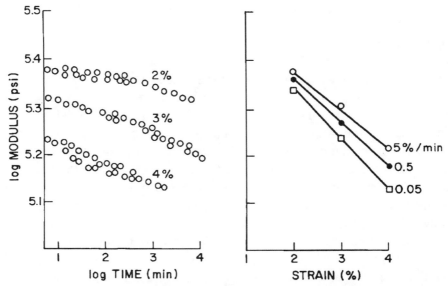

Figure 3.3.9   *Left*: Nonlinear viscoelastic relaxation modulus of polycarbonate. The vertical shift with ~ 6.8 × strain will superimpose those curves. *Right*: Secant modulus of the same can be reconstructed from the relaxation modulus by the scaling rule discussed in the text.

dominant factor for the nonlinearity. It means that the "curvature" of the stress-strain curve is almost totally due to the plasticity rather than the viscoelastic relaxation. Thus the stress strain curve can be drawn with the exponential function in $-c\varepsilon$, where c can be determined by the temperature dependence of the yield stress shown in Figure 3.3.5. The stress maximum occurs as a consequence of the monotonically decreasing value of the ratio of stress to strain, and the same function prevails before and *after* the maximum stress. This is shown in Figure 3.3.10. The stress strain curves in uniaxial compression also exhibit almost identical shape, including the maximum stress.

3.3.5 Engineering Scaling Rules for Creep, Relaxation, and Stress-Strain

As an example for comparing with the empirical nonlinear viscoelastic formulas mentioned earlier, we use a power law for $G(t)$ to be substituted into Equation 3.3.24 under the constant strain rate $\dot{\gamma}$. The power law is a good approximation when $t \ll \lambda$ and the KWW formula is not satisfactory:

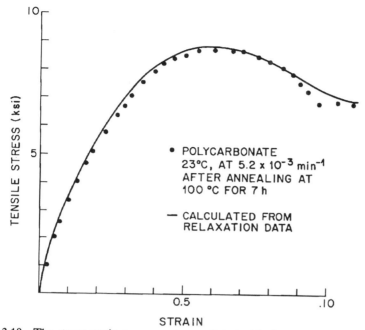

Figure 3.3.10   The stress-strain curve can be predicted with the secant modulus, which is a simple exponential function of $-\varepsilon$, and the curvature is almost totally due to the viscoplastic rather than viscoelastic dissipation of strain energy.

$$G(t) = G_0 \left[\frac{t}{t_0} \right]^{-n} \qquad \text{for } t > t_0 \qquad (3.3.26)$$

$$G(t) = G_0 \qquad \text{for } t < t_0$$

and from Equation 3.3.24, we obtain:

$$\sigma \Big|_{\dot{\gamma}} = G_0 \gamma_0 + G_0 \dot{\gamma} \int_{\gamma_0/\dot{\gamma}}^{\gamma/\dot{\gamma}} \left[\frac{t}{t_0} \right]^{-n} dt = \frac{G_0 \gamma}{1+n} \left[\frac{\gamma}{\gamma_0} \right]^{-n} \qquad (3.3.27)$$

where $\gamma_0 = \dot{\gamma} t_0$ and $n = \ln(\lambda/t_0)$. We incorporate the vertical shift factor as discussed in Section 3.3.3:

$$\frac{\sigma}{\gamma} = G_{0,T} \exp\left(-\frac{G_{0,T}}{\sigma_\infty^*} \gamma \right) \left[\frac{\gamma}{\gamma_0} \right]^{-n} \qquad (3.3.28)$$

The plot of $\log \sigma/\gamma$ vs. γ will be approximately a straight line, as shown in Figure 3.3.4, but we can carry this analysis even further. The value of 0.03

and m of 0.02 were calculated from Equation 3.3.4, which is based on the domain model, for polycarbonate at 25 °C. For $\dot{\gamma} = 5\%/\text{min}$, $t_0 = 0.1$ minute, $n = 0.035$, and $m = 0.023$, an exact fit with the data shown in Figure 3.3.4 is possible. An important difference between this agreement and those obtained by the empirical nonlinear model of Equations 3.3.9 and 3.3.10 is that our approach is based on independently verifiable parameters, to each of which a physical meaning can be attached. The theory of yield phenomena, which verified Gleisle's empirical rule with good physical reasoning, led to Equation 3.3.24, the basic formula for viscoplasticity. None were introduced because a particular functional form would give a good fit to some sets of data. The viscoplastic yield stress depends on the rate of strain. If the viscoelastic part of it can be characterized by the power law, we obtain the yield stress from Equation 3.4.2 or 3.4.3. Thus the yield stress increases in proportion to $(\dot{\gamma}\lambda)^n$, but it is always less than σ^*_∞. If the KWW formula is considered, one can use a substitution that

$$n = \beta \left(\frac{\gamma_e^*}{\dot{\gamma}\lambda} \right)^\beta \tag{3.3.29}$$

since $-n$ is the slope $d\ln G(t)/d\ln t$, but the KWW formula gives a poor approximation when $\dot{\gamma}\lambda \ll 1$.

Equation 1.3.8 for stress and strain in a viscoelastic material can be written in another form:

$$\frac{\sigma_i}{G_{0i}\dot{\gamma}\lambda_i} = \frac{\sigma}{G_0\dot{\gamma}\lambda_i} = \left[1 - \exp\left(-\frac{\gamma}{\dot{\gamma}\lambda_i} \right) \right] \tag{3.3.30}$$

for the ith element in the relaxation spectrum. The equation above makes it evident that all linear viscoelastic stress-strain curves under the constant rate $\dot{\gamma}$ will reduce to a single curve when plotted in the form $\sigma/G_0\dot{\gamma}\lambda_i$ vs. $\gamma/\dot{\gamma}\lambda_i$.

In our viscoplastic model, linear viscoelasticity prevails for each relaxation element until its *elastic* strain γ_e reaches the limiting γ_e^*. Thus, the plot of $\sigma_{\text{yield}}(\dot{\gamma}\lambda)^n/G_0\dot{\gamma}\lambda_i$ vs. $\gamma(\dot{\gamma}\lambda)^n/\dot{\gamma}\lambda_i$ for all λ_i's should reduce to a single curve for all $\dot{\gamma}$'s, in the range that $\gamma_e < \gamma_e^*$, (i.e., up to the yield). In short, for stress-strain curves obtained at different $\dot{\gamma}$'s, the corresponding states are established on the basis of equal γ_e's. For a given γ_e, the macroscopic strain $\gamma = \dot{\gamma}t$ and the stress σ are scaled for various rates of strain by the scaling factor $(\dot{\gamma}\lambda)^n$.

Thus we establish for the viscoplasticity the following scaling rules:

Scaling Rule 1 A stress-strain curve at $\dot\gamma_2$ can be predicted from an experimental stress-strain curve obtained at strain rate $\dot\gamma_1$ by multiplying the stress and strain in the experimental curve by the scaling factor s $(\dot\gamma_2/\dot\gamma_1)^n$ and $(\dot\gamma_2/\dot\gamma_1)^m$ for the stress and strain, respectively. These corresponding states are based on the isochronal states; that is, it takes the same time to reach σ_2,γ_2 as it does to reach σ_1,γ_1 by either relaxation, creep, or the constant rate of deformation starting from the zero stress state. The power coefficient m is for the creep, and it is typically two-thirds of n, the power for relaxation.

Scaling Rule 2 The parameter n is not a constant but, from Equation 3.3.4,

$$n \approx \frac{\beta}{[\log(\dot\gamma\lambda)]^2} \tag{3.3.31}$$

or if n_1 has been obtained experimentally, n_2 can be calculated from the equation:

$$n_2 = n_1\left[\dot\gamma_2\lambda_2/\dot\gamma_1\lambda_1\right]^{n_1} \tag{3.3.31a}$$

if n_1 and n_2 are not too far apart. Or, from Equation 3.2.10, assuming the similarity between the parameters n and β, we obtain:

$$\frac{1}{n_2} = \frac{1}{n_1} + \frac{H}{R}\left[\frac{1}{T_2} - \frac{1}{T_1}\right] \tag{3.3.31b}$$

Scaling Rule 3 When the temperature is changed, rule 2 can be used with respect to λ instead of $\dot\gamma$; that is, the scaling factor $(\lambda_2/\lambda_1)^n$ should be used.

Scaling Rule 4 Since the characteristic relaxation time follows the Adam-Gibbs formula, which becomes an Arrhenius equation in the nonequilibrium glassy state, we can introduce the scaling rule for the temperature change from T_1 to T_2:

$$\ln\frac{\lambda_2}{\lambda_1} = n\frac{\Delta\mu^*}{R}\frac{T_g - T_0}{T_g}\left(\frac{1}{T_2} - \frac{1}{T_1}\right)$$

$$= 8.8\times10^4\, n\left[\frac{1}{T_2} - \frac{1}{T_1}\right] \tag{3.3.32}$$

While for the vertical shift factor for the modulus is given by the equation:

$$\ln \frac{G_2}{G_1} = \ln \left[\frac{1 - T_2/T_c}{1 - T_1/T_c} \right] \qquad (3.3.33)$$

where T_c is the temperature for the zero overshoot yield stress described in Equation 3.3.16c.

These scaling rules work for the stress-strain curves, including the nonlinear range, for most glassy polymers.

Since the relaxation time λ is proportional to the aging time, the stress-strain curves can be scaled for the aging time as well. Care should be exercised, however, to ensure that the total effective aging time is taken. For example, an additional hour of aging for a given sample that has been aged the equivalent of 100 hours will hardly show a difference. It is important to establish the initial state of aging. By comparing the stress-strain curves for a sample of unknown history with a sample that has been well aged will help establish the thermal history of the former.

Scaling Rule 5 For a sample with aging time t_{a1} hours, a new history with additional t_{a2} hours of aging at the same temperature can be scaled by the factor $[(t_{a2} + t_{a1})/t_{a1}]^n$. The equivalence of the scaling factor for the aging time and the strain rate can be demonstrated by the stress-strain curves obtained in such a manner that the product $\dot{\gamma} t_a$ is constant. These stress-strain curves can be superimposed on top of each other as shown in Figure 3.3.11.

3.3.6 Invariants in Elasticity

Central to the theory of visco*plasticity* is the corresponding states of equal elastic recoverable strain γ_e, and the yield phenomenon was predicted on the basis of the critical value, $\gamma_e{}^*$. The real criterion, however, is the recoverable energy $\Delta\Psi = \Psi(\sigma) - \Psi(0)$,

$$\Delta\Psi = \int_0^{\gamma_e} \sigma d\gamma_e \qquad (3.3.34)$$

but σ or γ_e was used as a substitute measure for the recoverable (free) energy. In our viscoplastic model the viscoelastic part is linear and, therefore, the elastic part is also linear, i.e.,

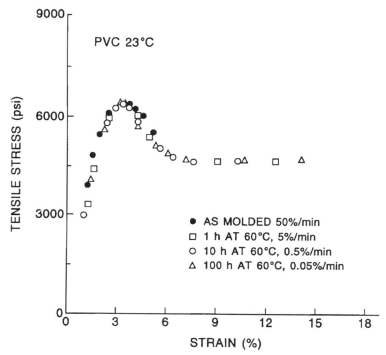

Figure 3.3.11   Stress-strain curves for polyvinyl chloride all are superimposed when the products of the strain rate and the aging period are the same.

$$\sigma(\gamma) = G_0 \, \gamma_e \qquad (3.3.35)$$

The mathematics of elasticity is applicable to all stress components as well as to elastic strains. For example, we can invoke the rules of strain invariants for elastic strains. Strain invariants are really various types of recoverable strain energy that, being scalar, are independent of (invariant in) the choice of coordinates.

The invariant of the first kind I_1 is the recoverable energy involved in stress-induced dilation and densification:

$$\tfrac{1}{2} I_1 \approx \varepsilon_x + \varepsilon_y + \varepsilon_z \qquad (3.3.36)$$

where ε's denote the recoverable tensile strains $\Delta l/l$. We will omit the subscript "e" for the recoverable strains in this section only. The invariant of the second kind I_2 is the recoverable strain energy, which includes an energy involving the change of shape:

$$\frac{1}{2} I_2 = \frac{1}{2} (\varepsilon_x^2 + \varepsilon_y^2 + \varepsilon_z^2) + \left(\frac{\gamma_{xy}}{2}\right)^2 + \left(\frac{\gamma_{yz}}{2}\right)^2 + \left(\frac{\gamma_{zx}}{2}\right)^2 \qquad (3.3.37)$$

We can also consider the invariant related *only* to the change of shape, $I_2{}'$, which is called the deviatoric strain invariant. By defining the deviatoric tensile strain $\varepsilon_x{}' = \varepsilon_x - \Delta V/3V$ etc., we obtain

$$\frac{1}{2} I_2{}' = \frac{1}{2} (\varepsilon_x{}'^2 + \varepsilon_y{}'^2 + \varepsilon_z{}'^2) + \left(\frac{\gamma_{xy}}{2}\right)^2 + \left(\frac{\gamma_{yz}}{2}\right)^2 + \left(\frac{\gamma_{zx}}{2}\right)^2 \qquad (3.3.38)$$

With Equation 3.3.37, we obtain the value of $I_2{}'$ when there is only the tensile stress in the x- direction, i.e.,

$$\varepsilon_x{}' = \frac{2(1+\nu)}{3} \varepsilon_x, \ \varepsilon_y{}' = \varepsilon_z{}' = -\frac{1+\nu}{3} \varepsilon_x$$

and

$$\left[\frac{1}{2} I_2\right]^{1/2} = \frac{1+\nu}{\sqrt{3}} \varepsilon_x \qquad (3.3.39)$$

We shall now obtain the value of $I_2{}'$ when there is only the shear strain γ_{xy}:

$$\left[\frac{1}{2} I_2\right]^{1/2} = \frac{\gamma_{xy}}{2} \qquad (3.3.40)$$

By equating the two values of these invariants in Equations 3.3.39 and 3.3.40, we establish the relationship between the tensile strain under uniaxial tension and the pure shear strain without tension that will meet the condition that the strain energies in the two cases be equal. The equation

$$\frac{1+\nu}{\sqrt{3}} \varepsilon_x = \frac{\gamma_{xy}}{2} \qquad (3.3.41)$$

will satisfy the equielastic energy condition. We can assume that $\varepsilon/\varepsilon_e = \gamma/\gamma_e$, where ε and γ here are the actual strains, and the relationship above holds for the macroscopic (measurable) strains when $\gamma_e < \gamma_e{}^*$. For the stress,

$$\sigma_{\text{tensile}} = E\,\varepsilon_x = 2(1+\nu)\,G\,\gamma_{xy}\,\frac{\sqrt{3}}{2(1+\nu)} = \sqrt{3}\,\sigma_{\text{shear}} \qquad (3.3.42)$$

In this section, we have extended the von Mises strain energy criteria beyond the original premise as yield criteria, but they apply to any stress levels before the yield. All stress components at any stage of relaxation can be calculated based on the deviatoric invariant $I_2{}'$ in the isotropic material.

From Equations 3.3.41 and 3.3.42, we can produce another scaling rule to obtain a shear stress-strain curve from the experimental tensile stress-strain data and vice versa:

Scaling Rule 6 Multiply the tensile strain ε by $2(1+\nu)/\sqrt{3} \approx 1.6$ to obtain the shear strain γ_{xy}, and multiply the tensile stress $\sigma_{tensile}$ by $1/\sqrt{3} = 0.58$ to obtain the shear stress σ_{shear}. Multiply the tensile strain rate $\dot{\varepsilon}$ by 1.6 to obtain the shear strain rate $\dot{\gamma}$, and adjust the calculated shear stress-strain curve with the new $\dot{\gamma}$. This scaling rule works well as illustrated in Figure 3.3.12, for polycarbonate. It is applicable not only to glassy polymers but also to crystalline polymers for which other scaling rules are different. It also works for polymer melts. These results support the contention that the elastic energy is in fact the correct criterion for the corresponding states for the viscoplastic (and viscoelastic) materials. The shear curve thus calculated from the tensile data can now be used to calculate the curve for uniaxial compressive stress vs. compressive strain, using the same scaling rules, except in this case the pressure affects the relaxation time because pressure and temperature are thermodynamic intensive quantities. Pressure will increase the relaxation time as temperature will decrease it. Consequently, the stress-strain curve is an almost symmetrical but slightly larger image of the tensile stress-strain curve. The compressive yield stress is greater than the tensile yield stress. This was shown in Figure 3.3.1. A very important aspect of this curve is the fact that yield occurs under compression in a manner not too different from that in tension. The simple free volume theory that yield is incurred through a strain-induced dilation is clearly unacceptable. The strain energy criterion for viscoplasticity is preferred. However, we have pointed out that if Doolittle's free volume equation is used to calculate the shortening of relaxation time under tensile dilation, a convincing value for the shift factor will result. When we calculate the entropy increase at yield using the Adam-Gibbs equation, we obtain also the same "right" values, since this equation also reduces to the Vogel equation in

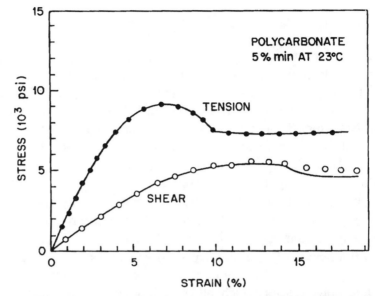

Figure 3.3.12   The stress-strain curves in tension and shear. Points are experimental. The line for the shear was calculated from the tensile data according to scaling rule 6.

equilibrium. The strain-induced entropy change is not an unreasonable concept. Staats-Westover[18] has constructed a machine that enables one to obtain data on tensile force vs. tensile deformation under hydrostatic pressure. An example is shown in Figure 3.3.13. The curves become bigger under higher hydrostatic pressure, supporting the reasoning for the difference between the tensile and compressive curves cited above.

We have proposed a group of scaling rules for predicting stress-strain curves at desired temperatures, strain rates, aging histories, and pressures, or converting from tension to shear to compression. The entire methodology has been programmed for more than 30 generic polymers in GWBASIC and is available from AT&T POLYMERS. The program also includes other

18. Staats-Westover, R. F., private communication.

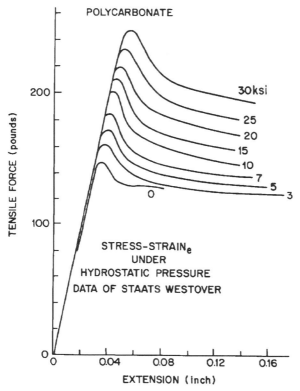

Figure 3.3.13 Stress-strain curves under the hydrostatic pressure. Raising the pressure will have the same effect on the thermodynamic state. as lowering the temperature.

engineering properties such as brittle transition temperatures, which depend on molecular weight and aging history, as well as creep and relaxation curves for the variable conditions listed above.

3.3.7 The Hypothesis of Domain Breakup During Yield

The behavior of the viscoplastic model we propose is partly viscoelastic and partly plastic, the border case being the element with its relaxation time $\lambda_i = \gamma_e{}^*/\dot{\gamma}$. With the relaxation cooperative model, the size z_i of a domain determines the magnitude of its relaxation time λ_i, the smaller domains relax in the viscoelastic fashion, while, as the limiting strain is reached in the larger domains, they begin to break up in to smaller sizes, thereby reducing their relaxation time. The final size depends on the imposed $\dot{\gamma}$, i.e., how fast the material is being made to deform. As an example, let us consider a group of 5 domains each consisting of 6 conformers each. When the strain limits of these domains are exceeded, they begin to break into 6 domains of 5 conformers each. The relaxation time will be reduced from λ_6 to λ_5 according to the equation:

$$\ln \lambda_5 = \ln \lambda_6 - \frac{\Delta \mu}{kT} (6 - 5) \tag{3.3.43}$$

and at $T = 300$ K and $\Delta \mu = 3.1$ kcal/mol, the resulting λ_5 is two orders of magnitude smaller than λ_6. Since the irreversible thermodynamic process follows a path of minimum free energy, the reduction of the relaxation time ought to be minimal, i.e., the final λ in the plastic flow regime should be equal to $\dot{\gamma}^{-1}$. When $\dot{\gamma} = \lambda^{-1}$, however, the final *elastic* strain in the viscoplastic material would have to be 1. For glassy polymers, however, the measurable yield strains are in the range of 5 to 10% instead of 100%. To reach σ^* at $\gamma = 10\%$ instead of $\gamma = 100\%$, $\dot{\gamma}$ must be 10 times greater than λ^{-1} for a single relaxation time, and 10^n times if there are multiple relaxation times of the type we have discussed. In such a case, a stress overshoot will be observed. Once the domains have been broken up to the final size, the effective γ_e will be 1, and Gleisle's rule as described in Equation 3.3.6 with $\gamma_e^* = 1$ will apply to the final steady state stress. Stress overshoot often has been called the apparent result of ignoring the necking of a specimen. We conducted a uniaxial compressive test of a cylindrical specimen and found that overshoot is observed in polycarbonate and polysulfone. This is therefore stress overshoot, and clearly it is NOT due to area reduction.

4

The Molten State

Before beginning this chapter, the reader might twist a piece of high molecular weight polyisobutylene, to see how it feels in the hand. This is a sample of polymer melt! Its T_g is -70 °C, and it is not crosslinked. Does it feel like "a piece of liquid"?!?

4.1 Elements of Melt Rheology

We have already covered some important concepts applicable to rheology of polymer melts, such as linear viscoelasticity, viscoplasticity, the distribution of relaxation times, temperature dependence, and the domains of cooperativity. As we apply these concepts to the melt, we shall be focusing on the major points of difference between the melts and the solids.[1] Perhaps the most important fundamental difference between the solids and melts is the molecular scale of the relaxation processes. In Chapter 2 we discussed the domains of cooperativity that consisted of the order of 10 conformers in solids, whereas the domains of cooperativity for the melt involve whole molecules with thousands of conformers. Near T_g, polymers in the equilibrium state manifest a shear modulus that compares with that of soft metals, and the high frequency end of the relaxation time spectrum can be seconds or even fractions of a second, whereas at that temperature, the maximum relaxation time for the melt can be thousands of years. The temperature range in which melt rheology is studied is the range in which polymers are extruded or molded: typically 50 to 100 degrees above the T_g. For example, for polystyrene melt, the shift in relaxation time when the temperature is changed from 100 °C to 160 °C (with $T_0 = 50$ °C) is obtained from the Vogel-Fulcher formula:

---

1. By solids here we mean, for example, the amorphous state near T_g, although the specimen has aged long enough to reach the equilibrium liquidus state.

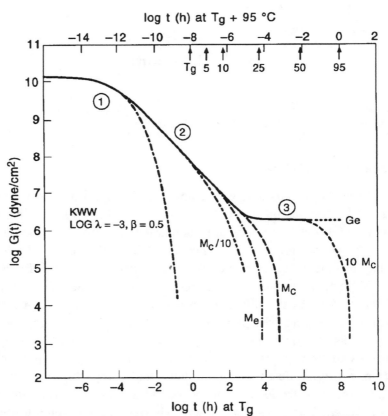

Figure 4.1.1   Master curve for the relaxation modulus of an amorphous polymer in thermodynamic equilibrium. The time scale at the bottom is for the reference temperature at its T_g. At the top, the time scale is for the temperature at T_g + 95 °C. Stage 1 is for conformational relaxation (unkinking), stage 2 is for intermolecular slippage involving a limited chain length, and stage 3 is the correlated relaxation of groups of long chain segments (blobs).

$$\log \frac{\lambda}{\lambda_g} = \frac{1}{2.3} \frac{\Delta\mu^*}{R} \left[\frac{1}{160\text{-}50} - \frac{1}{100\text{-}50} \right] \approx -7 \qquad (4.1.1)$$

and the master curve of Figure 1.4.1 is shifted by -7 decades. Figure 4.1.1 shows the same master curve, with addition of arrows indicating the 1-hour relaxation at each temperature marked by ΔT above T_g. For example, at T_g + 10 °C, the log (1 hour) mark is shifted to the original log (100 hours) = 2 at T_g. At T_g + 50 °C, the same 1-hour mark has now been shifted by 6 decades at the flat portion of the log $G(t)$ vs. log t curve, known as the "plateau" zone. At this temperature, the plateau zone starts at 3 decades earlier (i.e., at several seconds). If we conduct a stress relaxation experiment on the melt, we will most likely detect only the plateau modulus as the "initial" elastic modulus. The "transition" zone that precedes the "plateau zone" will have relaxed by the time the experimental strain has been attained. The plateau modulus, i.e., free energy the (unrelaxed) elastic shear modulus of polymer melt, is about 10^6 dynes/cm^2. The polymer melt is thus 10,000 times softer than the solid polymer, and its relaxation time is 10^8 times longer. From these numbers, it is understandable that the structural scale involved in the viscoelastic deformation of the melt is quite different from that of the glassy state.

As we shall discuss later, the width of the plateau depends on the molecular weight. From this, one suspects that the domain of cooperativity is in the scale of the order of the whole chain molecule. The local domains of conformers that we discussed for relaxation in solids are still important, since they constitute the factor for determining the temperature dependence of the relaxation times in the polymer melt, following the same Vogel-Fulcher formula of Equation 2.1.11. In polymer melts, however, the localized relaxation mode of cooperativity among the individual conformers occurs so fast that it is not observed by the viscoelastic measurement. Yet, as the same temperature dependence suggests, all three relaxation process stages are related. Stage 1 (unkinking) precedes stage 2 (chain slipping), followed by stage 3 (correlated blobs slipping). This is because only relaxations involving large segments of chains composed of many conformers are slow enough to be relevant for the polymer melt. Polymer chain conformations are calculated from the statistics of probability, and the rise and the dissipation of free energy are primarily influenced by the deformation of these *dynamic* chains on the scale of the whole molecule. A dynamic chain can assume many different conformations with the same internal energy. The most probable distribution of conformations means the lowest free energy, i.e., the equilibrium state. When perturbed by an external force, the most probable distribution of conformations is perturbed, and the free energy is raised. As the polymer is held in this deformed state, however, the chain molecules will gradually readjust themselves to relieve the externally initiated perturbation. At each step of molecular readjustment, the free energy thus raised is partially dissipated and eventually returns to the original unperturbed level. By this time, then, the conformational distribution will have returned to a distribution that is new but no less probable than that before the deformation was imposed. The probability of possible microstates that a polymer chain can assume is multiplicative, being the product of the number of all possible states. When this probability is expressed in the logarithmic term, it is of course additive, and this is the conformational entropy. A greater probability means a larger entropy, and a larger entropy means a lower free energy either in terms of Helmholtz free energy A:

$$A = U - TS \qquad (4.1.2)$$

or in terms of Gibbs free energy Ψ:

$$\Psi = H - TS \qquad (4.1.3)$$

The perturbed chains will be able to assume a smaller number of microstates, and the entropy decreases; that is, the free energy is raised. This is why the elasticity of a rubberlike material is sometimes referred to as the entropy spring. The elasticity arising from the conformational probability as described in a later section.

Whereas the units for cooperativity in solids are individual conformers, the units of cooperativity for melts are the "blobs," each consisting of a large portion of the polymer molecule. For every species of polymer, there is a critical molecular length that begins to manifest the rubbery plateau. Below this critical molecular length, the polymer melt exhibits low viscosity and very little elasticity, behaving similarly to ordinary fluids. Such a low molecular weight polymer in the solid state lacks plasticity and it is brittle.

Figure 4.1.2 depicts dynamic polymer molecules in the molten state. Each of the randomly placed loops is three-fourths of a circle, with its area being proportional to N, the number of conformers in the loop; its radius of curvature, however, is proportional to $\sqrt{N}$. Thus the cross-sectional width is proportional to $N^{1/4}$. If the molecular weight is less than the critical loop length, each loop will be disconnected and able to move independently.

Dynamic test results show that polymer melts exhibit linear viscoelasticity; that is, the modulus and dynamic viscosity are independent of the strain amplitude. It is particularly important to remember that the fast

Figure 4.1.2 A heuristic picture[2] of dynamic molecules in the molten state. The radius of curvature of each loop is drawn about the root-mean-square of the critical size for "entanglement."

rate of deformation experienced during a dynamic test, well in excess of the reciprocal of its longest relaxation time, will not cause nonlinear viscoelastic behavior. At frequencies well in excess of λ_1^{-1}, (λ_1 is the relaxation time of the fundamental mode, or the longest relaxation time of a spectrum), linear viscoelastic dynamic moduli are observed. This statement may at first seem to contradict the well-known shear-thinning behavior universally observed in polymer melts. Actually, however, the shear thinning, or the decrease of the apparent steady flow shear viscosity at higher shear rates, is a partially plastic, partially linear viscoelastic phenomenon, as we shall discuss in detail in the following sections. The plasticity is identified with yield phenomena governed by the deviatoric stress. Beyond the yield point, the stress at steady state is nearly independent of the rate of shear. We reason that the *postyield* stress divided by the shear rate (i.e., the steady state viscosity) thus

---

2. The choice of the words is by S. J. Muller, University of California, Berkeley.

decreases with increasing strain rate. Until the limiting elastic energy is reached, we have reason to believe that a polymer melt exhibits linear viscoelasticity. We are also aware of the well-studied nonlinearity invoking the BKZ theory, but this, too, can be explained within the framework of a combination of linear viscoelasticity and classical plasticity, as we discussed in Section 3.3 for solids, and we think this is why the "initial" modulus appears to be lower at a greater rate of strain in the stress relaxation test.

We have attributed the yield phenomenon in solid polymers to the breakup of domains of cooperativity into smaller sizes. This statement can be applied to the yield phenomenon in polymer melts, word for word. Only the size and nature of what constitutes a domain are grossly different for melts and for solids.

4.2 Rubber Elasticity

In Chapter 3, we discussed stage 1 relaxation in solids primarily in terms of a cooperative process among the conformers aimed at relieving the mechanically raised free energy. The distribution of conformations is essentially unchanged when a stress is suddenly imposed. "Unkinking" does not mean that all will end up in the *trans* conformations. A configurational change from *trans* to *gauche* might in fact relieve the stress, depending on the local structural environment. During relaxation, the average conformation on the scale of the whole molecule will change little and, after the stress has relaxed to 0, the distribution is essentially the same as before the stress was applied. The macroscopic strain involved is a few percent at the most, and little or no change in the relative concentration of *gauche* to *trans* conformations is expected before and after the relaxation.

Relaxation in the melt, on the other hand, is typically observed under a strain of the order of 100%. The driving force toward the elastic behavior is entropic, i.e., the tendency to return to the most probable conformational distribution from the oriented state under the strain. While the relative concentrations of the *gauche* and *trans* conformations are only slightly shifted under such strain, the number of the whole chain conformations under the strain is significantly reduced.

A conformation of an entire molecule can be specified by the sum of vectors with which the conformers along the molecule are represented. For a molecule with n conformers, there are $_{nc_1}P_{nc_1}$ conformations, where c_1 is the number of possible conformations a conformer can assume. From the total number of conformations the molecule can assume, the conformational entropy is calculated.

The traditional treatise[3] on the statistics of molecular conformations in the rubbery state has bypassed the problem of dealing with conformational states of individual conformers by introducing the concept of *submolecules*,[4] which is a large enough collection of conformers to be a dynamic chain. The size of such a submolecule is 20 to 40 conformers. The submolecule is the building block of the idealized *dynamic* polymer molecule. Each submolecule has average length *l*, and *n* such submolecules make up the entire polymer molecule, so that the contour length of the polymer molecule is *nl*. See the schematic illustration in Figure 4.2.1. We can apply the statistics of random walks to such a molecule because these submolecules are *freely* joined, i.e., at each joint the next step is equally likely to be taken in any direction. A particular conformation for a polymer molecule can be specified by the distance between the ends of the polymer molecule. The conformational probability can be calculated by the probability of the end-to-end distance for a given polymer of the contour length *nl*.

When one end of the polymer molecule is placed at the origin, $O\,(0,0,0)$, the probability $W(x,y,z)$ that the other end will be found in a little cube, dx by dy by dz located at $P\,(x,y,z)$ is given by the equation:

$$W(x,y,z)dx\,dy\,dz = \frac{\beta^3}{\pi^{3/2}}\,\exp[-\beta^2(x^2 + y^2 + z^2)]dx\,dy\,dz \qquad (4.2.1)$$

where

$$\beta^2 = \frac{3}{2nl^2} \qquad (4.2.2)$$

A simplified derivation of Equation 4.2.1 can be illustrated with a one-dimensional random walk, i.e., walking randomly either to the east or west. The final position after taking *n* steps corresponds to the position of the

---

3. Treloar, L. R. G., *The Physics of Rubber Elasticity*, Oxford University Press, London, 1958.
4. Kuhn, W., *J. Polym. Sci.* **1**, 380 (1946).

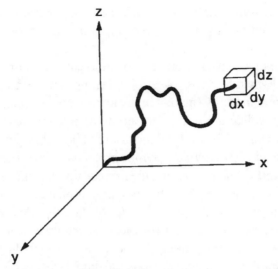

Figure 4.2.1 Molecular conformation is specified with the coordinate for the position of one end of the chain with respect to the other. The probability that the end will fall within the box dx dy dz at $P(x,y,z)$ is an equivalent of the probability for a conformation.

chain end. This probability is the same as the probability of flipping coins n times to find an exact number of times heads will show. The following will illustrate the problem.

Let $W(m)$ be the probability that "heads" will turn up m times out of n throws. Then

$$W(m) = \left(\frac{1}{2}\right)^n {}_nC_m = \left(\frac{1}{2}\right)^n \frac{n!}{m!(n-m)!}$$

In terms of $p = m - (n - m)$, that "heads" turn up p times more than "tails",

$$W(p) = \left(\frac{1}{2}\right)^n \frac{n!}{[(n+p)/2]![(n-p)/2]!}$$

The distance x reached at the end of n steps is $pl/\sqrt{3}$. With Stirling's formula, the equation above is rewritten:

$$= \left(\frac{1}{2}\right)^n n^{(n+1/2)} \exp(-n)(2\pi)^{1/2}$$

$$(\frac{n+p}{2})^{-[(n+p)/2+1/2]} \exp[(n+p)/2](2\pi)^{-1/2}$$

$$\left(\frac{n-p}{2}\right)^{-[(n-p)/2+1/2]} \exp[(n-p)/2](2\pi)^{-1/2}$$

$$=\left(\frac{1}{2}\right)^{n} n^{(n+1/2)} \left(\frac{n}{2}\right)^{-(n+p+1)/2} \left(\frac{n}{2}\right)^{-(n-p+1)/2}$$

$$\left(1+\frac{p}{n}\right)^{-(n+p+1)/2} \left(1-\frac{p}{n}\right)^{-(n-p+1)/2}$$

$$=n^{-1/2}\left(\frac{2}{\pi}\right)^{1/2} \exp\left[\frac{p^2}{n^2}\frac{(n+1)}{2}\right] \exp\left[\frac{2p}{n}\left(-\frac{p}{2}\right)\right]$$

$$=\left(\frac{2}{n\pi}\right)^{1/2} \exp\left(-\frac{p^2}{2n}\right)$$

$W(p)$ is the probability that the end of an n-step walk ends at p steps away from the start in the + direction (calling the "head" as a step in the + direction). To convert this form into the probability that the end will fall between x and $x + dx$, we must divide $W(p)$ by the distance that corresponds to the minimum increment in p. However, each single step in m means a change of 2 for p. Thus the distance that corresponds to the minimum incremental change in p is $2l/\sqrt{l}$, and we must *divide* $W(p)$ by this distance, which gives us:

$$W(x)\Delta x = \left(\frac{3}{2\pi n l^2}\right)^{1/2} \exp\left(-\frac{3x^2}{2nl^2}\right)\Delta x$$

This is the one-dimensional equivalent of Equation 4.2.1. The average distance between the ends can be taken in various forms. The most likely values for the other end of the chain in the x-direction is at $x=0$ as shown in Figure 4.2.2, and the same is true for the y and z coordinates. This does not mean, however, that the most likely place for the two ends is at the origin. It is merely the consequence of the symmetry of the distribution of the end positions. The scalar average of the end-to-end distance can be expressed in the polar coordinate:

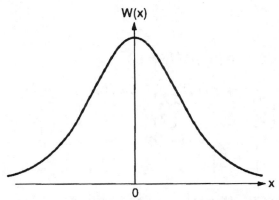

Figure 4.2.2 The probability $W(x)$ that a one-dimensional random walk will end at the distance x away from the origin.

$$<r> = \int_0^\infty r\, W(r)\mathrm{d}r = \int_0^\infty \frac{4\pi\beta^3 r^3}{\pi^{3/2}} \exp(-\beta^3 r^2)\mathrm{d}r \qquad (4.2.3)$$

which is evaluated to be $\dfrac{\sqrt{8n}}{\sqrt{3\pi}}l.$

The root-mean-square is another form of averaging the molecular dimension:

$$<r^2> = \int_0^\infty r^2 W(r)\mathrm{d}r = \int_0^\infty \frac{4\pi\beta^3 r^4}{\pi^{3/2}} \exp(-\beta^2 r^2)\mathrm{d}r = nl^2 \qquad (4.2.4)$$

which is shown in Figure 4.2.3, and

$$<r^2>^{1/2} = \sqrt{n}\,l \qquad (4.2.5)$$

For a tetrahedral chain, it can be shown that[5]

$$<r^2>^{1/2} = \sqrt{2n}\,l \qquad (4.2.5a)$$

The dimension of a *relaxed*, or the most probably shaped, molecule thus

---

5. See Bueche, F., *Physical Properties of Polymers*, Wiley-Interscience, New York, 1962, p. 27.

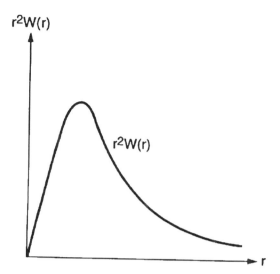

Figure 4.2.3 The root-mean-square, end-to-end distance is the average of $r^2W(r)$ and is equal to nl^2.

will double when the molecular weight is quadrupled, according to this simple model. One of the most serious roots of error in this freely joined molecular model is the omission of the excluded volume effect, namely that more than two segments may not occupy the same location. Accounting for the excluded volume effects will alter the power of $\frac{1}{2}$ to some other number (e.g., $\frac{2}{3}$).

When a freely jointed molecule is deformed, the most probable shape of the polymer chain will be altered. The new distribution under a mechanical strain can be calculated assuming that the change in the distribution of orientations of submolecules will be the same as the change of the macroscopic dimensions of the sample of that polymer, i.e., the *affine* deformation. Suppose the polymer sample in the shape of a square rod, L by D by D, is pulled in the L direction, such that the sample is deformed to the new dimension, $L + \Delta L$ by $D - \Delta D$ by $D - \Delta D$, as illustrated in Figure 4.2.4. Since the rubbery state is easily deformed but more difficult to dilate, the increase in the length is just about made up by the contraction in the lateral directions. The Poisson ratio is nearly 0.5. By defining the *extension ratio* α to be the ratio of the new length to the original length, the new probability, $W'(x,y,z)$, for the chain end under the deformation is obtained by

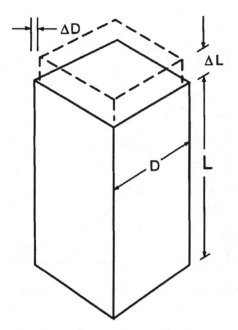

Figure 4.2.4 A prismatic bar before and after tensile deformation.

substituting x by αx, y by $y/\sqrt{\alpha}$, and z by $z/\sqrt{\alpha}$:

$$W'(x,y,z)\,dx\,dy\,dz = \frac{\beta^3}{\pi^{3/2}}\exp\left[-\beta^2\left(\alpha^2 x^2 + \frac{y^2}{\alpha} + \frac{z^2}{\alpha}\right)\right]dx\,dy\,dz \quad (4.2.6)$$

The entropy of a system that can be arranged in W different ways is $k\ln W$, where k is the Boltzmann constant. Accordingly, the entropy change Δs experienced by a chain by the deformation is:

$$\Delta s = -k\beta^2\left[(\alpha^2-1)x^2 + \left(\frac{1}{\alpha} - 1\right)y^2 + \left(\frac{1}{\alpha} - 1\right)z^2\right] \quad (4.2.7)$$

Now let us consider a collection of N chains, each nl long. Recalling that entropy is additive while probability is multiplicative, the total entropy change, ΔS, caused by the deformation is:

$$\Delta S = \Sigma \Delta s_i = -k\beta^2 \left[\left(\alpha^2 - 1 \right) \Sigma x_i^2 + \left(\frac{1}{\alpha} - 1 \right) \Sigma y_i^2 + \left(\frac{1}{\alpha} - 1 \right) \Sigma z_i^2 \right] \qquad (4.2.8)$$

In this expression Σx_i^2 is the sum of the square of the x components in the unstrained state of the system of collection of N polymer chains.

Since $\displaystyle\Sigma_i x_i^2 = \Sigma_i y_i^2 = \Sigma_i z_i^2 = \frac{1}{3} \Sigma_i r_i^2$ and $\displaystyle\Sigma_i r_i^2 = N <r^2>$

one obtains:

$$\Delta S = -\frac{1}{3} kN\beta^2 <r^2> \left[\alpha^2 + \frac{2}{\alpha} - 3 \right] = -\frac{1}{2} Nk \left[\alpha^2 + \frac{2}{\alpha} - 3 \right] \qquad (4.2.9)$$

which no longer depends on the arbitrary constants related to n and l, the number and the dimension of the submolecules.

Now, the recoverable strain energy is the integral of the stress with respect to the elastic strain. The recoverable energy is thermodynamically equivalent to the free energy. Accordingly, the stress σ, or the force per unit area, is the derivative of Helmholtz free energy A per unit volume (e.g., in 1 cm^3) with respect to the extension ratio α:

$$\sigma = \frac{dA}{d\alpha} = \frac{dU}{d\alpha} - T\frac{dS}{d\alpha} \qquad (4.2.10)$$

where U is the internal energy, which, in this idealized rubbery polymer, is not affected by the deformation and, therefore,

$$\sigma = -T\frac{dS}{d\alpha} = NkT\left(\alpha - \frac{1}{\alpha^2} \right) \approx 3NkT\frac{\varepsilon}{1+\varepsilon} \quad \text{when } \varepsilon \ll 3 \qquad (4.2.11)$$

where the tensile strain $\varepsilon = \alpha - 1$, and N is the number of molecules per unit volume (e.g., cm^3), and $Nk = (\rho/M)R$ where ρ is the density (in, e.g., cm^3), and M is the molecular weight of the whole chain. Equation 4.2.11 predicts that the stiffness of the rubbery polymer will decrease with strain in tension and increase under compression. Also, the stiffness increases proportionally to the absolute temperature, according to Equation 4.2.11. The theory is compared with data in Figure 4.2.5. The compressive data in fact fit the theory better than the tensile data. In case of the simple shear, the external force can be in the x direction (y-z plane), such that $\alpha = 1$ in the y and z directions and then it can be shown that

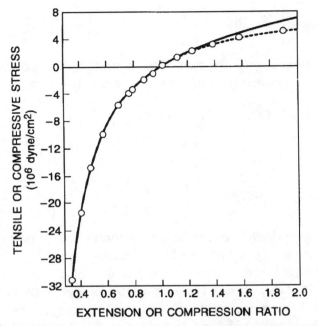

Figure 4.2.5 Rubber elasticity in the relatively small strain range. The line is from the theory in the text (Equation 4.2.11).

$$\sigma = NkT\gamma = \frac{\rho RT}{M}\gamma \tag{4.2.12}$$

where γ is the shear strain and σ is the shear force per unit area. Note that the shear modulus is one-third of the tensile modulus when the strain is very small. This can be predicted from purely geometric considerations, which leads to the well-known relationship among the tensile modulus E, the bulk modulus K, the shear modulus G, and the Poisson ratio ν:

$$E = 3K(1 - 2\nu) = 2(1 + \nu)G \tag{4.2.13}$$

which suggests that for a hard material $(E \approx K)$, ν is $\frac{1}{3}$, whereas for a soft material $(G/K \approx 0)$, ν is $\frac{1}{2}$. It has nothing to do with the magnitude of compressibility. The compressibility of a rubbery polymer is very large, in fact.

When polymer chains are chemically crosslinked, the conformers at the points of crosslinking are prevented from undergoing conformational change under strain. Only the portion of the chain between crosslinked points can undergo conformational change, and the strand of the molecular chain between the crosslink points becomes the basis of the entropic spring. The number of the strands N_c would be equal to the total length $n_0 l$ of the primary chain (the original chain before crosslinking), divided by the length of the network chain nl. This, however, neglects the segments with uncrosslinked ends and, if one accounts for them, one obtains the formula:

$$N_c = \frac{n_0 l}{nl} \left[1 - \frac{2nl}{n_0 l} \right] \tag{4.2.14a}$$

and by substituting the ratio of the (number average) molecular weight M_n of the primary chains over the M_c of the network strands between crosslinks for the ratio n_0 over n in the equation above,

$$N_c = \frac{M_n}{M_c} \left[1 - \frac{2M_c}{M_n} \right] \tag{4.2.14b}$$

is obtained.

For a crosslinked polymer, we can write for the shear stress σ, from Equation 4.2.12,

$$\sigma = N_c kT \gamma = \frac{\rho RT}{M_e} \gamma \tag{4.2.15}$$

where M_e is the effective average molecular weight between the crosslinks. This equation plays a useful role when we attempt to understand the elasticity in the plateau region of viscoelasticity in the next section.

The equations above pertain only to small strains of less than 1, where the network conformational distribution is Gaussian. The tensile modulus decreases with strain according to Equation 4.2.11 and Figure 4.2.5.[6]

---

6. The well-known Mooney-Rivlin formula will not change this aspect, and it has been shown that its second coefficient $C_2 \rightarrow 0$ at equilibrium: Ciferri, A., and Flory, P. J., *J. Appl. Phys.* **30**, 1498 (1959).

However, a model for the elasticity of a real molecule must include a provision for the unassailable boundary condition that, when the molecule is completely stretched, its modulus should be that of stretching the C-C bonds, or practically the infinity in the scale of the concern. L angevin's model of the ordering of magnetic dipoles in a magnetic field has the essential feature that, the more dipoles are in the parallel direction to the field, the more difficult it is to further increase the orientation. The random state contains as many parallel dipoles as the antiparallel dipoles, and the average angle between the dipoles and the field is 90°. Any perturbation in orientation will produce work: $W = Fl \cos \theta$, where F is the force, and θ the angle between a dipole and the field. According to the Boltzmann distribution law, the probability that the segment makes an angle θ with the direction of the force is proportional to $\exp(-W/kT)$. The average value of the component of the vector l in the direction of the field, which will be defined as the x-axis, will be

$$\frac{<l_x>}{l} = \frac{\displaystyle\int_0^{\pi} (\cos\theta)(2\pi \sin\theta \; d\theta)\exp(Fl\cos\theta/kT)}{\displaystyle\int_0^{\pi} 2\pi\sin\theta \; d\theta\exp(Fl\cos\theta/kT)}$$

or

$$\frac{<l_x>}{l} = \left[\coth\left(\frac{Fl}{kT}\right) - \left(\frac{kT}{Fl}\right)\right] \equiv L\left(\frac{Fl}{kT}\right)$$

where $L(x)$ is the Langevin equation of x. $<l_x>$ is the change in the net projection of l in the x- direction under the force F, which was zero without the force. Thus $<l_x>$ represents the deformation per segment. The strain is the deformation over the unperturbed dimension. Thus, we rewrite Equation 4.2.16:

$$\frac{<r_x>}{nl} = L\left(\frac{F}{kT}\right) \qquad (4.2.16')$$

where n is the number of beads per molecule, and

$$\frac{Fl}{kT} = \mathbf{L*}\left(\frac{<r_x>}{nl}\right) = \left[3\left(\frac{<r_x>}{nl}\right) + \frac{9}{5}\left(\frac{<r_x>}{nl}\right)^3 + \ldots\right] \quad (4.2.17)$$

where $\mathbf{L*}$ is the inverse Langevin equation, and for $<r_x>/nl^2 = \varepsilon \ll 1$,

$$F = 3kT\frac{<r_x>}{nl^2} = 3NkT\varepsilon \quad (4.2.18)$$

which is Equation 4.2.11 as $\alpha \to 1$, where N is the number of polymer molecules per cubic centimeter.

For larger strains, F/NkT = inverse Langevin function of $(\alpha - 1)$ is characterized by a rapidly increasing slope toward the strain of several hundred percent. Such a curve is illustrated in Figure 4.5.5 in Section 4.5.

4.3 Linear Viscoelasticity Without Entanglement: Stage 2

Beyond stage 1, the polymer segments are pulled past the surrounding molecules. The early part of this process is stage 2. One point of view of Stage 2 relaxation was presented in Section 2.2.2, dealing with the statistical probability of various modes of relaxation represented by the chain length. Stage 2 is typified by the viscoelastic behavior of polymer melts having molecular weight less than the critical value for the entanglement. With Equation 4.2.12, we have shown that the shear modulus is proportional to N, the number of strands per cubic centimeter of the sample. When this sample is suddenly strained to γ_o, the stress will rise to $NkT\gamma_o$. The entropy decreases and the Helmholtz free energy rises, but as we hold the strain constant, the molecules will readjust toward the most probable conformational distribution. The square of the end-to-end distance of a molecule, which initially rose from $<r^2>$ to $<r'^2>$, will in time return to $<r^2>$, as the macroscopic strain is held constant. The stress will decay back to zero and the experimental strain γ_o is now "set", that is, the sample has attained a new permanent shape. In the process of returning from $<r'^2>$ to $<r^2>$, a molecule must move against its surroundings, and in so doing it will experience frictional resistance. The frictional coefficient ς, or the force over the velocity, is the molecular equivalent of the viscosity η and it is proportional to the length of the molecule, i.e.,

$$\varsigma = \varsigma_0 \frac{M}{M_0} \tag{4.3.1}$$

where ς_0 is the frictional coefficient per conformer and M_o is the molecular weight of one conformer.

The steady state viscosity is the steady state stress divided by the rate of strain. For a linear viscoelastic material with a single relaxation time λ,

$$\eta = \frac{\sigma_{ss}}{\dot{\gamma}} = \lim_{t \to \infty} \frac{\sigma_{\dot{\gamma}}}{\dot{\gamma}} = \lim_{t \to \infty} \frac{G\lambda\dot{\gamma}[1 - \exp(-t/\lambda)]}{\dot{\gamma}} = G\lambda \tag{4.3.2}$$

For a sample that consists of $N = \rho/M$ molecules/cm^3 (ρ is the density), $G = \rho RT/M$, and the apparent steady flow viscosity η is

$$\eta = \frac{\rho RT}{M} \lambda \tag{4.3.3}$$

From Equations 4.3.1 and 4.3.3, the molecular weight dependence of relaxation time λ is obtained:

$$\lambda = \frac{\varsigma_0}{M_0} \frac{M^2}{\rho RT} \tag{4.3.4}$$

while for the molecular weight dependence of the modulus G, we already have (Equation 4.2.12):

$$G = \frac{\sigma}{\gamma} = \frac{\rho RT}{M} \tag{4.3.4'}$$

Thus, the shear modulus G is inversely proportional to the molecular weight M. The viscosity η is proportional to M, and the relaxation time λ is proportional to M^2.

The relaxation time λ cited here is the relaxation time involving a uniformly distributed stress over the entire length of the molecule. Conceivably, however, the stress can be nonuniformly distributed along the chain, and such a locally concentrated stress can be relaxed completely through the relaxation of a part of the molecule. Thus a polymer molecule is capable of undergoing the relaxation with a fraction of a whole molecule with the relaxation time $\lambda_p = (\varsigma_0/M_0)(M^2/p^2)\, 1/(\rho RT) = \lambda_1/p^2$, where the pth mode is for a $1/p$ long segment of the chain. (The subscript 1 denotes the whole chain.)

The relaxation spectrum $H(\ln\lambda)$ is the intensity for the mode for the relaxation time λ per interval $\Delta\ln\lambda$. The relaxation modulus is, therefore, given by the formula:

$$G(t) = \int_{\ln\lambda_{min}}^{\ln\lambda_{max}} H(\ln\lambda)\exp\left(-\frac{t}{\lambda}\right)\, d\ln\lambda \qquad (4.3.5)$$

For the pth mode, the strand length $M_p = M/p$, the viscosity η_p is proportional to the strand size:

$$\eta_p = \eta\frac{M_p}{M} = \frac{\eta}{p} \qquad (4.3.6)$$

and from Equation 4.3.4′,

$$H_p = H(\ln\lambda_p) = \frac{\rho RT}{M_p} = \frac{\rho RT}{M}p \qquad (4.3.7)$$

and

$$\lambda_p = \frac{\eta_p}{H_p} = \frac{\eta}{p}\frac{M}{\rho RT}\frac{1}{p} = \frac{\lambda_1}{p^2} \qquad (4.3.8)$$

Since $d\ln\lambda_p = -2dp/p$, we obtain from Equation 4.3.5:

$$G(t) = \frac{2\rho RT}{M}\int_{1}^{p_{max}} \exp\left(-\frac{t}{\lambda_1/p^2}\right)\, dp \qquad (4.3.9)$$

or, in terms of the discrete spectrum :

$$G(t) = \frac{2\rho RT}{M}\sum_{p=1}^{p_{max}} \exp\left(-\frac{t}{\lambda_1/p^2}\right) \qquad (4.3.10)$$

where p_{max} signifies the minimum size of strands or the highest mode harmonics for the *external* frictional relaxation of stage 2. This is where the relaxation function joins the *internal* frictional relaxation of stage 1, and it is estimated to be around the point at which the relaxation modulus $G(t)$ takes the value of ca. 10^9 dynes/cm^2, or time t of 1 hour at $T = T_g - 5$ °C in the equilibrium state. Equation 4.3.10 is essentially the same as the formula derived from the Rouse model,[7] except for the factor 2 for the modulus. The Rouse formula can be obtained from Equation 4.3.8 for the pth mode relaxation time, by letting the elastic modulus to be σ_p/γ_p. Here σ_p is the stress, the force per square centimeter, due to the pth mode strands, which are p times as numerous as the fundamental mode involving the whole molecule. γ_p is the strain, or the strain per strand times the number of strands per cubic centimeter, which again is p times that of the whole molecule. Thus the modulus is $p(\rho RT/pM) = \rho RT/M$, and p cancels out for the modulus for the pth mode. Thus we obtain:

$$G(t) = \frac{\rho RT}{M}\sum_{p=1}^{p\,\text{max}}\exp\left[-\frac{t}{\lambda_1/p^2}\right] \qquad (4.3.11)$$

From Equations 4.3.7 and 4.3.8, it is evident that the slope for the $\ln H(\ln\lambda)$ vs. $\ln\lambda$ is -0.5. Hence, according to Equation 1.5.3, the same is true of the slope for the $\ln G(t)$ vs. $\ln t$.

For the creep retardation spectrum $L(\ln\lambda)$, we can utilize the same procedure as above, provided

$$L_p = L(\ln\lambda_p) = \frac{M}{\rho RT}\frac{1}{p} \qquad (4.3.12)$$

and

$$\frac{1}{\eta_p} = \frac{p}{\eta} \qquad (4.3.13)$$

and we obtain for the creep compliance:

$$\int_1^{p\,\text{max}}\frac{2}{p^2}\frac{M}{\rho RT}\left[1-\exp\left(-\frac{t}{\lambda_1/p^2}\right)\right]dp \qquad (4.3.14)$$

and in terms of the discrete spectrum:

7. Rouse, R. E., Jr., *J. Chem. Phys.* **21,** 1272 (1953).

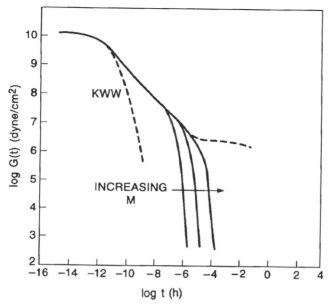

Figure 4.3.1 Schematic diagram for the relaxation modulus in stage 2, for various molecular weights.

$$J(t) = \frac{2M}{\rho RT} \sum_{p,\text{odd}} \frac{1}{p^2} \left[1 - \exp\left(-\frac{t}{\lambda_1/p^2} \right) \right] \qquad (4.3.15)$$

where only odd valued ps were taken to contribute for the diffusion of strands.[8]

According to Equation 4.3.12, the slope for the plot of $\ln L$ ($\ln \lambda$) vs. $\ln \lambda$ should be $+0.5$, and the discrete spectrum $J_p = J_1/p^2$ rapidly increases toward the fundamental mode value, instead of remaining constant as in the case of the modulus. The dielectric spectrum is essentially the retardation spectrum, so that the transition zone has a slope of 0.5. This will be illustrated for the case of dilute solutions in Section 6.3.

8. Gross, B., *J. Polymer Sci.* **20**, 123 (1956).

A slope of ca. -0.5 is obtained for the *relaxation* spectrum derived in Equation 2.2.20 in Section 2.2.2, where the Gaussian distribution was assumed for the probability density of all normal modes. The center of the distribution according to that analysis is about 20 conformers. Tobolsky and Murakami[9] have shown that in the transition zone, or stage 2, the increase in the molecular weight results in the increase of the maximum λ_1, coupled with the decrease of the maximum modulus G_1 as shown schematically in Figure 4.3.1, and as described by Equations 4.3.4 and 4.3.4´. All the equations above were derived based on the theory that viscosity is proportional to molecular weight. This is true as long as the molecular weight is not so small as to become diluted by a large population of chain ends. The conformer units at the chain ends are always at a higher energy level than the same conformer within the chain.[10] This effect from the excessive population of chain ends is evident when T_g becomes noticeably lower as a result of the reduced molecular weight. The dependence of viscosity on molecular weight is shown in Figure 4.3.2.[11] Above the critical molecular weight for the entanglement, the slope is 3.4. This is stage 3 relaxation, and it is discussed in the following section. Below the critical molecular weight, the slope of the log-log plot is 1.

The upper limit of p is determined by the smallest segment of the molecule that can still be considered to be part of the dynamic chain. To estimate the limit of p in the high frequency limit requires some assumptions. As we continue to subdivide the chain into smaller and smaller segments, the corresponding relaxation time λ_p will begin to overlap with the conformational relaxation time of the intermolecular cooperative mode, i.e., the unkinking mode, discussed in detail in Chapter 2. The *inter*molecular mode in the melt temperature range, however, typically involves ca. 2 to 3 conformers, as shown by the formula:

---

9. Tobolsky, A. V., and Murakami, K., *J. Polym. Sci.* **40**, 443 (1959).

10. See Table 2.2, Section 2.1.

11. Berry, G. C., and Fox, T. G., *Adv. Polymer Sci.* **5** 261 (1968); also in Ferry, J. D., *Viscoelastic Properties of Polymers,* Wiley, New York, 1970, p. 270.

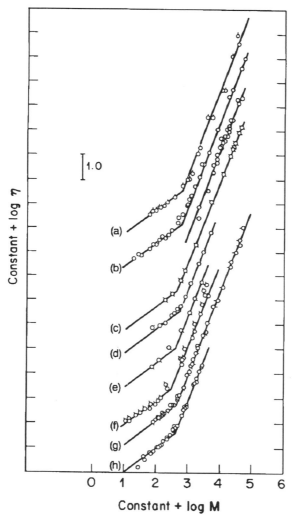

Figure 4.3.2 Steady state viscosity vs. molecular weight for transition zone (stage 2) relaxation where $M < M_e$ and entanglement zone (stage 3) relaxation where $M > M_e$ for many different polymers. The slope in stage 2 is slightly greater than 1 primarily because the chain ends, which act as diluents, increase their concentration at the lower molecular weight range, giving an additional effect of molecular weight. This effect is accompanied by a drop in the glass transition temperature.

$$z = \frac{T^* - T_0}{T^*} \frac{T}{T - T_0} = 2.3 \tag{4.3.16}$$

with the characteristic relaxation time of 10^{-6} second (See Figure 2.1.8). The monomeric friction coefficient ς_0 is the force required to move a monomer-sized segment over a unit distance in a second. Following the example by Ferry,[12] the effective local viscosity η_{eff} can be calculated based on Stokes' law for an isolated sphere of radius r:

$$\varsigma_0 = 6\pi\eta_{\text{eff}} r \tag{4.3.17}$$

For a molar volume of 100 cm^3 (2 conformers of polystyrene) at $T = T_g + 100$ °C, the experimental value of ς_0 is ca. 10^{-7} dyne-cm/s, whereas at T_g, it is 10^2 dyne-cm/s. The value of r (per monomer unit, rather than a conformer) is obtained from $[3/\pi \times 100/6 \times 10^{23}]^{1/3} = 5.4 \times 10^{-8}$ cm and we obtain a convenient expression: $\eta_{\text{eff}} = \varsigma_0 \times 10^6$ dynes/cm^2-s or poise. At $T = T_g + 100$ °C, we obtain η_{eff} of 0.1 poise and at T_g 10^8 poises. The latter value is compared to the internal viscosity for the conformation relaxation, $G_0\lambda_c \sim 10^{8.5} \times 3 \times 10^3 = 10^{12}$ poises, and clearly the latter is the controlling mechanism near T_g. At $T = T_g + 100$ °C, however, the (conformational) internal viscosity is $10^8 \times 10^{(-11)} \sim 10^{-3}$ poise, as compared to the external viscosity of 10^{-1} poise, in which case the external viscosity is the controlling mechanism.

In the range $T \sim T_g$ to $T - T_g + 100$ °C, the temperature dependence of the domain size is a significant factor for the large apparent activation energy, because the latter includes the factor dz/dT; i.e.,

$$\Delta H = \frac{d}{d(1/T)} \frac{\Delta\mu^*}{(T - T_0)} = T^2 \frac{\Delta\mu^*}{(T - T_0)^2} \tag{4.3.18}$$

will obtain 195 kcal!!!, whereas the "real" $\Delta\mu^* z \sim 14.7$ kcal for a constant value of $z = 4.3$ and $\Delta\mu^* = 3.4$ kcal from Equations 2.1.4 and 2.1.7, at 100 °C for the polymer with $T_g = 100$ °C and $T_0 = 50$ °C. At 200 °C, ΔH, in Equation 4.3.18, is 35 kcal, whereas $\Delta\mu^* z$ is 7 kcal when $z = 2$. The Vogel-Fulcher formula no longer holds at high temperatures, as the external viscosity becomes the controlling factor, and the domain size, small as it is at

---

12. Ferry, J. D., *Viscoelastic Properties of Polymers*, Wiley, New York, 1970, p. 369.

high temperatures, is not expected to change significantly with temperature, such that at high enough temperatures the Arrhenius formula:

$$\ln \eta \propto \frac{\Delta H^*}{kT} \tag{4.3.19}$$

will fit data better. ΔH^* is the flow activation energy and depends on the monomeric friction coefficient ς_0, and it is best evaluated from the zero-shear rate viscosity. For linear polyethylene, ΔH^* is about 6 kcal, while for branched polyethylene it is 12 kcal.

The value of ς_0 varies from polymer to polymer by four orders of magnitude. However, as Ferry points out, the value 10^{-6} dyne-s/cm divides polymers with disubstituted backbone chain atoms (methacrylate polymers and polyisobutylene) from polymers with a monosubstituted backbone. It is conceivable that the presence of short branches can offer a higher local viscosity.[13]

Since the friction coefficient is the force required to move a segment over a unit distance in a second, it is related to the self-diffusion coefficient D:

$$\varsigma = \frac{kT}{D} \tag{4.3.20}$$

Experiments have been performed on the diffusion of a small foreign molecule through polymer media. A slight complication could arise because the free energy levels of dimers and trimers are higher than those of the two or three segments in the middle of a chain. However, for normal paraffins, ς is found approximately proportional to the molecular length.[14] What seems to be interesting is that the activation energy necessary for the friction coefficient for a conformer to slip (jump) is about the same as $\Delta \mu$ for the rotational relaxation (ca. 3 to 4 kcal/mol). We believe that this is why the Vogel-type temperature dependence of relaxation phenomena in the melt is carried to the high temperature range with the same values of parameters obtained *for the equilibrium state* near the glass transition temperature.

---

13. Polydimethyl siloxane is a resounding exception with $\varsigma_0 \sim 10^{-8}$ dyne-cm/s, a class by itself.
14. Chen, S. P., and Ferry, J. D., *Macromolecules* **1**, 270 (1968).

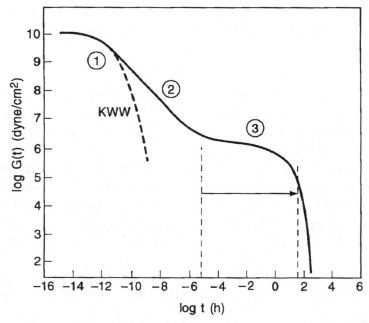

Figure 4.4.1 Simplified picture of how the Dirac delta jumps to stage 3 from stage 2 when the critical molecular weight for the entanglement is exceeded.

4.4 Linear Viscoelasticity with Entanglement: Stage 3

The proportionality relationship between molecular weight and melt viscosity does not go on too far among high molecular weight polymers. In the Rouse-like stage 2 regime (the "transition" zone) discussed in Section 4.3.1, the viscosity dependence ($\propto M$) and the relaxation time dependence ($\propto M^2$) on molecular weight are different. In the "plateau" region, which we are about to discuss, the relaxation time increases, as does the viscosity, with the 3.4th power. Unlike in the "transition" zone, where the modulus for the terminal (the slowest) relaxation process decreases with $\propto M^{-1}$, the modulus in the plateau region is independent of molecular weight. Clearly, above the critical molecular weight M_c, M_c, as illustrated in Figure 4.4.1, the apparent number of strands remains constant regardless of the real molecular weight. The value of the plateau modulus is about 10^6 to 10^7

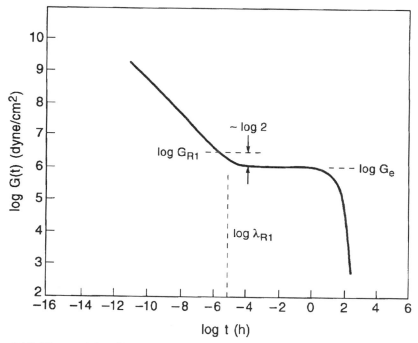

Figure 4.4.2 The modulus G_{RI} for the longest relaxation mode in stage 2 is about twice as large as G_e, the modulus at the entanglement plateau.

dynes/cm² for most polymers. Since the modulus depends on the moles per cubic centimeter of the strands, the modulus G_e of an entanglement strand M_e long, is given by

$$G_e = N_e kT = \frac{\rho RT}{M_e} \tag{4.4.1}$$

where N_e is the number of strands per unit volume. $G_e = 2 \times 10^6$ dynes/cm³ $= 5 \times 10^{-2}$ cal/cm³, and $T = 400$ K, $\rho = 1$ g/cm³, will obtain $M_e = 1.6 \times 10^4$. G_e is the modulus value to which the tail end of the stage 2 relaxation modulus approaches as if it were the final equilibrium modulus in a chemically crosslinked polymer. This is the value to which the slowest relaxing species in the stage 2 spectrum will relax. The last and the longest of the stage 2 relaxation times in the $\eta \propto M$ regime (stage 2), which we shall

Table 4.1 Critical Molecular Weight for Entanglement From Viscosity Measurement

Polymer	Temp. °C	M_c	$n_c{}^a$
Polyvinyl acetate	155	24,500	570
Polymethyl methacrylate	217	27,500	550
Polystyrene	183	33,000	640
Polyisobutylene	217	15,200	540
Polyethylene glycol	80	4,400	300
Polydimethyl siloxane	25	24,500	660
1,4-Polybutadiene	27	5,900	440
Polyethylene	150	3,800	270
Polydecamethylene adipate	110	5,000	320

$^a n_c$ is the number of conformers per chain.

call λ_{R1} for Rouse, will have relaxed to $1/e$ at $t = \lambda_{R1}$, for which the corresponding initial G_{R1} is of course greater than G_e. The corresponding viscosity $\eta_{R1} = \int_0^\infty G(t)\mathrm{d}t$ is the last in the $\eta \propto M$ regime, since the next relaxation mode will exhibit the $\eta \propto M^{3.4}$ relationship. G_{R1} can be $e \approx 2.7$ times the value for G_e if we consider a discrete spectrum, or $\sqrt{e} \approx 1.7$ times G_e if we consider a continuous spectrum.

Experimentally, G_{R1} is about $2G_e$. The critical M_c for the viscosity (to change the slope from 1 to 3.4) should not be called the "molecular weight between the entanglement points," as M_e should be called. M_c is then $2M_e$. This is shown schematically in Figure 4.4.2, Table 4.1 tabulates the values of M_c. It is noted that variations in M_c among different polymers are much greater than the variations in the critical number of conformers, M_e/M_o. For polyisobutylene, the molecular weight of the conformer was calculated by dividing the repeat unit by 2, the usual practice for vinyl polymers. The conformer of polyisobutylene for stage 1, the glass transition, shown in Table 2.3, is half of the unit of transport referred here. In certain cases, we must assume different size conformers for the conformational relaxation of stage 1 from the translational relaxation of stages 2 and 3. These polymers in Table 4.1 are mostly aliphatic hydrocarbons. No aromatic backbone polymers, which should show very different values for n_c, were included. This means that the fundamental criterion for the transition from M type to $M^{3.4}$ type viscoelastic behavior is not G_e, which depends on the number *and* the molecular weight of the conformers, but it is the viscosity, which depends only on the number of conformers, according to Equation 4.3.7. When the frictional coefficient $\varsigma = \varsigma_0 M / M_0$ reaches a critical value $\varsigma_c = \varsigma_0 M_c / M_0$, stage 2 is replaced by stage 3. The theories based on the analogy between the critical strand length for entanglement and the molecular length between the points of chemical crosslinking are not, in the words of Tobolsky,[15] derived in a truly a priori fashion. In this sense, the reptation theory is the only cogent theory, since it is a model with which we can understand the physics of why the friction factor could be the criterion for η and λ to change to the "M^3" behavior.

We now take the same dynamic molecules shown in Figure 4.1.2 and subject them to the shearing field, as shown in Figure 4.4.3. The dark areas are the load-bearing portions of the entwined molecules. We can now assign the scaling values to the picture. Assuming $N = 600$, r is equal to 25 segments or sections, and since one loop is $\sqrt{N}$ long but contains N segments, the cross-sectional diameter is 1/5th of $2 \times r$. The picture was drawn with such a scale in mind. If the molecular weight of the whole molecule is less than that of one loop, there would be only one dark spot per molecule at the most, and the molecules would be pulled easily past their neighbors. No "cooperativity" would be needed among the loops. On the other hand, with molecular weight greater than the critical value for "entanglement," the loops are connected as shown in Figure 9.4.4, and the "knot" must move in a coordinated manner, or "reptate."

The reptation theory, which is based on the idea of a molecule worming its way through a medium consisting of similar molecules, was conceived and completed by Doi and Edwards,[16] and de Gennes.[17] A polymer molecule is embedded in an imaginary tube and it is forced to move following its contour. There are a number of points along the chain which the chain is not allowed to cross, indicated by dots in Figure 4.4.4. According to de

15. Tobolsky, A. V., *Properties and Structure of Polymers,* Wiley, New York, 1962, p. 170.

16. Doi, M., and Edwards, S. F., *J. Chem. Soc. Faraday Trans. II,* **74**, 1789, 1818 (1978).

17. deGennes, P.-G., *J. Chem. Phys.* **55**, 572 (1972); *Scaling Concepts in Polymer Physics,* Cornell University Press, Ithaca, New York, 1979, p. 224.

Figure 4.4.3 The dynamic polymer molecules from Figure 4.1.2, subjected to the shear field represented by the arrows. Dark areas indicate the sections of chains that are bearing tensile loads. Because the molecular length exceeds the contour length of one "loop" (see Figure 4.1.2), the load is shared by several loops in the same chain. Similarly, because the loops in the different molecules are intertwined, the load is shared by many chains.

Gennes, reptation is similar to unraveling a knot. This is shown in the right-hand sketch of Figure 4.4.4. The average knot size, or the loop A-B-C in the figure, is M_e. (More precisely, its unrelaxed modulus is $2G_e$ and its relaxed modulus is G_e with viscosity of η_c and the relaxation time of λ_c). If the molecule is smaller than the size of the knot, it will not form a knot and its migration will depend on the conventional frictional coefficient $\varsigma = \varsigma_0 M / M_0$. A detailed statistical description of the fluctuations of the tube length and their dynamic effects can be found in the original articles by these authors. The essential features of the model, which results in the steady state viscosity dependence on the third power of the length, i.e., $(M/M_e)^3$, can be simply described by the following three accounts:

1.   The friction coefficient is M/M_e times ς_e, and $\varsigma_e = (M_e)/(M_o) \varsigma_0$.

2.   The length that the molecule must worm through is M/M_e times the size of a "knot" with the loop size of M_e.

3.   The time for the tube, from which the chain has moved out, to be filled (healed) with the surrounding molecular segments is proportional to M/M_e.

Thus, the steady state viscosity is $(M/M_e)^3$ times the viscosity of the

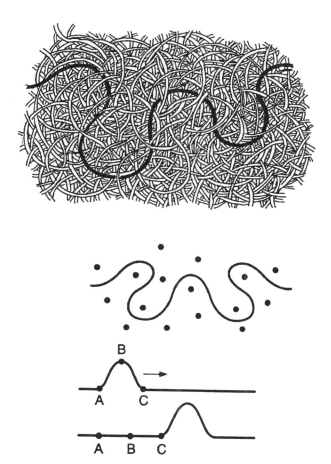

Figure 4.4.4 One chain was picked from the picture of Figure 4.1.2 and colored dark. For this chain to move, it must snake through the environment surrounded by neighbors consisting of chains with loops having similar radii of curvature. The schematic picture of one pinned bundle follows the concept of Doi-Edwards, whereas the series at the bottom represents the worming through of the knot after de Gennes' concept.

"knot"-sized chain with M_e. The relaxation time λ_1 (the subscript 1 is used to note for $p = 1$, the maximum relaxation time pertaining to the whole molecule) is the ratio of the unrelaxed elastic modulus to the steady state viscosity,

$$\eta_1 = \lim_{t \to \infty} G_e \lambda_1 \left[1\text{-exp}\left(-\frac{t}{\lambda_1} \right) \right] G_e \lambda_1 \qquad (4.4.2)$$

and, therefore,

$$\lambda_1 = \lambda_c \left(\frac{M}{M_e} \right)^3 = \frac{G_e}{\eta_c} \left(\frac{M}{M_e} \right)^3 = \frac{2G_e}{\eta_c} \left(\frac{M}{M_c} \right)^3 \qquad (4.4.3)$$

where $2\,G_e$ is used in place of G_c as discussed previously.

The reptation model thus predicts $\lambda_1 \propto M^3$ instead of the empirically found $M^{3.4}$ dependence. It is entirely possible, however, that the difference between 3 and 3.4 merely indicates a difference between the molecular relaxation time, on the one hand, and the (experimental) *retardation* time, on the other. Earlier, in Figure 1.3.4, by numerically obtaining the time-dependent strain under constant stress for a material with a single relaxation time λ_γ, we showed that the time λ_σ for the creep strain to reach the value e times the initial strain, or the retardation time, is greater than λ_γ, the material's intrinsic relaxation time, also illustrated in Figure 1.3.4. In fact, the difference in log t scale: $\Delta\log\lambda = \log\lambda_\sigma - \log\lambda_\gamma$ is about 0.4. This will result in the 3.4th power relationship:

$$\lambda_{\sigma_1} = \lambda_{\sigma_c} \left(\frac{M}{M_e} \right)^3 = \lambda_{\gamma_c} \left(\frac{M}{M_e} \right)^{3.4} \qquad (4.4.4)$$

The constant strain rate results in the "relaxation" time $\lambda_{\dot{\gamma}}$, which is even greater than the retardation time λ_σ. Among the three kinds of "relaxation" time, the constant strain type λ_γ reflects the molecular relaxation time, since it deals with the dissipation of the perturbed free energy. According to this argument, the physics of the reptation model is sound and it is the phenomenological aspect of the dynamic data that needs to be carefully analyzed.

Figure 4.4.5 shows the dynamic moduli obtained by Marin and Graessley[18] for polystyrenes with various molecular weights. The shift factor

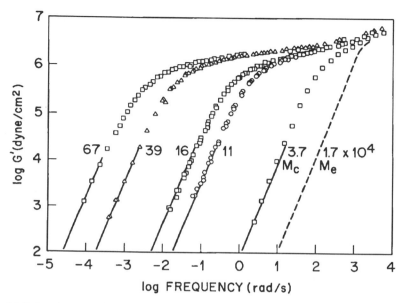

Figure 4.4.5 In-phase modulus of narrow molecular weight polystyrenes at 160 °C (Marin and Graessley).

with molecular weight is the 3.4th power for the moderate molecular weight range, but it is the 3.6th power for higher molecular weight samples. A very important reminder from this figure concerns the criterion for nonlinearity: if nonlinear viscoelasticity does occur, then at what frequency or what strain magnitude? Clearly, linear viscoelasticity is maintained at frequencies well above the reciprocal value of the maximum relaxation time; in fact, all data shown are in the range $\omega \lambda_1 > 1$. In the next section, we will take up the subject of shear thinning, the phenomenon of the apparent decrease in steady state viscosity as the flow rate increases. We will attribute this phenomenon to viscoplasticity, i.e., the yield phenomenon. At present, we continue our discussion on the linear viscoelastic relaxation process.

18. Marin, G., and Graessley, W. W., *Rheol. Acta,* **16,** 527 (1977).

The dynamic in-phase modulus depends on the relaxation spectrum in the form indicated by Equation 1.3.7, i.e.,

$$G' = \sum_p G_p \frac{\omega^2 \lambda_p^2}{1 + \omega^2 \lambda_p^2} \tag{4.4.6}$$

and if either $\lambda_1 \gg \lambda_2$ or $G_1 \gg G_2$, G' at small ω will appear as though it is a sole function of λ_1. The low frequency end of a $\log G'$ vs. $\log \omega$ plot will be a straight line with a slope of 2. This is precisely as observed in Figure 4.4.5. The curve with $M = 3.7 \times 10^4$ still exhibits a trace of the entanglement plateau. This molecular weight corresponds to M_c for the critical η_c. A calculated G' for $M_e = M_c/2$ will show no plateau, again supporting the contention that G_e based on M_e is the unrelaxed modulus for the reptation, but at the same time it is the relaxed modulus value of the "knot."

The formulation of a relaxation spectrum proposed by Doi and Edwards (see note 16) starts with a Rouse-like relationship between consecutive relaxation times λ_i and $\lambda_i + 1$, but the weight for the modulus diminishes rapidly with the square of p, or

$$G(t) = G_e \sum_{p \text{ odd}} \frac{1}{p^2} \exp\left(- \frac{t}{\lambda_1/p^2} \right) \tag{4.4.7}$$

This distribution is too narrow to fit data. Instead of this distribution, suppose that a knot can be found at a randomly chosen position along a chain. For the knot that is located at $1/p$ of the length from one end, the effective length of the chain *and* the tube is M/p. The retardation time $\lambda_{\sigma p}$ is $\lambda_1/p^{3.4}$. The modulus G_p is proportional to the concentration of the *effective* strands of the length M/p per unit volume. While there are N such strands, only $1/p$ of them are effective, and therefore, $G_p = G_e/p$. Following Doi's argument that only the odd p terms contribute to relaxation, we obtain the formula:

$$G(t) = G_e \sum_{p \text{ odd}} \frac{1}{p} \exp\left(- \frac{t}{\lambda_1/p^{3.4}} \right) \tag{4.4.8}$$

This equation fits well with both G' and G'' data for all molecular weights. An example with $M = 3.9 \times 10^5$ is shown in Figure 4.4.6. The short time end of stage 3 is marked by $p_{\max} = M/M_e$.

One more aspect of the viscoelastic relaxation of the melt remains to be

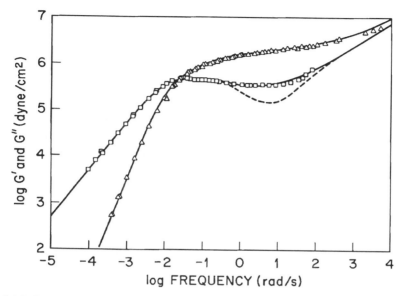

Figure 4.4.6 Comparison of our model spectrum described by Equation 4.4.8 (solid line) and data. The dashed line is G'' calculated from Doi's spectrum described by Equation 4.4.7.

discussed, namely the apparently strain-dependent characteristics of the relaxation modulus. The nonlinear relaxation modulus has been proposed to be a product of two independent functions, one solely dependent on the absolute strain and the other solely on the time, i.e.,

$$G(\gamma,t) = h(\gamma) g(t) \tag{4.4.9}$$

It has been believed that the relaxation modulus is nonlinear and with above $h(\gamma) \propto \exp(-c\gamma)$, where c is a constant. We have shown in Section 3.3 that this type of nonlinear behavior is observed in solids. Our discussion in Section 3.3 is summarized as follows:

1. The initial stress was achieved not instantaneously but through a finite strain rate increase.

2. The stress thus achieved is a viscoplastic stress, and is proportional to $\gamma \exp(-c\gamma)$.

3. If this stress is used as the initial step for the stress relaxation experiment to follow, the modulus over the entire time range will of course depend on the strain, but this is a linear viscoelastic behavior.

4. A range of application for Equation 4.4.9 is limited, even if it were justfiable, to some simple time history of strains (e.g., the relaxation followed by constant rate deformation and steady state viscosity).

Thus we conclude this section by remarking that linear viscoelasticity prevails in melt behavior and that a fast rate of strain alone or strain magnitude alone is unlikely to produce a nonlinear effect.

4.5 The Melt Flow

When a polymer melt is being "processed," it means, for example, that a polymer at well above T_g (and T_m if it is a crystallizable polymer) is being forced to move through a narrow channel of the extruder head or an injection runner or the gate at a cavity. Rheologically it is a forced irreversible deformation under varying deformation rate.[19] The number of variables in such a complex problem is staggering indeed. The methodologies of sorting them out are diverse, but we will continue to maintain our emphasis on materials aspects, particularly aspects that have molecular significance. A good starting point for connecting the materials side of polymer rheology to the continuum mechanical side is probably the steady state viscosity. For a single relaxation model, the steady state shear viscosity $\eta_s = G\lambda$ under the constant rate of shear, i.e.,

$$\eta_s = \lim_{t \to \infty} \frac{\sigma(t)}{\dot{\gamma}} = \lim_{t \to \infty} G\lambda \left[1 - \exp\left(-\frac{t}{\lambda} \right) \right] = G\lambda \qquad (4.5.1)$$

where $\sigma(t)$ in this case is the viscoelastic stress that builds up under the constant shear rate $\dot{\gamma}$, approaching the final steady state level of $\sigma_{ss} = G\lambda\dot{\gamma}$. The topic areas relating to σ_{ss} were covered in Sections 1.3 and 3.2, but we have not yet discussed the molecular aspects in the melt. The modulus G

---

19. We prefer "deformation rate" to "flow rate" because of the contribution momentum to the free energy rise is negligible compared to that from the elastic strain energy.

depends on M_e and is a material constant. In a polymer solution, however, G reflects the concentration of the elastically active strands, which decreases with dilution. Similarly, in the melt, if species with molecular weight of less than M_c are present, G will be lower, reflecting a decrease in the population of strands with $M > M_e$. (M_e is the molecular weight of the "knot" as discussed in Section 4.4). Thus the steady state stress σ_{ss} and viscosity η_s decrease with the increase of the species that are shorter than the size of a knot, $M < M_e$.

The relaxation time λ increases with $M^{3.4}$. The steady state stress (and η_s) will depend on polydispersity according to the concentration of these species. If we consider only the terminal relaxation time of each molecule, i.e., if we neglect all higher order terms in each molecule, we can write

$$\eta_s = \frac{\sigma_{ss}}{\dot{\gamma}} = \sum_i \left(\frac{M_i}{M_r}\right)^{3.4} \tag{4.5.2}$$

where the subscript r is referred to a reference molecular weight.

In the linear viscoelasticity regime, the steady state stress increases proportionately with the strain rate $\dot{\gamma}$, regardless of polydispersity in molecular weight; hence the viscosity η_s is independent of $\dot{\gamma}$. It is customary to call this regime of slow $\dot{\gamma}$ the Newtonian flow, although it has nothing to do with laminar flow as opposed to turbulent flow, nor with the kinetic energy of the flowing media. Stress in viscoelastic media is always a measure of the recoverable (elastic) strain energy. When G is constant, the recoverable energy is proportional to σ_{ss}^2, and therefore to $\dot{\gamma}^2$ also. The recoverable strain energy is stored in the molecules and remains constant at steady state, while the flow energy is continuously dissipated. As the viscoelastic material is deformed at higher and higher strain rates, the stored energy at steady state becomes greater and greater. The elastic deformation in any material cannot increase without limit, however. In metals, the yield phenomenon is associated with the irreversible deformation of polycrystalline grains, involving the migration of defects aimed at relieving stress. We proposed in Chapter 3 that in polymer solids, the cooperative domains are broken and rearranged into smaller sizes with shorter relaxation times. In this case, the yield process consists of the three steps: (1) the linear viscoelastic stress increases under the constant $\dot{\gamma}$, (2) the limiting strength of the domains with λ is reached, where the strength limit set by the intermolecular energy is reached, and (3) conformers are regrouped into smaller domains with the new relaxation time λ' equal to the reciprocal of the prevailing strain rate $\dot{\gamma}$ (i.e., $\dot{\gamma}\lambda' = 1$) and the steady stress $G\dot{\gamma}\lambda' = G$ is established and maintained.

In Chapter 3, we called the yield phenomenon in viscoelastic media "viscoplasticity." The term viscoplasticity also applies to polymer melts. Step 1 above takes place in the melt just the same. Step 2 is the destruction of a cooperative structure (a knot) by force. In polymer melts, the cooperativity among neighboring molecules is the controlling factor for relaxation and the factor gives rise to M^3 dependence. If the melt is strained by force beyond the "strength" of the intertwined molecular environment, it will certainly have to deform by another mechanism, which is akin to the plastic deformation observed in other materials. Chain scission under high shear rates is commonly observed during the processing of polymer melts. One could argue that a destruction of one crucial point in the vicinity of a knot (Figure 4.4.4) would immediately release the local stress there. A chemically crosslinked rubber (with the modulus of 10^8 dynes/cm^3) exhibits the maximum tensile elongation of 500 to 1000% before fracture. The fracture energy of 2×10^{10} ergs/cm^3 translates to only 500 calories/cm^3, or 7 kcal of C-C bonds if the conformer is assumed to be a methylene unit. The point here is to obtain a numerical comparison between the destruction of the chemically crosslinked rubber network and that of the knots, which prevent an easy path of relaxation in the uncrosslinked but entangled network. In step 3, after a sufficient number of knots have been destroyed either by scission or by forced, quick unkinking, the structure will come to a point where the new relaxation rate with fewer knots is in balance with the ongoing strain rate $\dot{\gamma}$. In other words, the destruction of knots has continued until the new $\lambda' \approx \dot{\gamma}^{-1}$ is attained. This steady state viscoplasticity condition will lead, as shown in Section 3.3.4, to Gleisle's and Cox-Merz's empirical laws. We can add another step concerning the yield phenomenon in the melt. Step 4 is the recovery of λ' to the original λ (or close to it, depending on how much the average molecular weight has been preserved despite the shear degradation). The rate of strain recovery should slow down as the relaxation time λ' increases toward λ_1, but overall, it should be closer to $1/\lambda'$ than to $1/\lambda_1$.[20]

Now that the viscoplasticity model for polymer melts has been briefly and qualitatively described, let us discuss in detail the flow properties that deviate from linear viscoelastic behavior. The viscoplastic yield criterion is the limiting stress, which is determined by the strength of the material. We shall call this yield stress σ^*. For convenience, σ^* is defined in shear for the time being, although it can be converted to a tensile stress through the invariant of deviatoric stresses ($I_2{}'$, Equation 3.3.38): that is essentially the von Mises strain energy criterion.

We shall first discuss the ideal viscoplasticity, which exhibits no stress overshoot at yield. In such a case, as long as the material is deformed at a rate of less than $\dot{\gamma} = \sigma^*/G\lambda_1$, σ^* is never reached and the material behavior is entirely viscoelastic. The prevailing relaxation time is λ_1, a material constant. If this rate of strain exceeds the rate that equals $\sigma^*/G\lambda_1$, then σ^* is reached at time $t = -\lambda\ln[1 - \sigma^*/(G\dot{\gamma}\lambda_1)]$; less time is needed if $\dot{\gamma}\lambda_1$ is greater. The cooperativity network is destroyed temporarily, and the material is deformed at a rate dictated by the externally enforced condition, $\dot{\gamma}$. The structure is reduced until the population of knots is reduced to the point at which forceful destruction is no longer necessary. Now the number of knots per molecule has been reduced. The effective relaxation time λ_1 is reduced to the new value $\lambda' = \dot{\gamma}^{-1}$. The new steady state stress σ_{ss} is smaller than the yield stress σ^* and is equal to

$$\sigma_{ss} = G_e\lambda'\dot{\gamma} = G_e\dot{\gamma}^{-1}\dot{\gamma} = G_e \qquad (4.5.3)$$

The corresponding elastic (recoverable) strain at the steady state is 1. The steady state viscosity after the yield is

$$\eta_s = \frac{\sigma_{ss}}{\dot{\gamma}} = \frac{G_e}{\dot{\gamma}} \qquad (4.5.4)$$

and, for single relaxation materials only, the slope of log η vs. log $\dot{\gamma}$ is -1. The conditions that determine whether a material will behave according to linear viscoelasticity or plasticity are summarized below:

---

20. A similar discussion was presented for solids in Chapter 3.

1.   When $\dot{\gamma}\lambda_1 \ll \sigma_{ss}/G_e = 1$, linear viscoelasticity prevails and $\sigma_{ss} = G_e\dot{\gamma}\lambda_1$.

2.   When $\dot{\gamma}\lambda_1 \gg \sigma_{ss}/G_e = 1$, plasticity prevails and $\sigma_{ss} = G_e$.
     Both these conditions can be approximated, conveniently, by one equation,

$$\sigma_{ss} = G_e\dot{\gamma}\lambda\left[1 - \exp\left(-\frac{1}{\dot{\gamma}\lambda}\right)\right] \tag{4.5.5}$$

or by another:

$$\sigma_{ss} = \frac{G_e\dot{\gamma}\lambda}{[1 + (\dot{\gamma}\lambda)^2]^{1/2}} \tag{4.5.6}$$

in either Equations 4.55 or 4.56 it is true that (1) if $\dot{\gamma}\lambda \gg 1$, then $\sigma_{ss}\rightarrow G_e$, and (2) if $\dot{\gamma}\lambda \ll 1$, then $\sigma_{ss}\rightarrow G_e\dot{\gamma}\lambda$. While these equations look familiar to rheologists, these formulas are among perhaps many expressions that may satisfy the conditions 1 and 2 above. The stress in Equation 4.5.5 is, of course, equal to the stress at $t = 1/\dot{\gamma}$ that a single relaxation time body would experience under the constant strain rate $\dot{\gamma}$, i.e., for the material with the relaxation modulus

$$G(t) = G_e\exp\left(-\frac{t}{\lambda}\right) \tag{4.5.7}$$

under the constant strain rate $\dot{\gamma}$, the stress at t is

$$\sigma(t) = \int_0^t G(t)\dot{\gamma}\,dt = G_e\dot{\gamma}\lambda\left[1 - \exp\left(-\frac{t}{\lambda}\right)\right] \tag{4.5.8}$$

and at $t = 1/\dot{\gamma}$,

$$\sigma(t = \dot{\gamma}^{-1}) = \int_0^{\dot{\gamma}^{-1}} G(t)\dot{\gamma}\,dt = G_e\dot{\gamma}\lambda\left[1 - \exp\left(-\frac{1}{\dot{\gamma}\lambda}\right)\right] \tag{4.5.9}$$

which is the same as Equation 4.5.5.
     The integral in Equation 4.5.9 is not limited to a single relaxation time material, but it can be applied to more general cases with a spectrum of

relaxation times. σ^* at a different strain rate. Conversely, at a given strain rate $\dot{\gamma}$, some relaxing units with large λ's will eventually reach σ^*, while some other relaxing units with small λ's will never reach σ^*. However, for each relaxing unit, conditions 1 and 2 hold, and for each unit, the integral in Equation 4.5.8 applies. Therefore, integrating over each unit that is part of the whole relaxation spectrum, the total steady state stress σ_{ss} can be described by the equation:

$$\sigma_{ss} \mid _{\dot{\gamma}} = \dot{\gamma}\sum\left[1 - \exp\left(-\frac{1}{\dot{\gamma}\lambda_i}\right)\right] = \int_0^{\dot{\gamma}^{-1}} G(t)\,dt \qquad (4.5.10)$$

This equation is Gleisle's well-known rule (Equation 1.6.8 in Chapter 1). Physically, it does not "prove" that the linear viscoelastic relaxation spectrum has anything to do with nonlinear viscosity. It means only that the transition from linear viscoelastic behavior to a (nonlinear) postyield flow process occurs in order from the longest λ to the shortest λ at a given strain rate $\dot{\gamma}$. The rate dependence of the yield stress can thus be predicted from the distribution of linear viscoelastic relaxation times.[21] Starting with Equation 4.5.6, the same procedure that led to Gleisle's rule will lead to Cox-Merz's empirical law (Equation 1.6.12 in Chapter 1), which simply states that the steady state viscosity can be calculated by equating it to the magnitude of the complex dynamic viscosity $|\eta(\omega)|$ by substituting $\dot{\gamma}$ for its ω.

We shall now discuss the rheological data as they relate to the viscoplasticity. Starting with the polystyrene dynamic mechanical data by Marin and Graessley, shown in Figure 4.4.5, we formulated our distribution function of relaxation times for a narrow molecular weight distribution using Equation 4.4.8. We were satisfied with our equation that fit to all dynamic mechanical data, shown in Figure 4.4.5, which can be shifted by the 3.4th power of the molecular weight with the respective M_w/M_n, all at 160 °C. We then shifted the data to 183 °C using the Vogel-Fulcher equation, and calculated σ_{ss} for polystyrenes with molecular weight of 4.85×10^4, 11.7×10^4 17.9×10^4, 21.7×10^4 and 24.2×10^4 using Equation 4.5.10. The plot of

---

21. As was demonstrated for glassy polymers in Chapter 3.

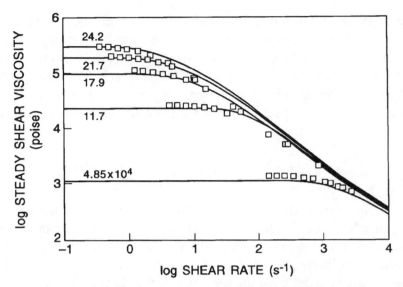

Figure 4.5.1 Steady shear viscosity vs. shear rate (in log-log scale) for polystyrene at 183 °C. Data by Stratton (note 22). The lines are calculated from the linear viscoelastic data by Marin and Graessley (see note 18), using Equation 4.5.10 after shifting for the temperature change using the WLF equation. The linear viscoelastic data fit the distribution of relaxation time of Equation 4.4.8.

$\log \eta_s = \log(\sigma_{ss}/\dot{\gamma})$ vs. $\log \dot{\gamma}$ is shown with real lines in Figure 4.5.1, giving excellent agreement with Stratton's data.[22] The slope of the $\log \eta_s$ vs. $\log \dot{\gamma}$ curve in the postyield regime is no longer -1, because even a monodispersed polymer exhibits a distribution of λ's according to Equation 4.4.8. The steepest slope for the polymer melt with no polydispersity is -0.81. This slope, which is the power n for the power law for the viscosity-shear rate relationship:

---

22. Stratton, R. A., *J. Colloid Interface Sci.* **22**, 517 (1966); also, Ferry, J. D., *Viscoelastic Properties of Polymers,* Wiley, New York, 1978, p. 428.

$$\eta_s(\dot{\gamma}) = \eta_0 \left(\frac{\dot{\gamma}}{\dot{\gamma_0}} \right)^{-n} \tag{4.5.11}$$

can be evaluated from the linear viscoelastic data as indicated below. The plateau region of the in-phase dynamic mechanical modulus is not flat but is an increasing function of the frequency due to the distribution of relaxation times that exists even in a monodispersed polymer. The slope m of the plateau region, i.e.,

$$G'(\omega) = G_e \left(\frac{\omega}{\omega_0} \right)^{m} \tag{4.5.12}$$

is related to the relaxation modulus

$$G(t) = G_e \left(\frac{t}{t_0} \right)^{-m} \tag{4.5.13}$$

as can be shown from Equation 1.5.5. Hence, the steady state viscoplastic stress (postyield stress) σ_{ss} depends on the strain rate $\dot{\gamma}$:

$$\sigma_{ss}(\dot{\gamma}) = \sigma_{ss\,0} \left(\frac{\dot{\gamma}}{\dot{\gamma_0}} \right)^{m} \tag{4.5.14}$$

and the viscosity η_s depends on the shear rate $\dot{\gamma}$:

$$\eta_s = \frac{\sigma_{ss}}{\dot{\gamma}} = \eta_0 \left(\frac{\dot{\gamma}}{\dot{\gamma_0}} \right)^{m-1} \tag{4.5.15}$$

Thus, taking the slope m of the plateau in the log G' vs. log ω curve, one can estimate the slope of n of the viscosity power law by the formula:

$$n = 1 - m \tag{4.5.16}$$

For example, for the very narrow molecular weight polystyrenes of Figure 4.4.5, we estimate m to be about 0.2. This gives the slope of the viscosity power law as -0.8, which is what we estimated as nearly the maximum absolute value for the slope.

So far, we have treated only the shear flow. As we discussed in Chapter 1, however, all elastic stresses are interrelated through the scalar elastic recoverable energy.[23] The elastic invariants of the recoverable strains are the

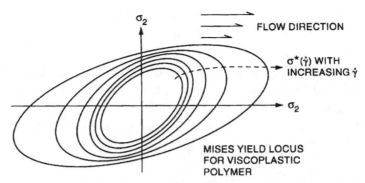

Figure 4.5.2 von Mises stress locus for viscoplastic flow in two dimensions: σ^* will increase with mth power of the flow rate, (i.e., the ellipse will grow while maintaining the 45° tilt) until the flow-induced orientation makes the modulus anisotropic. The ellipse will grow in the direction of the higher modulus, or the direction of flow.

unique functions of the sum of all stresses at a given point in the body, and they can be used to convert the shear stress to the tensile stress. Thus we were able to calculate all stresses in solids by knowing the stress boundary conditions at any time t and $\dot{\gamma}$ (or $\dot{\varepsilon}$).

For the yield criterion, we used the deviatoric elastic strain energy following the von Mises criterion, which in material terms means the maximum deformation energy that a unit volume of material can store. From Equation 1.6.1, for the two-dimensional example, an ellipse was drawn for the stresses that make up the deviatoric invariant shown in Figure 1.6.2. Since the steady state stress in a given plane depends on $\dot{\gamma}^m$, we can make this ellipse strain rate dependent for the viscoplastic yield phenomenon by drawing a series of concentric ellipses with $\dot{\gamma}$ as the parameter as shown in Figure 4.5.2. With increasing $\dot{\gamma}$, the size of the ellipse increases by $\dot{\gamma}^m$, where $m = 1 - n$, and n is the power law exponent of the non-Newtonian steady state viscosity η_s. As we continue to increase $\dot{\gamma}$, the flow induces a greater

---

23. The elastic energy as the conservative stress parameter has been proposed by Leonov for his formulation of nonlinear viscoelasticity.

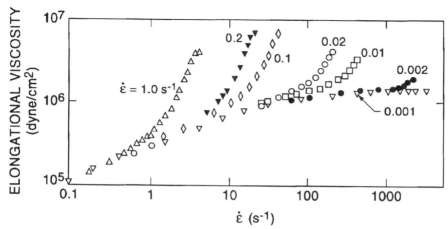

Figure 4.5.3 Elongational viscosity vs. elapsed time under constant strain rates, for low density polyethylene. (From Bird, R. B., Armstrong, R. C., Curtis, C. F., *Dynamics of Polymeric Liquids,* Vol. 2, Wiley, New York, 1977.)

orientation among molecules. The state of orientation produces anisotropic modulus and yield stress, since the strength is greater in the direction of chain molecules. The ellipsoidal diagram for the stress locus, which originally was inclined at 45° to the x- axis, now becomes elongated more in the x- direction (flow direction) as shown by the dashed line in Figure 4.5.2.

Anisotropy can be introduced in the von Mises criterion with the coefficient α, which is proportional to the orientation function:

$$\sigma^{*2} = \frac{1}{2}(\alpha\sigma_x - \sigma_y)^2 + \frac{1}{2}(\sigma_y - \sigma_z)^2 + \frac{1}{2}(\sigma_z - \sigma_x)^2$$
$$+ 3\alpha\sigma_{xy}^2 + 3\sigma_{yz}^2 + 3\alpha\sigma_{zx}^2 \qquad (4.5.17)$$

which is the condition of the elongational flow. This same modification of Equation 1.6.1 will be used in the yield of crystalline polymers in a later chapter, since they can be drawn into a fiberlike configuration with an extremely high modulus in the draw direction.

Elongational flow has often been regarded as a type of flow totally different from shear flow. Even a different activation energy for it has been proposed, to leave a provision for the transition from a shear flow. With the viscoplasticity model, elongational flow is predicted to occur when the shear stress is high enough to cause a pronounced molecular orientation, which in turn results in anisotropic yield stress. The knots in the reptation model are severely depleted, and the molecules are lined up in the flow direction. This

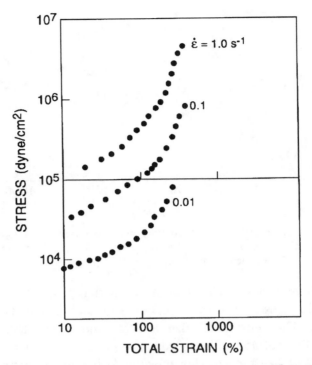

Figure 4.5.4 Tensile stress vs. macroscopic strain curves derived from the elongational flow data of Figure 4.5.3.

kind of highly anisotropic structure in turn will allow the flow stress σ_{ss} to further increase in the flow direction, as shown in Figure 4.5.2. The elongational "viscosity" (i.e., $\sigma_{ss}/\dot{\varepsilon}$ in the flow direction) increases with the rate of flow.

Figure 4.5.3 plots $\log \eta_{\dot{\varepsilon}}$ vs. log time under various rates of strain $\dot{\varepsilon}$. First we shift these curves horizontally by $\Delta\log \dot{\varepsilon}$ to convert the abscissa into log strain, then vertically by $\Delta\log\dot{\varepsilon}$ to change the ordinate into log stress.

The result is shown in Figure 4.5.4, a macroscopic stress-strain curve at three strain rates (log-log scale, of course). The stress is always smaller than the theoretical yield stress because some of the viscoelastic elements with short relaxation times always relax before reaching this maximum stress. When we discussed yield phenomena in solids, we pointed out that the distribution of multiple relaxation times causes the shear stress, which is dependent on the rate of strain $\dot{\varepsilon}$, to be less than the theoretical plastic

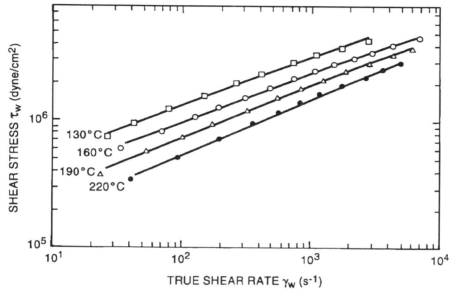

Figure 4.5.5 Stress vs. shear rate for low density polyethylene, with slope ca. 0.5.

stress. We have shown, moreover, that such a rate dependence could be approximated by the power law:

$$\frac{\sigma}{\sigma_0} = \left(\frac{\dot{\varepsilon}}{\dot{\varepsilon}_0}\right)^m \tag{4.5.18}$$

where m is the same power as in the relaxation modulus in Equation 4.5.13. The power n in the power law for the melt viscosity is $n = 1 - m$. The shift factor of about 0.5 per decade of vertical scale will superimpose these curves, or $m \approx 0.5$, a typical value for a polydispersed molecular weight. Although not for the same sample, the plot of shear stress vs. shear rate for a commercial grade, low density polyethylene is shown in Figure 4.5.5. The slope m for the log-log plot in fact is about 0.5.

The stress-strain curve for a crosslinked rubber is compared in linear scale in Figure 4.5.6, which is qualitatively supported by the rubber elasticity at small strains (Equation 4.2.11) and the Langevin expression at large strains (Equation 4.2.17).

The similarity between the stress-strain relationship of the rubber and the melt in tension suggests that the recoverable part of the elongational stress-strain relationship is equivalent to the molecular stress-strain

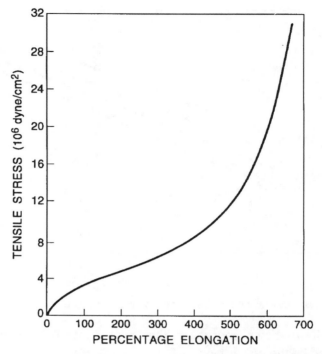

Figure 4.5.6 Tensile stress-strain curve of crosslinked rubber. From Treloar, L.R.G.; The Physics of Rubber Elasticity, Oxford 1958. The stress in this diagram corresponds to the stress in Figure 4.5.2.

relationship in the rubbery state, i.e., the molecular orientation in the flowing media gives rise to the increased steady state stress in the elongational flow.

4.6 Additional Comments

4.6.1 The Vertical Shift Factor and the BKZ Theory

In Section 1.3, we derived the convolution integral for the linear viscoelastic stress:

$$\sigma = \int_0^t G(t-x)\frac{d\gamma}{dx}\,dx \qquad (1.3.6)$$

for any strain history, provided $G(t)$ satisfies the linear viscoelasticity condition, i.e., to be independent of the strain magnitude. Only when such a condition is met can the responses to all strain histories be superimposed to obtain the final stress $\sigma(t)$. Actually, for materials that satisfy Equation 1.3.6, three other similar integrals apply. All four equations are shown below:

$$\sigma = \int_0^t G(t-x) \frac{d\gamma}{dx} \, dx \qquad (4.6.1)$$

$$\sigma = \int_0^t \frac{dG(t-x)}{dx} \gamma(x) \, dx \qquad (4.6.2)$$

$$\sigma = \int_0^t G(x) \frac{d\gamma(t-x)}{dx} \, dx \qquad (4.6.3)$$

$$\sigma = \int_0^t \frac{dG(x)}{dx} \gamma(t-x) \, dx \qquad (4.6.4)$$

The physical picture is perhaps clearest with Equation 4.6.1, which we have consistently used. The others are not as easily visualized, but mathematically their validity can be shown readily. Although linear viscoelasticity is a basic assumption for these equations, a certain type of nonlinear viscoelasticity can be accommodated by modifying these equations. The simplest such modification is with the modulus, which can be factored out into the strain-dependent part $h(\gamma)$ and the time-dependent part $G(t)$ such that:

$$G(\gamma, t) = G(t) \, h(\gamma) \qquad (4.6.5)$$

which is nearly the same as Equation 3.3.9 in Section 3.3. When $G(\gamma, t)$ is substituted into Equation 4.6.1, and if $h(\gamma)$ can be taken out of the integral, the stress thus calculated is obviously nonlinear.

The well-known BKZ theory[24] is, according to Larson,[25] "a class of

24. Bernstein, B., Kearsley, E. A., and Zappas, L. J., *J. Res. NBS*, **68B**, 103 (1964).

25. Larson, R. G., *Constitutive Equations for Polymer Melts and Solutions*, Butterworths, London, 1988.

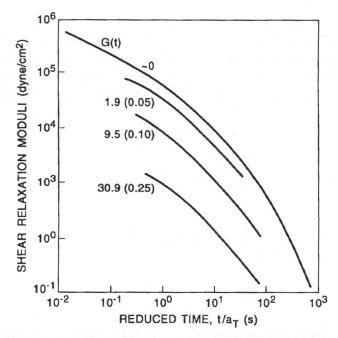

Figure 4.6.1 Nonlinear viscoelastic relaxation in a polymer melt. The curves represent the relaxation moduli at different strain magnitudes obtained after the constant rate of strain, rather than instantaneously.

constitutive equations that admits a great variety of behavior, without specific sets of nonlinear parameters." Its underlying principles involve the applicability of the originally linear convolution integrals, especially of the type exemplified by Equation 4.6.1, to certain types of nonlinear behavior, particularly with a modulus that can be characterized by the factorability of two independent functions as shown by Equation 4.6.5. A simple example can be given with the neo-Hookean rubberlike elasticity that can be described by a suitable $h(\gamma)$. In such a case, the origin of the nonlinear elasticity is known from independent theory and is supported by data, and the applicability to nonlinear behavior is probably acceptable.

More frequent use of the BKZ theory is found in the analysis of nonlinear behavior of the polymer melt, even including the non-Newtonian flow. Very well known analyses by Wagner[26] and Osaki[27] have dealt with the nonlinear shear modulus, such as shown in Figure 4.6.1, the data by Laun.[28]

The log $G(t)$ vs. log t curves are displaced by the vertical shifts, which are in apparent agreement with Wagner's empirical formula for the strain dependent part of the modulus:

$$h(\gamma) = \exp(-c\gamma) \qquad (4.6.6)$$

We have proposed an alternative view that this behavior is due to a combination of linear viscoelasticity and plasticity, and that the apparent decline in the magnitude of the modulus with increasing strain amplitude is a consequence of the domains' reaching the critical stress at different strain levels, which can be calculated by Gleisle's rule, arrived at under the constant strain rate.

The viscoplasticity formulas were derived for constant rates of deformation. However, the same formula should apply to the stress relaxation modulus if the initial strain is arrived at by taking the same finite amount of time. This is equivalent to stating that the faster relaxing species have already reached the yield condition at the beginning of relaxation test, and greater the strain, the more species have reached this state. Thus in place of Wagner's empirical formula, one obtains the formula:

$$h(\gamma) = \exp\left(-\frac{\gamma}{2\gamma_e{}^*}\right) \qquad (4.6.7)$$

which applies both to the constant rate of strain process and, as in the relaxation experiment, the constant strain experiment.

4.6.2 Stress Overshoot

So far, the relationship between steady state stress and rate of strain has been discussed, but the subject of stress overshoot in polymer melts has not been touched. Stress overshoot in polymer solids, however, was discussed in

26. Wagner, M. H., *Rheol. Acta,* **15**, 136 (1976).

27. Osaki, K., *Proc 7th International Congress of Rheology,* Gothenburg, Sweden, 1976.

28. Laun, H. M., *Rheol. Acta,* **17**, 1 (1978).

Chapter 3, and it was shown to be a real effect because the stress maximum is observed not only in tension but under uniaxial compression, where no reduction in cross-sectional area occurs. The maximum stress level reached in stress overshoot is the yield stress in the true sense, since it reflects the mechanical strength of the structure, or in this case the limit at which the knots can reptate without tearing through the polymer melt. The steady state is reached when the relaxation time that is characteristic of the new structure under the ongoing strain rate is equal to the reciprocal of the strain rate, or $\dot{\gamma}^{-1}$. If the rate of strain happens to be less than the reciprocal of the original relaxation time, the polymer can reptate without destroying the original structure, and viscoelastic relaxation ensues. In plasticity, steady state stress is determined by the ongoing rate of strain, whereas in viscoelasticity it is determined by the natural relaxation time. The virtual elastic strain $\dot{\gamma}\lambda$ in plastic flow is thus 1, or 100%, at least for the case of shear flow (vs. elongational flow) of flexible (vs. liquid crystal type stiff) chain molecules. Stress overshoot means that the yield stress exceeds the steady state stress, hence it occurs when the plastic yield strain is greater than 1 ($\dot{\gamma}\lambda$). As seen in the stress-strain curve of the rubbery material shown in Figure 4.5.6, the structural limit of the *tensile* elongation, is about 500%, beyond which an increase in the elastic deformation becomes very difficult. The level of this tensile stress is about 10^7 dynes/cm^2. The shear stress that corresponds to this tensile stress is 4×10^6 dynes/cm^2, to sustain the same deviatoric strain energy level as discussed in Section 3.3.6. The steady state stress is about the same value as the unrelaxed rubbery modulus itself, or twice the plateau modulus. Thus the yield stress exceeds the steady state stress by a factor of 2, and that should result in stress overshoot. As the structure begins to break up after the start of stress overshoot, the theoretical yield stress is never reached as the relaxation is accompanied. This situation can be modeled by setting the continuously decreasing relaxation time as a function of stress in excess of the steady state value. Two experimental curves for a polystyrene melt with a not very narrow molecular weight distribution are shown in Figure 4.6.2.[29]

---

29. Maxwell, B., and Nguyen, M., *Polym. Eng. Sci.* **19**(16), 1140 (1979).

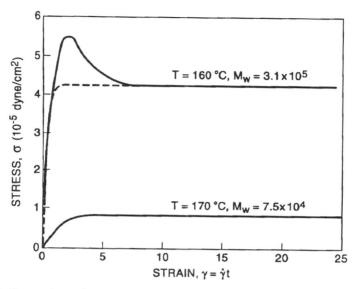

Figure 4.6.2 Comparison of stress-strain curves between a high molecular weight polymer at low temperature and a low molecular weight polymer at high temperature. Polystyrene melt by Maxwell and Nguyen.

The curve labeled $M_w = 3.1 \times 10^5$ is for a high molecular weight polystyrene, for which the strain rate exceeded the limit of linear viscoelasticity, and depicts the plasticity with an overshoot. The other curve is for a lower molecular weight sample at a higher temperature, and this is a typical linear viscoelastic deformation in which the relaxation process prevented the stress from reaching the yield stress level.

4.6.3 Normal Stresses

When an *elastic* cylinder is twisted, there is a second-order effect that tends to constrict the body laterally and force it to bulge axially in the manner shown in Figure 4.6.3.

This is known as the Poynting effect.[30] The pressure is highest in the

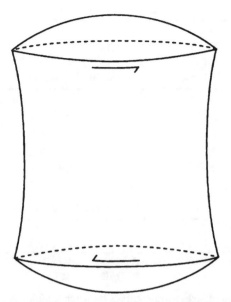

Figure 4.6.3 Schematic picture of the second-order strain in a twisted cylinder, alluding to the similar effect known to occur in the elastic components in a viscoelastic medium.

center and diminishes to zero at the edge. In contrast, if normal stress were directly a result of elastic shear strain, then normal stress in the center of a twisted cylinder should be less than the stress at the edge, where strain is the greatest.

The average normal pressure required to prevent this bulge can be shown to depend on the elastic strain γ_e:

---

30. Rivlin, R. S., *J. Appl. Phys.* **18**, 444 (1947)

$$\frac{\int p \, dA}{\int dA} = cG_0\gamma_e^2 \qquad (4.6.9)$$

where c is a proportionality constant to average the pressure distribution.[31] For viscoplastic flow,

$$\gamma_e = \frac{\sigma_{ss}{}^*}{G_0} = \frac{\dot{\gamma}\eta_{ss}}{G_0} \qquad (4.6.10)$$

where the subscript ss refers to the steady state. Thus we obtain that

$$\sigma_{ss}{}^* = \sigma_{11} - \sigma_{22} = cG_0\left(\frac{\dot{\gamma}\eta_{ss}}{G_0}\right)^2 = c\frac{(\dot{\gamma}\eta_{ss})^2}{G_0} \qquad (4.6.11)$$

For the single relaxation time model, the log-log plot for the normal stress difference vs. shear rate would exhibit a slope of 2 at small $\dot{\gamma}$, leveling off at higher $\dot{\gamma}$. For a broader distribution of relaxation times, the flat portion will exhibit a moderate slope and the initial slope will become *less* than 2, much as the dynamic modulus G' behaves in response to the broader molecular weight distribution.

---

31. When Hooke's law is extended into the finite strain regime, the introduction of the Almansi measure of finite strain gives $c = 1/2$ in Equation 4.6.9. Introducing the Green measure gives $c = 1/4$. The actual value of this constant is not essential to this analysis.

5

The Crystalline State

Polymers behave very differently in solution and in the molten state, primarily because of the intermolecular interference from the neighbors in the latter. It is an oversimplification to suppose that a solution-crystallized morphology is a model for crystals formed in a supercooled melt.

5.1 Melting and Crystallization

The apparent melting point depends on crystallite size and shape. The thermodynamic melting point is the temperature at which a crystal of infinite size melts. At this temperature, the Gibbs free energy of the crystalline state is equal to that of the molten state, i.e.,

$$H_{\text{crystal}} - T_m S_{\text{crystal}} = H_{\text{melt}} - T_m S_{\text{melt}} \tag{5.1.1}$$

The heat of fusion, $\Delta H_u = H_{\text{melt}} - H_{\text{crystal}}$, is in balance with the increase of entropy, $\Delta S_u = S_{\text{melt}} - S_{\text{crystal}}$, and

$$\Delta H_u - T_m \Delta S_u = 0 \tag{5.1.2}$$

Now, the increase in the conformational entropy at melting, ΔS_c, is, from Equation 2.1.7 in Chapter 2,

$$\Delta S_c = \frac{T^* s^*}{T^* - T_0} \frac{T_m - T_0}{T_m} \tag{5.1.3}$$

Recalling, from Equation 2.1.3, that at T^*,

$$s^* = N_A k \ln c_1 \tag{2.1.3}$$

and from Equation 2.1.21

$$\frac{T^*}{T^* - T_0} = \frac{\ln M}{\ln M_0} \tag{2.1.21}$$

we obtain:

$$\Delta S_c = k \frac{\ln M}{\ln M_0} \ln c_1 \frac{T_m - T_0}{T_m} \qquad (5.1.4)$$

where M_0 is 9.62. The value of c_1, the rotational isomeric state probability, 3 if the energy differences among the possible bond angles are negligible; otherwise, the temperature dependence must be accounted for, and c_1 becomes less than 3. In polystyrene, one bond angle is forbidden, so the maximum value is 2 instead of 3.

For linear polyethylene with the values of $T_m = 140$ °C, $T_0 = -160$ °C, $M = 14$, we calculate, by assuming $c_1 = 3$, to obtain $\Delta S_c = 1.9$ eu per mole of -CH_2-. The total entropy of fusion is larger than ΔS_c, because it is equal to the increase in entropy from zero to the rotational isomeric state at T_m, or $s*$ at T_m. Therefore,

$$\Delta S_u = \Delta S_c \frac{T_m}{T_m - T_0} = \frac{\ln M}{\ln M_0} k \ln c_1 \qquad (5.1.5)$$

and ΔS_u of 2.5 eu (cf. 2.34 in Table 5.1) is obtained for polyethylene. Multiplying it by T_m will give ΔH_u of 1033 cal/mol (cf. 960 in Table 5.1) of -CH44. For isotactic polypropylene, $T_m = 176$ °C, $T_0 = -80$ °C, $M = 21$, and we obtain $\Delta S_c = 1.7$ eu and $\Delta S_u = 2.9$ eu per conformer. The conformer is half the repeat unit for polypropylene as the average size, and multiplying the entropy of fusion by 2 and by T_m will yield the latent heat of 2640 calories per repeat unit. Those numbers for polypropylene are in close agreement with the experimental values shown in Table 5.1.[1] However, the assumption $c_1 = 3$ leads to a slight overestimation of the entropy. All other equations that we have used, including the Adam-Gibbs formula, include the ratio of an entropy to $s*$, and the absolute value of $s*$ is not needed. The value of c_1 depends on the temperature as $\ln c_1 \sim \Delta H / kT$, where ΔH is the energy difference between the *trans* and *gauche* configurations. In addition, c_1 is affected by the tacticity as well as the severe steric hindrance. Allowing two out of three configurations will result in ΔS_u of 1.7 for isotactic polystyrene, and 1.5 for 1,4-*cis*- polyisoprene (natural rubber). Allowing five

---

1. From Mandelkern, L., *Crystallization of Polymers,* McGraw-Hill, New York, 1964.

Polymer	T_m, °C	ΔH_u, cal/mole	$\Delta H_u/M_0$, cal/g	ΔS_u/bond, cal/deg
Polyethylene	137.5*	960	68.5	2.34
Polypropylene	176	2,600	62.0	2.9
Poly(isoprene), 1,4-*cis*	28	1,050	15.3	1.15
Poly(isoprene), 1,4-*trans*†	74	3,040	45.1	2.92
Poly(styrene)	239	2,000	19.2	1.95
Poly(chloroprene), 1,4-*trans*‡	80	2,000	22.6	1.89
Poly(chlorotrifluoroethylene)	210	1,200	10.3	1.25
Polyvinyl fluoride	197	1,800	39	1.9
Poly(decamethylene adipate)	79.5	10,200	36	1.60
Poly(decamethylene sebacate)	80	12,000	35	1.55
Poly(decamethylene azelate)	69	10,000	31	1.39
Poly(nonmethylene azelate)	65	10,300	33	1.52
Poly(decamethylene terephthalate)	138	11,000	36	1.91
Poly(hexamethylene terephthalate)	160.5	8,500	34	1.95
Poly(tetramethylene terephthalate)	230	7,600	33	1.9
Poly(tetramethylene isophthalate)	152.5	10,100	45	3.0
Poly(N,N'-sebacoyl piperazine)	180	6,200	24.5	1.25
Poly(decamethylene sebacamide)	216	8,300	24.5	0.77
Poly(decamethylene azelamide)	214	8,800	27	0.86
Cellulose tributyrate	207	3,000	8.1	3.1
Cellulose trinitrate	>700	900–1500	3.0–5.0	0.75
Cellulose (2.44) nitrate	617	1,350	5.2	0.76
Cellulose tricaprylate	116	3,100	5.7	4.0
Polyethylene oxide	66	1,980	45	2.68
Polymethylene oxide	180	1,590	53	3.5
Polyacrylonitrile	317	1,200	23	1.0
Collagen	145§	2,250	24	1.95
Poly(ethylene terephthalate)	267	5,500	28.1	1.7
Poly(ethylene sebacate)	76	8,000	30.5	1.65
Poly(hexamethylene adipamide)	267	10,300	45	1.36
Poly(hexamethylene sebacamide)	226	12,000	43	1.32
Poly(caproamide)	225	5,100	45	1.46
Polymethylene oxide	180	1,780	59.2	3.94
Poly(tetrafluoroethylene)	327	1,460	14.6	1.45

Table 5.1 Thermodynamic Quantities of Fusion for Polymers

* The melting point of a high molecular weight fraction has been determined as 138.5 °C.
† For the higher melting polymorph.
‡ Extrapolated to the *all*-1.4-trans polymer.
§ Extrapolated from the melting point of ethylene glycol mixtures.

out of six configurations will give 3.1 for 1,4-*trans* polyisoprene (gutta percha). In all those cases, if c_1 is assumed to be 3, the values of the entropy of fusion would be much greater than the values shown in Table 5.1.

From Equation 2.1.16, we can derive an expression for free volume increase accompanying the conformational entropy increase ΔS_c:

$$\frac{\Delta V_u}{V} = \Delta S_c T_m \frac{\Delta \alpha}{\Delta C_p} \tag{5.1.5}$$

For polyethylene, with $\Delta S_c = 1.7/14 = 0.2$ eu and $\Delta C_p/\Delta \alpha = 2.5 \times 10^2$ cal/g from Figure 2.1.5, we obtain $\Delta V_u/V = 0.20$, and for $V_{crystal}$ we have 1.05 cm^3/g at T_m, $\Delta V_u = 0.21$ cm^3/g. This volume of fusion ΔV_u is the volume difference between the melt and the crystalline unit cell, both at T_m. It is greater than most directly measured values even for highly crystalline polymers. The Clausius-Clapeyron equation relates the melting point rise to hydrostatic pressure:

$$\frac{dT_m}{dp} = \frac{\Delta V_u}{\Delta S_u} \tag{5.1.6}$$

The value of dT_m/dp is ca. 30 °C/kbar,[2] and for ΔS_u of 2.3/14 eu/g, we obtain ΔV_u of 0.21 cm^3/g. The experimentally measured specific volume of the molten linear polyethylene is 1.25 cm^3/g, and that of the unit cell is 1.05 cm^3/g, which agrees with the value above for the volume of fusion. Now,

$$T_m = \frac{\Delta H}{\Delta S_u} = \frac{1}{V_c} \frac{\Delta V_u}{\Delta S_u} \frac{\Delta C_p}{\Delta \alpha}$$

and

$$T_g = \frac{E_h}{S_{c,g}} = \frac{1}{V_g} \frac{\Delta V_g}{S_{c,g}} \frac{\Delta C_p}{\Delta \alpha}$$

Assuming that the same ratio of the free volume increase to the conformational entropy increase is maintained at all temperatures,

---

2. Matsuoka, S., *J. Polym. Sci.* **57**, 569-588 (1962).

$$\frac{\Delta V_g}{S_{c,g} V_g} = \frac{\Delta V_u}{\Delta S_c V_c}$$

and we obtain

$$\frac{T_g}{T_m} = \frac{\Delta S_c}{\Delta S_u} = \frac{T_m - T_0}{T_m} = \frac{T_m - T_g + 50}{T_m}$$

and finally

$$\frac{T_g}{T_m} = 0.5 + \frac{50}{T_m} \tag{5.1.7}$$

According to this formula, the ratio of T_g/T_m is 1/2 for high melting materials, and for the low melting material such as $T_m = 0$ °C, the ratio is 2/3. Most polymers fall within these limits. The rule that

$$\frac{1}{2} < \frac{T_g}{T_m} < \frac{2}{3} \tag{5.1.8}$$

is known as Boyer-Beaman's rule,[3] and Equation 5.1.7 is probably a useful formula.

There are always density fluctuations in the molten state. These fluctuations can be considered to be temporary islands of a higher density, some of them comparable to the crystalline density. The population distribution of these "heterophase" fluctuations is determined according to their size; the larger ones are further away from the equilibrium conditions and are less populous than the smaller ones. The Gibbs free energy $\Delta\Psi$ of a particle consisting of g conformers is made up from the bulk free energy $g[H_{cryst} - H_{melt} - T(S_{cryst} - S_{melt})]$ and the surface free energy $g^{2/3}\sigma$, where σ is the surface free energy per unit area.

Now, instead of conditions above the melting point, we consider conditions below the melting point. If liquid is quenched from temperature above T_m, it can stay in the supercooled state until crystals nucleate and grow. The Gibbs free energy of the heterophase fluctuation consisting of g

---

3. Boyer, R. F., *Rubber Chem. Technol.* **36**, 1303 (1963).

conformers is:

$$\Delta\Psi(g) = \Psi_{crystal}(g) - \Psi_{melt}(g) = \Delta S_u(T - T_m)g + \sigma g^{2/3} \qquad (5.1.9)$$

This equation has a maximum in g at the critical size g^*:

$$g^* = \left[\frac{2}{3}\frac{\sigma}{\Delta S_u(T_m - T)}\right]^3 \qquad (5.1.10)$$

and only when $g > g^* \times 9/4$ will $\Delta\Psi(g)$ be negative and the crystallite become progressively more stable as the size increases further. Nuclei having size g^* are the least populous, and the degree of their abundance is the rate-controlling factor for crystallization; i.e., the concentration $n(g^*)$ of the critical size nuclei is

$$n(g) = A\exp\left[-\frac{\Delta\Psi(g^*)}{kT}\right] \qquad (5.1.11)$$

For polymers, the surface energy is anisotropic, σ_s being the lateral surface energy and σ_e being the end surface energy. The end surface energy is much greater than the lateral surface energy. This means that a crystallite can grow much faster in the lateral direction (perpendicular to the chain direction) than by increasing its thickness. The natural shape of a crystalline domain would be disclike, with chains perpendicular to the surface of the disc. The free energy of a crystallite l cm thick and r cm in radius is

$$\Delta\Psi = 2\pi r^2 l \Delta S_u(T - T_m) + 2\sigma_e \pi r^2 + \sigma_s 2\pi rl \qquad (5.1.12)$$

where the thermodynamic quantities are now per cubic centimeter. For linear polyethylene, $\sigma_s = 10$ ergs/cm^2 and $\sigma_e = 60$ ergs/cm^2. By taking $\partial\Delta\Psi/\partial r = 0$, we find that $\Delta\Psi$ becomes maximum when $l = \sigma_e/\Delta S_u(T_m - T)$ for $l\sigma_s \ll r\sigma_e$.[4] We find that:

---

4. For this l^*, $r^* = l^*/100$ so r can be assumed to be always greater than r^*, and l^* becomes THE controlling dimension of crystallization.

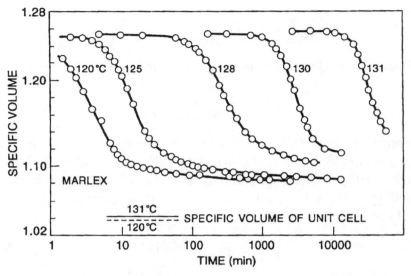

Figure 5.1.1 Isothermal crystallization of linear polyethylene measured by the specific volume change.

$$\Delta\Psi^* = 2\pi rl^*\sigma_s = 2\pi r\frac{\sigma_s\sigma_e}{\Delta S_u(T_m - T)} \qquad (5.1.13)$$

The quantity $2\pi r$ is the perimeter of the disc-shaped crystallite. For the 1 cm wide growing crystal surface,

$$\Delta\Psi_s^* = \frac{\sigma_s\sigma_e}{\Delta S_u(T_m - T)} \qquad (5.1.14)$$

The rate of growth K in the radial direction is

$$K = A\exp\left[-\frac{\sigma_s\sigma_e}{\Delta S_u(T_m - T)kT}\right] \qquad (5.1.15)$$

Figure 5.1.1 shows the volume change of linear polyethylene during isothermal crystallization.

By measuring how much these curves are shifted horizontally with temperature, the temperature dependence of log K can be obtained. The curves fit well with Equation 5.1.5 with the values cited in the foregoing discussion in this section.

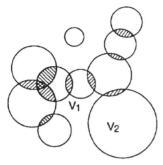

1. ISOKINETIC
2. OVERLAPPED REGIONS ARE COUNTED ONCE.
3. V_1 = SPECIFIC VOLUME OUTSIDE OF GROWING
   SPHERES (LIQUID PHASE)
4. V_2 = SPECIFIC VOLUME INSIDE OF GROWING
   SPHERES (SPHERULITE SPECIFIC VOLUME,
   INDEPENDENT OF TIME)

$$\text{IN } \frac{V - V_2}{V_1 - V_2} = - Kt^n$$

Figure 5.1.2 A schematic representation of Avrami's formula for relating the radial growth rate to the growth of spheres in a given space.

The shape of the curves in Figure 5.1.1 can tell us much about the mode of the crystal growth. The crystallization process comes to a virtual halt well below 100% crystallinity. Presumably many amorphous regions become trapped between lamellae and are not able to be integrated into the crystalline domains. The amount that remains uncrystallized in linear polyethylene is dependent on the molecular weight: the *higher* the molecular weight, the *less* the final degree of crystallinity. For M_w of 10^6, about one-third remains in the amorphous state. The portion of the crystallization curve in Figure 5.1.1 up to this final degree of crystallinity follows Avrami's formula[5] for growing spheres with a constant radial growth rate to fill the space, as shown in Figure 5.1.2. The formula is:

$$\ln \frac{V - V_\infty}{V_0 - V_\infty} = Kt^n \tag{5.1.16}$$

where V is the specific volume, and the subscripts 0 and ∞ refer to the initial and final conditions, respectively. The value of the exponent n corresponds approximately to the dimension of growth (i.e., $n = 3$ means a three-dimensional sphere growing with a constant radial growth rate), and this value fits the data if V_∞ is set at the leveling-off point of the isotherm. The

5. Avrami, S., *J. Chem. Phys.* **7**, 1103 (1939); **8**, 212 (1940).

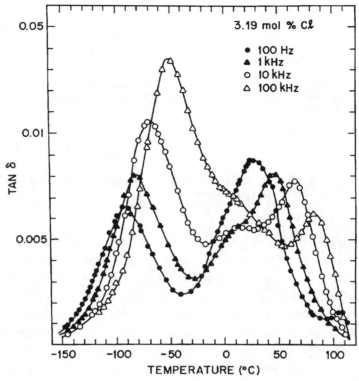

Figure 5.2.1 Dielectric tan δ vs. temperature at four frequencies for linear polyethylene chlorinated to 3.19%, then crystallized.

remaining portion of the isotherm is reminiscent of the physical aging process, because a careful analysis of this portion reveals that n continues to decrease from the initial value of 1. Fischer et al.[6] have shown that this

6. Fischer, E. W., and Schmidt, G. F., *Angew. Chem. Int. Ed. Engl.* 1, 488 (1962).

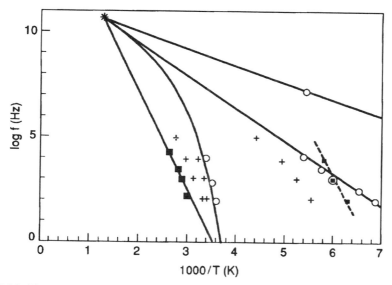

Figure 5.2.2 Transition map for the α, β, and γ transitions of linear (solid squares), branched (open circles), and 3.19% chlorinated linear (+) polyethylene. The straight line going through one circle would be drawn if the γ transition involved one methylene unit as the β conformer. That particular circle is for the temperature the frequency for methyl group rotation, obtained by NMR spectrometry.[7]

process is accompanied by the increase in lamellar thickness l, following $l \propto K \ln t$.

Some comments can be made on the surface energy σ_s and σ_e. A cubic centimeter of linear poylethyelene with the density of 1 g/cm³ contains $N_A/14$ conformers. This cube contains $(N_A/14)^{1/3} = 3.5 \times 10^7$ layers of plates 1 cm × 1 cm × 1 conformer thick. If we slice this cube in the direction parallel to the chain, the total surface energy for separating all of the layers is $\sigma_s = 10$ ergs/cm² × 3.5 × 10⁷ = 35 J/cm³, and for a cube of 1 mole of conformers, this is 117 cal/mol. Similarly, for slicing perpendicular to the chain, we use σ_e, which is 6 times as great, and obtain 700 cal/mol. There

7. McCall, D. W., *U.S. Nat. Bur. Stand. Publication* **301**, Washington, DC, 1968.

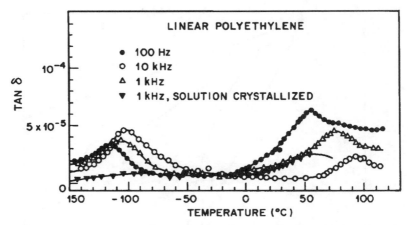

Figure 5.2.3 Dielectric loss tan δ for linear polyethylene, including the solution-crystallized sample.

are three orthogonal ways to cut this cube: two in the parallel direction and one perpendicular to the chain. When this is done, and each surface has been separated from the initial crystal dimension to the final liquidlike distance, and after all that IS the definition of the interfacial energy used here, we will have melted 1 cm^3 of polyethylene crystal. The addition of 117 $\times$ 2 + 700 will yield 934 cal/mol, and the heat of fusion of polyethylene is 960 cal/mol (cf. Table 5.1).

The surface free energy is thus the difference between the crystal interface and the liquid interface. If the chain folds are to be formed out of randomly coiled polymer chains, the energy for forming, say, six consecutive *gauche* conformations from six *trans* conformations, is 6×3 kcal/mol which translates to σ_e of 1500 ergs/cm^2! Even if half were already in the *gauche* conformation to begin with, it is still 750 ergs/cm^2, compared to σ_e of 60 ergs/cm^2. In comparison, the actual thermodynamic driving potential toward crystallization is only 23 cal/mol at 10 °C supercooling.

During the discussion on the melting of crystalline polymers, we considered homopolymers only. When noncrystallizable co-mer is introduced, the crystallizable sequence is interrupted, and the entropy of the crystalline state is increased, the entropy of fusion is reduced, and the temperature range within which partial melting occurs is widened.

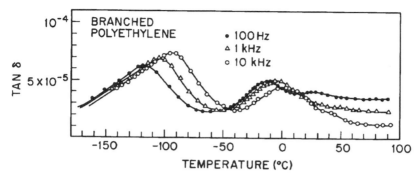

Figure 5.2.4 Dielectric tan δ for branched polyethylene.

An expression for the melting point depression of copolymers has been introduced by Flory[8]

$$\frac{\Delta H_u}{R}\left[\frac{1}{T_m^o} - \frac{1}{T_m}\right] = \ln p \qquad (5.1.17)$$

where T_m^o is the melting point of the homopolymer, T_m is that of the copolymer, and p is the sequence propagation probability of the crystallizable conformer along the chain. If it is a random copolymer, p is nearly equal to the mole fraction of the crystallizable conformers. If it is a block copolymer, p will be greater than this fraction. We can test the theory on four polyethylenes having the mole fractions of methyl groups: (I) 3.3%, (II) 1.8%, (III) 0.85%, and (IV) 0.3%. The sequence propagation probability was calculated, and the following effective amorphous fractions $(1-p)$ were found: (I) 8.3%, (II) 6.9%, (III) 4.7%, and (IV) 1.4%. If the values of $(1-p)$ had been *smaller* than the actual fraction, this result would have been attributable to a possible block-forming tendency, but such is not the case and the opposite was true. Equation 5.1.17 was perhaps too simple and needed modification. Let us now consider a portion of a homopolymer chain in a crystalline lamella with the thickness of l^* cm or g^* in number of

---

8. Flory, P. J., *Trans. Faraday Soc.* **51**, 848 (1955).

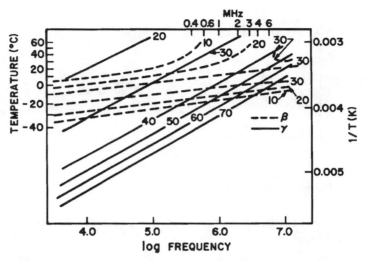

Figure 5.2.5 Contour of tan δ for β and γ processes for branched polyethylene. Data of Reddish et al. (Note 10).

conformers. This is a "stick" of a straight chain of length g^*. We consider 100 of these sticks, which are contiguously and laterally stacked. If the homopolymer is now replaced by one of the copolymers containing ϕ mol % of branches, then these 100 sticks will contain ϕg^* methyl groups. The probability that a randomly picked stick among these 100 will contain a branch is $\phi g^*/100\%$. If we assume that only sticks that do NOT contain any methyl group can crystallize, Flory's p in Equation 5.1.17 will have a new meaning:

$$1-p = \phi g^* \times 10^{-4} \tag{5.1.18}$$

The value of g^* is the critical thickness of the lamella (in number of conformers) that has persisted upon heating until final complete melting has taken place. Since lamellae thicken during slow heating before the final melting, g can vary depending on the heating rate and the type of the polymer. The final g^* tends to be larger for homopolymers that thicken more easily.

To fit the values of the methyl group content and the melting point to

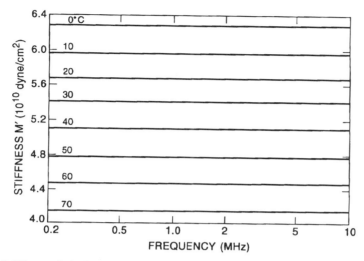

Figure 5.2.6 Ultrasonic bulk modulus for very high molecular weight linear polyethylene.

the modified Equation 5.1.17, we obtain g^* for the examples mentioned above: (I) 250, (II) 110, (III) 550, and (IV) 470 conformers thick. The basic thermodynamics of Equation 5.1.17 is sound, but it needs the value of g^*, which is an adjustable parameter unless it is determined independently. This equation in the empirical form is, however, useful for obtaining the temperature dependence of the degree of crystallinity for copolymers and, therefore, the temperature dependence of the stiffness of the crystalline domain for viscoelastic analysis.

5.2 Relaxation of Semicrystalline Polymers as Composite Structures

There are typically three transitions observed in crystalline polymers, named α, β, and γ transitions in the order of decreasing temperature. That the α transition involves the crystalline regions is supported by data that show its intensity increasing with degree of crystallinity. The β transition is usually the glass transition temperature in the amorphous regions, which really corresponds to the α transition in totally amorphous polymers such as were discussed in Chapter 3. The γ transition in crystalline polymer typically

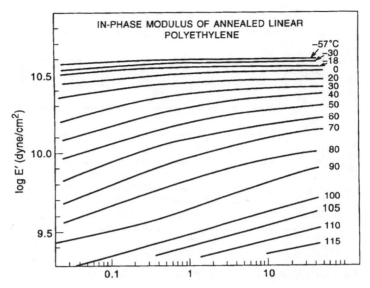

Figure 5.2.7 In-phase modulus of annealed linear polyethylene.

corresponds to the β transition in glassy polymers, the local *intra*molecular relaxation at well below T_g. Figure 5.2.1 is the plot of dielectric tan δ vs. temperature at four frequencies for a linear polyethylene that was chlorinated to the mole fraction of 3.19%.

This set of data is part of an extensive study[9] made on a series of linear polyethylene samples chlorinated to different mole fractions. The degree of crystallinity of this particular sample is found to be equal to that of a branched polyethylene having the same mole percent of methyl groups. At 10 kHz, all three transitions can be resolved, whereas the β peak in

9. Matsuoka, S, Roe, R. J., and Cole, H. F. *Dielectric Properties of Polymers,* Karasz, F. E., Ed., Plenum, New York, 1972, p. 255.

particular becomes swamped by the α peak at low frequencies and by the γ peak at high frequencies. Clearly, the β transition has a higher *apparent* activation energy than either α or γ. The apparent activation energy for the equilibrium liquid near the glass transition is high, because the temperature dependence of the true activation energy, $\Delta\mu\, z$, contains the term $\Delta\mu\, dz\, /dT$ in addition to the term $\Delta\mu z$. The term $\Delta\mu z$ is the physically viable energy barrier, and not the slope of the curve in the transition map. This point was brought up regarding Equation 2.1.24 in Section 2.1. This explains why the β process that occurs at a lower temperature than the α process can exhibit a higher *apparent* activation energy. The transition map for this polymer is compared to those for linear and branched polyethylenes in Figure 5.2.2.

All curves except the γ transition for the linear polyethylene point toward ln λ^* at $T^* = 500$ °C. The curves for T_β for the 3.2 mol % chlorinated polymer and the branched polyethylene with 3.2 mol % methyl group obviously represent the same kind of glass transition. The results from other chlorinated samples with varying extent of chlorination also exhibited the same T_β map, though the intensities varied with the amorphous fraction. These curves follow the familiar Vogel-Fulcher formula or, the WLF or Doolittle formulas, with $\Delta\mu^*$ of 3.5 kcal/mol. Aspects of intermolecular cooperativity in the conformational (stage 1) relaxation were discussed in Chapter 2. The β peak is usually not observed in linear polyethylene, while the α and γ peaks are prominently displayed, as shown in Figure 5.2.3. The apparent activation energy of ca. 11 kcal/mol for the γ transition is definitely higher than the γ transition in the branched polyethylene, with ca. 6.5 kcal/mol, as shown in Figure 5.2.4. The significantly lower value of the latter is supported repeatedly by many studies, including the data by Reddish,[10] shown in Figure 5.2.5.

All these data suggest unequivocally that the γ transition in linear polyethylene is different from that in other polymers. However, our thermodynamic analysis of the glass transition in Chapter 2 indicated that T_g of one methylene group as a conformer (i.e., linear polyethylene) ought to be -110 °C as shown in Table 2.3. Since T_g as we defined it is 50 °C above T_0,

---

10. Reddish, W., *J. Polym. Sci.* **C14**, 123 (1966)

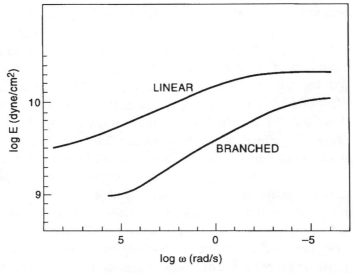

Figure 5.2.8 Master curves for the tensile in-phase moduli of linear and branched polyethylene at 30 °C.

the latter should be -160 °C. If we use these numbers in the Vogel-Fulcher formula, we obtain apparent activation energy near -100 °C of 10 kcal/mol, a higher value than $\Delta\mu$ arising as a result of the additional term $\Delta\mu/dT$, when the fictive temperature is changing with the real temperature. Thus, if the methylene units in the amorphous state were to undergo the glass transition, it would occur at just about the region of the γ transition for branched polyethylene. The latter is a traditional β process in amorphous glassy polymers having T_g = -30 °C, and a constant activation energy with the value of $\Delta\mu z_\beta$ = 7 kcal. This argument is supported by the fact that solution-crystallized linear polyethylene exhibits no γ transition and contains no amorphous regions. Although not shown here, extended chain crystals produced under high hydrostatic pressure also lack the γ transition. Linear polyethylene and branched polyethylene are, therefore, different polymers. The difference in their T_g values leads to different melt behaviors as well. Linear polyethylene exhibits an apparent activation energy of 6 kcal for the

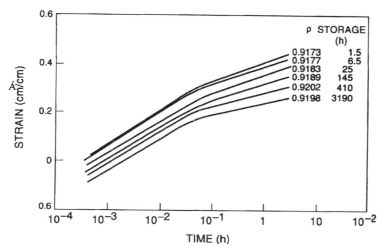

Figure 5.2.9 Log creep compliance against time on an arbitrary scale: data by Ogorkiwicz indicate two regimes of creep (or relaxation) for branched polyethylene.

melt viscosity, while branched polyethylene with higher T_g exhibits 12 kcal. The γ transition in linear polyethylene (which should be called β, but this would make it hopelessly confusing) will converge to the T^* point via a curved line typical of the Vogel-Fulcher equation. The slope of the γ relaxation for polyethylene, shown by the dashed line in Figure 5.2.2, is much higher than that of the branched polyethylene.

The converging feature of the α and γ transitions with constant slopes strongly implies the restricted or intramolecular cooperative rotation of the main chain bonds as the basic mechanism in both transitions. The higher transition temperatures among the different polymers mean that more conformers (the larger values for $\Delta\mu z$) are involved. The α transition is an Arrhenius process with the constant activation energy of 28 kcal/mol for linear polyethylene (progressively lower for the lesser crystalline, lower melting point homologues), implying the onset of the cooperative relaxation of six (the activation energy is divided by $\Delta\mu$, not $\Delta\mu^*$) conformers. Hoffman's model[11] features the rotation of the whole segment of a chain between the folds in the crystalline region, in which the activation energy depends on the thickness of the crystal. Above T_α, the dipoles are allowed to rotate cooperatively, with the frequency in the order of kilohertz. At this temperature the polymer appears transparent and can be drawn to a fiber form readily, without whitening. Above T_α there is no additional dielectric transition, and no peak is observed at the melting of crystals. These features are reminiscent of liquid crystals in which rotational relaxation can occur freely while the center of mass of each conformer remains fixed in the orderly array of a crystal. The fluctuation that culminates in 6 consecutive conformers gaining 28 kcal of Gibbs free energy may be pictured as a group of 29 conformers having an average of energy equaling the heat of fusion, and the total energy is localized from time to time to the 6 conformers in the center (29 is derived from 960 cal for heat of fusion). It means that the the central 6 conformers are surrounded by four neighboring chains, forming body-centered orthorhombic cell. Incidentally, six consecutive conformers melt at 88 °C according to Equation 5.1.17, and this temperature *is* in the range of the α transition for linear polyethylene.

The intensity of the α transition is complementary to the γ transition, because if the conformers are able to relax with the smaller number of cooperative conformers (i.e., γ process), they would do so. The intensity depends on the frequency and the temperature.

Perhaps the best known model for the viscoelastic behavior of semicrystalline polymers is the one by Takayanagi.[12] This model is in fact a generalized model for composites with two distinctly different viscoelastic properties, and it has been demonstrated to work well with the two phase systems such as the ABS terpolymer in which the rubbery spheres are dispersed in the glassy matrix. The tensile modulus E of a composite structure is calculated according to the formula:

11. Hoffman, J. D., *J. Polym. Sci.* **C14**, 173 (1968).
12. Takayanagi, M., *Mem. Fac. of Eng., Kyushu Univ.* **13**, 41 (1963).

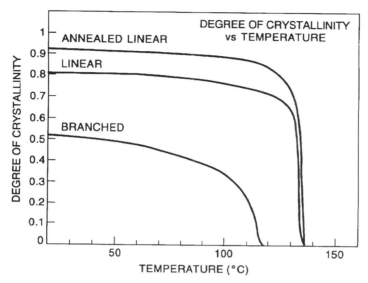

Figure 5.2.10 Degrees of crystallinity vs. temperature calculated from specific volume for three polyethylene samples.

$$E = \left[\frac{\phi}{\lambda E_A + (1\text{-}\lambda)E_c} + \frac{1-\phi}{E_C} \right]^{-1} \qquad (5.2.1)$$

where ϕ is the effective amorphous fraction in the longitudinal direction of force and λ is that in the cross-sectional direction. Neither ϕ nor λ is a simple ratio of the volume fraction of the amorphous regions but can be calculated from the formulas:

$$\lambda = [2 + 3(1\text{-}x)]/5 \qquad (5.2.2a)$$

and

$$\phi = 5(1\text{-}x)/[2 + 3(1\text{-}x)] \qquad (5.2.2b)$$

where x is the degree of crystallinity. This formula is due to Kerner,[13] and

Takayanagi and coworkers have applied it to a number of polymer systems including some highly anisotropic systems. When the following quantities are substituted (for linear polyethylene) into the equations above: $x = 0.8$, $\lambda = 0.52$, $\phi = 0.38$, $E_C = 2.5 \times 10^{10}$, and $E_A \leq 10^7$ dynes/cm^2, $E = 1.77 \times 10^{10}$ dynes/cm^2 is obtained. The value for E_A below 10^7 dynes/cm^2 does not affect E, which is already very small. This resulting value for E, then, is the calculated value for the completely relaxed modulus of the composite. The amplitude of the relaxation $\Delta \log(E_C/E) = 0.15$ is the maximum value according to this calculation. This value is too small for the entire relaxation, as the dynamic mechanical modulus could increase by this amount by simply changing the frequency by less than 3 decades or sometimes by less than 2 decades *isothermally*. The effect of the rigid crystalline matrix is too great according to this assumption. Alternatively, we can assume that there are enough conformers in the amorphous state interrupting the apparently coherent lamellar structure that the crystalline domains may be considered to be islands and the amorphous domains the matrix, even though the crystalline fraction is 80%. This is done by letting x in Equation 5.2.2 be the *amorphous* fraction rather than the crystalline fraction. Calculation in this way results in the relaxed modulus of $E = 3.27 \times 10^9$ dynes/cm^2, and the amplitude of the isothermal relaxation $\Delta \log(E_C/E) = 0.88$ is obtained. As we shall see, this is in close agreement with the data. This is a somewhat unexpected result, and it has not been seen before in part because it is extremely difficult to separate out the relaxed modulus after a short time at high temperature from the relaxed modulus after a long (years!) time at room temperature.

A linear polyethylene with molecular weight of over a million typically crystallizes only up to 67%. No spherulites are observable. Its viscoelastic behavior, however, can be predicted with the approach shown above. This is certainly a case in which the concept of the continuous amorphous regions is more plausible.

To separate the effect of temperature on the viscoelastic properties into the two distinct contributions, one for reducing the relaxation time with the

---

13. Kerner, D. H., *Proc. Phys. Soc.* **B69**, 808 (1956).

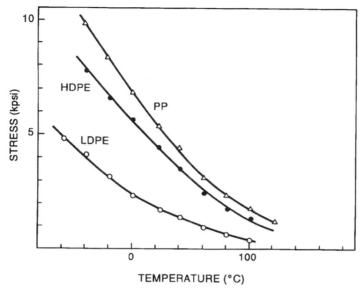

Figure 5.2.11 Yield stress observed under a strain rate of 5% per minute deformation rate for linear and branched polyethylenes and for polypropylene

horizontal shift, and the other for reducing the stiffness of the crystalline region with the vertical shift, each much be measured independently. The conventional wisdom of matching the shapes or the slopes of consecutive isotherms is at best inaccurate, since all give nearly straight lines. That technique often ends up shifting everything horizontally with a huge time span for the master curve.

Figure 5.2.6 shows the ultrasonically measured bulk modulus of linear polyethylene over 2 decades of frequency about 1 MHz.[14] Similar data for branched polyethylene, not shown, exhibit a definite frequency dependence,

---

14. Matsuoka, S., and McSkimin, S., unpublished data.

while the completely flat, straight feature of all the curves shown here suggests that for linear polyethylene this time-temperature range corresponds to the unrelaxed modulus regime. The bulk modulus K is related to the tensile modulus E by the formula:

$$K = \frac{E}{3(1 - 2\nu)} \qquad (5.2.3)$$

where ν is the Poisson ratio, ca. 0.4 for polyethylene. This will make log K/E about 0.22, though an accurate absolute value for this is not needed for our analysis here.

Using the temperature dependence of the ultrasonic bulk modulus as a guide for the "vertical shift" factor, the isotherms shown in Figure 5.2.7 were shifted both vertically and horizontally to obtain the master curves for linear and branched polyethylenes. For the branched polyethylene, its own bulk modulus curves were used as the vertical shift factor. The master curves for $T = 30\ ^{\circ}\text{C}$ are shown in Figure 5.2.8. For another temperature, these curves would have to be shifted not only horizontally to account for the shift in the relaxation times, but also vertically by the amount that the ultrasonic modulus shifts with the temperature.

The horizontal shift factor for linear polyethylene followed the Arrhenius expression with the activation energy of 30 kcal/mol, a value close to 28 kcal for the α process. The horizontal shift factor for branched polyethylene is complicated because the β shift factor for the amorphous regions enters at the short time end with Vogel-Fulcher type dependence, but above 30 $^{\circ}\text{C}$ it is mostly the α process having an activation energy of about 24 kcal. These two separate relaxation mechanisms in branched polyethylene are observed in the creep data by Ogorkiwicz[15] shown in Figure 5.2.9.

Two distinct regimes are observed: the fast relaxing process with the steeper slope is affected by the amorphous region, which is relaxed after about 2 minutes (3×10^{-2} h) and is followed by the crystalline-dominated process, which has a typical slope of 0.04 to 0.1, comparable to that of the

---

15. Ogorkiwicz, R. M., *Engineering Properties of Thermoplastics,* Wiley, New York, 1970.

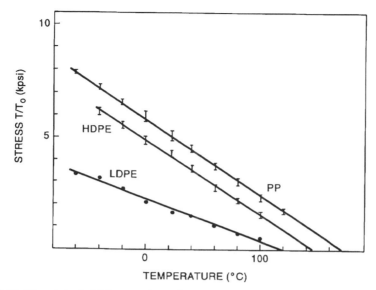

Figure 5.2.12 The plot of yield stress times the temperature for the three polymers of Figure 5.2.11 results in straight lines when plotted against temperature.

linear polyethylene. The effect of aging in crystalline polymers is different from that in glassy polymers. It is primarily the stiffness increasing in the crystalline region that will shift the creep curve down and the relaxation curve up vertically. This feature of a vertical shift with aging is also seen for linear polyethylene. From the master curve for linear polyethylene in Figure 5.2.8, the modulus drop for the isothermal relaxation of $\Delta \log E = 0.8$ and a power law slope of 0.08 is obtained. The former number is in good agreement with the calculation made from Equation 5.2.1 with the amorphous region as the matrix, and the latter number is in agreement with the stress-strain data as will be discussed.

Figure 5.2.10 shows the temperature dependence of the degree of crystallinity for branched, linear, and annealed linear polyethylenes. Below 100 °C, the degree of crystallinity does not change much for the linear polyethylene, yet even the ultrasonic bulk modulus was observed to decrease from 0 °C and up. Clearly, the stiffness of the crystal, aside from its own relaxation time change, is affected by the temperature much more drastically than the crystallinity change would indicate. As it turns out, it is not the elastic modulus of the crystal itself but the local and microscopic plasticity in the crystalline region that affects the "vertical shift" for the viscoelastic modulus, just as it is the case of the glassy state and also for the melt, as discussed in the foregoing chapters.

The yield stress at 5% per minute is plotted against temperature in Figure 5.2.11. The yield stress decreases as the temperature is increased, but not linearly as is the case of glassy polymers shown in Chapter 3 (Figure 3.3.5). For glassy polymers, the straight line between yield stress and temperature was argued based on the model (i.e., Equation 3.3.16a):

$$\sigma^* \propto strain\ energy\ at\ yield = \Delta H^\dagger - T\Delta S^\dagger \qquad (5.2.4)$$

where $\dagger$ indicates the increase in enthalpy or entropy at the yield condition; i.e., when the deviatoric strain energy exceeds the energy needed to break up the domain structure, the yield phenomenon occurs. Hence the yield stress σ^* decreases linearly with T following Equation 5.2.4. The curves for the crystalline polymers become straight, however, when $T\sigma^*$ rather than σ^* is plotted against T, as shown in Figure 5.2.12. In other words,

$$\frac{T}{T_b}\sigma^* = \Delta H^\dagger - T\Delta S^\dagger \qquad (5.2.5)$$

where T_b is the extrapolated temperature at which the crystalline modulus becomes the same as that of the glassy state, at which point the Equation 5.2.4 becomes operative, since the polymer acts as in the glassy state. This will be further supported by the stress-strain curves shown later in this chapter. Equation 5.2.5 suggests that the yield process in crystalline structures involves an increase in entropy as the criterion, as opposed to the enthalpy in glassy polymers in Equation 5.2.4. The application of the stress increases the excess entropy, and when the latter reaches a critical value, yield occurs. This is like the fusion process except the structure, instead of being loosened by thermal agitation, is initiated by strain. However, the amount of $\Delta S^\dagger$ is about 1/20 of the entropy of fusion, the value of $\Delta S^\dagger$ being only 0.01 eu per mole of $-CH_2-$ conformer. The ratio is reminiscent of the ratio of the critical energy for yield in the glassy state being about 1/30 of the heat of fusion of a conformer, as discussed earlier in connection with

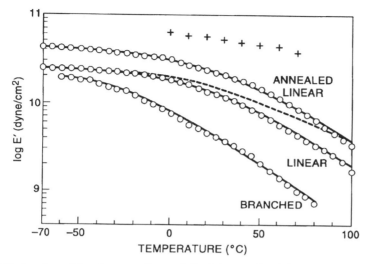

Figure 5.2.13 Isochronal in-phase tensile moduli of three polyethylene samples. Dashed line is relative yield stress for linear polyethylene matched at -40 °C. Plus signs indicate bulk moduli obtained for the very high molecular weight linear polyethylene shown in Figure 5.2.6.

Equation 3.3.16c, and we suggested in Chapter 3 that the structural change must be local in nature. Following the method of calculation of Equation 5.1.12, the surface energy involved in the yield process was calculated to be 2 or 3 ergs/cm^2, about a quarter of the lateral surface energy σ_s of 10 ergs/cm^2.[16]

The isochronal moduli for the three polyethylene samples are shown in Figure 5.2.13.

The dashed line is a plot of the relative change in yield stress with temperature, shifted to match the modulus of linear polyethylene at -40 °C.

---

16. The interfacial energy discussed here is not the surface energy of liquids in contact with a solid surface, which is typically 50 ergs/cm^2, or the energy required to separate the interface to the infinite distance; our interfacial energy requires that the liquidlike distance be removed from the solidlike distance.

The ratio of the absolute values of the yield stress and the modulus was 1:46 at -40 °C, (cf. 1:30 for glassy polymers), which translates to 2.2% for the yield strain in molecular scale at -40 °C. The yield stress does not decrease as fast as does the isochronal modulus with temperature, begause the shortening relaxation time further reduces the latter. σ^* is really a measure of the critical strain energy for the plastic deformation. This critical energy is equal to the energy required to break up the microstructure in the crystalline region, and its value decreases as the temperature is increased. Its temperature dependence is found to be nearly equal to that of the unrelaxed modulus and the vertical shift factor. The relationship between σ^* and the linear viscoelastic modulus thus can be calculated with Equation 3.3.21, Gleisle's rule. Takayanagi's[17] $\alpha_c{}'$ transition at a temperature higher than α, in our opinion, is a manifestation of this plasticity. It is identified by Takayanagi as the breaking up of the mosaic structure in the lamellae. The apparently nonlinear effect that occurs at a frequency and a temperature different from that of the α transition can be interpreted as another loss mechanism. The onset of such a nonlinearity can be as small as a fraction of a percent strain.[18] Takayanagi has also observed the strong nonlinearity in the viscoelasticity of solution-crystallized linear polyethylene with the vertical shift factor of the form $\exp(-\varepsilon)$, where ε is the tensile strain. This is true for glassy as well as molten polymers, as discussed in Chapters.

SUMMARY

1. The α transition for crystalline polymers involves intramolecular cooperativity in the crystalline regions. The β transition is the glass transition for the amorphous domains. The γ transition is the local intramolecular cooperative relaxation in the glassy regions. Linear polyethylene is an unusual case: the transition at -100 to -110 °C is the glass transition, while the transition in the same temperature range found in branched polyethylene is in the class of local relaxation such as the β transition in glassy polymers.

---

17. Takayanagi, M., *J. Polym. Sci.* C, 113 (1964).
18. Matsuoka, S., unpublished results.

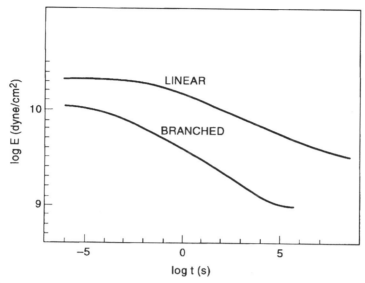

Figure 5.3.1 Master curves for the relaxation moduli for linear ergs/cm², or the energy required to separate the master dynamic mechanical data shown in Figure 5.2.8.

2. The isothermal dynamic data must be shifted for the different temperatures not only horizontally to account for the change in relaxation time but also vertically to account for the change in the unrelaxed modulus. The vertical shift for the unrelaxed modulus can be obtained from the ultrasonic bulk modulus that depends on the temperature, which nearly coincides with the temperature dependence of the yield stress on the relative scale.

5.3 Engineering Properties

The curves in Figure 5.2.8 can be flipped around the y-axis to obtain the master curves of relaxation modulus, which is shown in Figure 5.3.1.

The master curve can also be obtained from isochronal dynamic mechanical modulus at all temperatures above T_g by the following procedure:

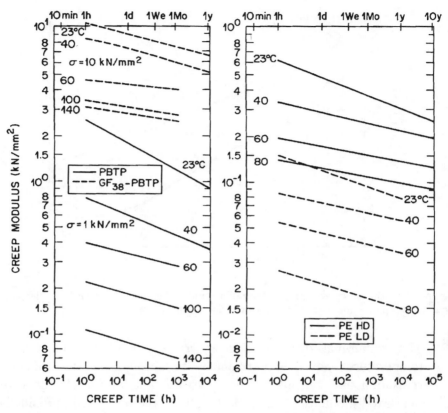

Figure 5.3.2 Creep moduli of linear and branched polyethylenes and polybutylene terephthalete. GF stands for glass-filled.

1.   Decide on the reference temperature T_r (e.g., 25 °C. The time is $t_r = 1/\omega_r$ radians⁻¹ sec $= 1/2\pi f\,\text{Hz}^{-1}$.

2. $E(t)$ at T_r is obtained from $E'(\omega)$ at T by shifting vertically, so that

$$E(t)\ \Big|\ _{T_r} = E'(\omega_r)\ \Big|\ _T \frac{T_r}{T}\frac{T_c - T_r}{T_c - T} \tag{5.3.1a}$$

and horizontally, so that

$$\log t = \frac{H}{2.3R}(\frac{1}{T_r} - \frac{1}{T}) + \log\omega_r \tag{5.3.1b}$$

The horizontal shift must be consistent with the following equation involving the loss tangent,

$$\tan \delta = \frac{E''}{E'} = \frac{1}{E'} \frac{dE'}{d\ln \omega} = \frac{d\ln E'}{dT} \frac{RT^2}{H} \qquad (5.3.1c)$$

where H is the apparent activation energy for the relaxation time.

3. Below T_g, the crystalline polymer behaves as if a glassy polymer, following the characteristics described in Chapter 3.
    The relaxation modulus is approximated by the power law:

$$E(t) = E_0 \qquad \qquad \text{for } t < t_0 \qquad (5.3.2a)$$

$$E(t) = E_0 \left(\frac{t}{t_0}\right)^{-n} \qquad \text{for } t > t_0 \qquad (5.3.2b)$$

For linear polyethylene, $\log E_0 = 10.3$ (dynes/cm^2) and $n = 0.08$ at 25 °C, and $\log t_0 = -2$ (seconds). For branched polyethylene, $\log t_0 = -4$ (seconds), $\log E_0 = 10.0$ (dynes/cm^2), $n = 0.12$.

A highly crystalline polymer should exhibit a final "plateau" modulus. This is apparent from Takayanagi's formula, Equation 5.2.1. For given degree of crystallinity, the values of parameters λ and ϕ are fixed. Depending on those values, there is a minimum value of the modulus E_A for the amorphous component, below which the overall modulus E is no longer affected. The value of the minimum E_A for the linear polyethylene cited in this chapter is $\sim 10^7$ dynes/cm^2, and the minimum E is $\sim 3.3 \times 10^9$ dynes/cm^2 or $\log E_{min} = 9.5$. Similarly, the plateau modulus for branched polyethylene is 10^9 dynes/cm^2. The plateau value of E will decrease with temperature according to Equation 5.3.1a above. The total span of modulus change ΔE is typically one decade.

We pointed out in Chapter 1 that even the linear viscoelastic modulus is not a reciprocal of the creep compliance, and in Chapter 3 we showed that the creep curve tends to spread on the time axis more than the relaxation curve. Even for a material that exhibits a single relaxation time, its creep modulus ($=$ compliance^{-1}) would be a stretched exponential function with the KWW $\beta = 1.2$.[19] In Chapter 3, Figure 3.2.6, we further demonstrated that for the KWW β of 0.5 and $\lambda = 1$ minute, the relaxation modulus corresponds to β' of 0.33 and λ' of 0.2 minute for the creep modulus. In general, β' is two-thirds of β.[20]

In general, it is possible to predict the relaxation modulus from the creep modulus, or vice versa, by two approaches:

1. Changing n for the power law (or KWW β) to m for the creep modulus:

$$m = \frac{2}{3}n \qquad (5.3.3a)$$

2. $\log t_{0,n}$ for relaxation to $\log t_{0,m}$ for creep:

$$\log t_{0,m} = \log t_{0,n} - 0.8 \qquad (5.3.3b)$$

The creep moduli of linear polyethylene, branched polyethylene, and polybutylene terephthalate are shown in Figure 5.3.2.[21]

The creep power of $m = 0.053$ is observed at 23 °C, while our value of n for the relaxation-dynamic modulus of 0.08 is about 3/2 times the value of m, in agreement to Equation 5.3.3a. At higher temperatures, nonlinear effects are more pronounced for the creep data and the value of m appears to decrease. The strictly linear value of m, however, can be assumed to be constant over a wide range of temperatures, as is true of n for relaxation.

In Chapter 3, we introduced a scheme to predict creep or relaxation behavior from stress-strain data obtained under a constant rate of deformation. The central theme for that methodology was to treat the isochronal stress-strain states as corresponding states. If it takes the same time interval to reach a certain stress σ_1 and strain ε_1 as it does to reach σ_2 and ε_2, by either relaxation, creep, or constant rate deformation, we said that these two states corresponding states. If the state $\{\sigma_1, \varepsilon_1\}$ is reached at the

---

19. It was stated in Chapter 4 that the exponent on the molecular weight can be 3 for the relaxation, but the exponent for the creep modulus could be $3 \times 1.2 = 3.6$.

20. Whereas $\beta = 0.5$ is a frequently found value for stress relaxation, dynamic mechanical modulus, or compliance, and for the dielectric permittivity, $\beta' = 0.33$ is a frequently found value in creep, known as the Andrade formula.

21. Oberbach, K., *Kunststoff - Kennwerte für Konstrukture,* Hanser, Munich, 1975.

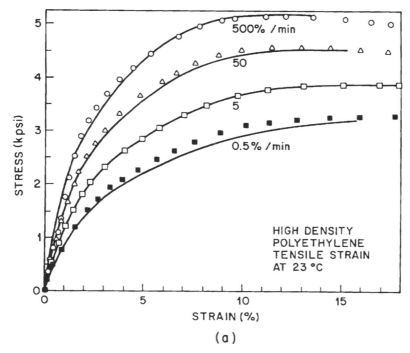

Figure 5.3.3a Stress-strain curves of linear polyethylene: (a) at 23 °C at strain rates of 0.5, 5, 50, and 500% per minute, calculated according to Equation 5.3.5 of scaling rule 1′ (below) based on data at 5% per minute, and (b) at 5% per minute at various temperatures.

deformation rate of $\dot{\varepsilon}_1$, and $\{\sigma_2, \varepsilon_2\}$ at $\dot{\varepsilon}_2$, then σ_2 could be obtained by multiplying σ_1 by factor $(\dot{\varepsilon}_2/\dot{\varepsilon}_1)^n$, and ε_2 by multiplying ε_1 by $(\dot{\varepsilon}_2/\dot{\varepsilon}_1)^m$. This scheme is justified because all stress-strain curves are reducible to one master curve for the normalized relative values of stress and strain as a function of the dimensionless time or the rate of strain.

For a composite structure such as a crystalline polymer, this scheme would not work, however. Under a constant rate of strain, the amorphous regions initially add to the overall stiffness, but relax and become soft by the time the stress nears the yield condition. Stress is greater at a given strain when the strain rate is faster, since stress during the relaxation experiment is greater at a shorter time. The equivalence between the two stresses works

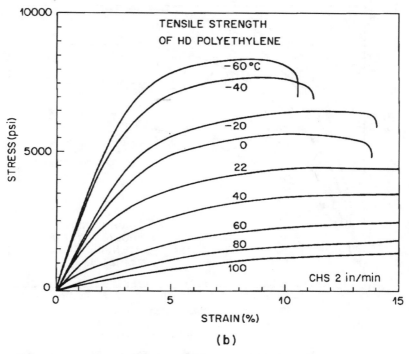

Figure 5.3.3b Stress strain curves at 5% per minute at various temperatures.

well in the nonlinear regime according to the viscoplastic model proposed earlier. For glassy polymers, the stresses between two isochronal states were scaled by the formula:

$$\frac{\sigma_2}{\sigma_1} = \left(\frac{\dot{\varepsilon}_2}{\dot{\varepsilon}_1} \right)^n$$

(5.3.4)

and the same factor was applied for the strains, thereby achieving the similar "shape" for all stress-strain curves. However, the strain cannot be scaled by the same factor $\dot{\varepsilon}^n$ for crystalline polymers because the initial stress is much higher as a result of the large contribution from the amorphous regions. The stress in crystalline polymers, which are composites of two phases, rises faster than in a homogeneous system consisting of either of the two

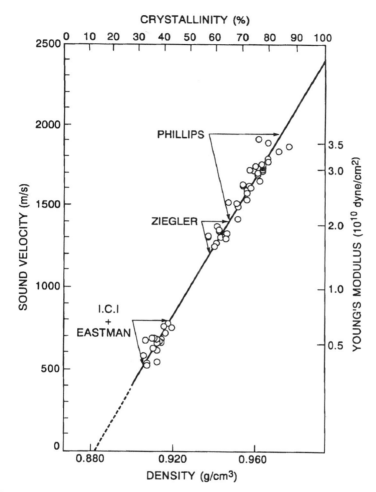

Figure 5.3.4 The velocity of sound and Young's modulus vs. density in several classes of polyethylenes. Data by Davidse et al. The scale for the modulus was calculated using Equation 5.3.11.

components. As the stress rises, the course of the stress-strain relationship is kept at the minimum possible free energy levels. The strain energy level can thus be used as the criterion for the corresponding states in crystalline polymers. The underlying principle is that of the von Mises criterion, which we expanded earlier to specify the equivalent stress-strain levels in a viscoplastic body, using deviatoric strain invariants. Between two stress-strain curves at different strain rates, the following relationship should stand:

$$\varepsilon \frac{\Delta \sigma}{\Delta \dot{\varepsilon}} + \sigma \frac{\Delta \varepsilon}{\Delta \dot{\varepsilon}} = 0 \tag{5.3.5}$$

which is rewritten, for the change in the strain rate of $\Delta \dot{\varepsilon} = \dot{\varepsilon}_2 - \dot{\varepsilon}_1$, to lead to the relationship:

$$\ln \left(\frac{\sigma_2}{\sigma_1} \right) + \ln \left(\frac{\varepsilon_2}{\varepsilon_1} \right) = 0 \tag{5.3.6}$$

or

$$\frac{\sigma_2}{\sigma_1} = \frac{\varepsilon_1}{\varepsilon_2} \tag{5.3.7}$$

The condition above is satisfied when we scale a stress-strain curve from another by multiplying the stress and dividing the strain by the factor $(\dot{\varepsilon}_2 / \dot{\varepsilon}_1)^n$, i.e.,

$$\frac{\sigma_2}{\sigma_1} = \left(\frac{\dot{\varepsilon}_2}{\dot{\varepsilon}_1} \right)^n \tag{5.3.8}$$

$$\frac{\varepsilon_2}{\varepsilon_1} = \left(\frac{\dot{\varepsilon}_2}{\dot{\varepsilon}_1} \right)^{-n} \tag{5.3.9}$$

Stress-strain data for linear high density polyethylene are shown in Figure 5.3.3. The curves for the strain rates of 0.5, 50, and 500% per minute were calculated from the curve obtained at the strain rate of 5% per minute. The points are experimental data, and the curves were obtained by calculating from the data at 5% per minute using Equations 5.3.8 and 5.3.9. The good agreement between calculated results and data supports the scaling scheme of Equation 5.3.6, which may be restated as follows:

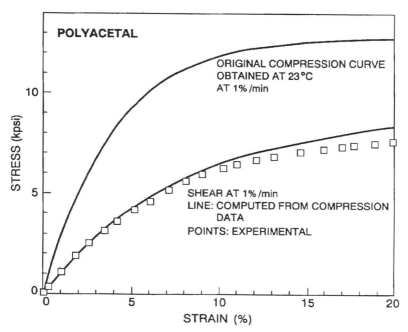

Figure 5.3.5 Stress-strain curves in compression and shear for polyacetal, a crystalline polymer. The shear curve has been calculated from the compression data points by the application of scaling rule 6´ or 6.

Scaling Rule 1´ A stress-strain curve at strain rate $\dot{\gamma}_2$ (or $\dot{\varepsilon}_2$) can be predicted from the experimental stress-strain curve obtained at the strain rate of $\dot{\gamma}_1$ by multiplying the stress and dividing the strain by the scaling factor $(\dot{\gamma}_2/\dot{\gamma}_1)^n$.

Scaling Rule 2´ The parameter n can be treated as independent of temperature, since it depends on the amplitude of the isothermal relaxation: $\Delta \ln G = \ln G(t = 0) - \ln G(t \rightarrow \infty)$.

Scaling Rule 3´ When the temperature is changed, the scaling factor λ_2/λ_1 should be used. Figure 5.3.3 shows the temperature dependence of the stress-strain curves for linear polyethylene.

Scaling Rule 4´ The effect of temperature on the characteristic relaxation time λ_c follows the Arrhenius equation. The vertical shift factor for the modulus is obtained from the equation:

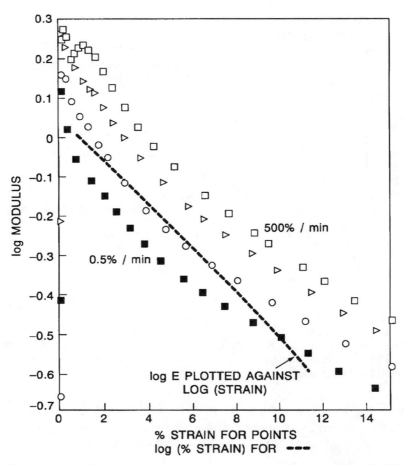

Figure 5.3.6 The logarithm of the secant modulus vs. strain for linear polyethylene. The dashed line is plotted against the logarithm of strain, which makes it a straight line.

$$\ln \frac{G_2}{G_1} = \ln \left[\frac{T_1(1 - T_2/T_m)}{T_1(1 - T_1/T_m)} \right] \qquad (5.3.10)$$

Scaling Rule 5′ Physical aging affects crystalline polymers by increasing the crystallinity and the unrelaxed modulus, as shown in Figures 5.2.9 and 5.2.10.

The effect is totally on the vertical shift. Davidse et al.,[22] have shown that the linear relationship between the velocity of sound v, density ρ, and Young's modulus E depends on these two quantities by the relationship

$$E = v^2 \rho \qquad (5.3.11)$$

as shown in Figure 5.3.4.

The density of a semicrystalline polymer increases during secondary crystallization, which does not follow the Avrami expression with a constant exponent but, instead, manifests the exponential integral as in physical aging in glassy polymers, which is best approximated by a continuously decreasing exponent with time. The temperature dependence of the rates of secondary crystallization follows Equation 5.1.15, i.e., $\exp[c/T\Delta T]$, where ΔT is the degree of supercooling, $T - T_m$. The scaling is done from the change in the density.

Scaling Rule 6´ It is interesting to observe that, from Equations 3.3.41 and 3.3.42, the products $\sigma_{tensile}\varepsilon_x$ and $\sigma_{shear}\gamma_{xy}$ are equal when the Poisson ratio ν is precisely 0.5. This means that the von Mises criterion is an energy criterion for "incompressible"[23] solids. When $\nu = 0.5$, the tensile energy exceeds the shear energy, although slightly, according to the deviatoric invariant rule. This means that the shear stress tends to be greater than $\sigma_{tensile}/\sqrt{3}$. At any rate, the same scaling rule as scaling rule 6 for glassy polymers applies for crystalline polymers, between either the tensile or compressive stress-strain and the shear stress-strain states, as illustrated in Figure 5.3.5, in which the shear stress and strain were scaled from the uniaxial compressive stress and strain for polyoxymethylene (polyacetal).

The "shape" of the stress-strain curves depends on the rate of strain for crystalline polymers. However, when $\log \sigma/\varepsilon$ is plotted against ε, as shown in Figure 5.3.6, these curves are separated from each other by *ca* $n \log(\dot{\varepsilon}_2/\dot{\varepsilon}_1)$ with $n = 0.8$, which is about the value found for the dynamic modulus.

When plotted against $\log \varepsilon$, the curves become straight, as shown by

---

22. Davidse, P. D., Waterman, H. I., and Westerdijk, I. B., *J. Polym. Sci.* **59**, 389 (1962).
23. A misnomer. A better word would be "nondilatable."

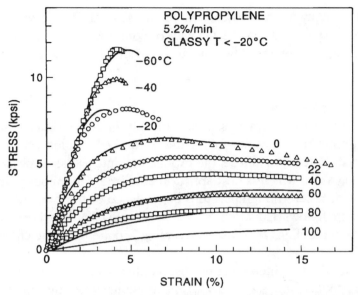

Figure 5.3.7 Stress-strain curves for isotactic polypropylene deformed at the rate of 5.2% per minute. Below the glass transition temperature of ~ -20 °C, the stress-strain curves of polypropylene are scaled following the rules for the glassy polymers, ΔT is the degree of supercooling, $T - T_m$. The polymers are applicable.

Equation 5.3.12, which was derived as Equation 1.6.17 assuming the power law for the relaxation modulus:

$$\frac{\sigma}{\varepsilon} = E_0\varepsilon^{-n}(\dot{\varepsilon}\,t_0)^n \tag{5.3.12}$$

At a temperature below T_g of the amorphous regions, crystalline polymers can be treated as if they are glassy polymers, and all the scaling rules for glassy polymers can be applied. This is shown in Figure 5.3.7 for polypropylene.

6

Related Topics

This chapter, which deals with aspects of polymer properties that are strongly affected by molecular relaxation mechanisms, may be considered to be the application of what has been discussed in the foregoing chapters.

6.1 The Glass Transition in Crosslinked Polymers (Thermosets)

Although the epoxy system is a very complicated system to serve as an example for thermosets, it is perhaps the most widely known system. For this reason, our discussion centers around experimental data derived with this system and, in particular, with cresol novolac with phenolic hardener.

It is well known that a densely crosslinked network of polymer molecules exhibits a high equilibrium modulus. The dependence of the modulus on the crosslink density can be derived from the theory of rubber elasticity. The elastic modulus is proportional to the change of entropy per strain per unit volume, and therefore it is proportional to the number of chains per unit volume. From Equation 4.2.12, the shear modulus is shown to depend on the number N_c of the chains per unit volume:

$$G = N_c kT \qquad (6.1.1)$$

In a crosslinked system, the longest unit of conformational change is the length between crosslinked points, and N_c is the number of those strands per unit volume. G can be an equilibrium modulus only if there is so much crosslinking that each polymer is crosslinked at least once at some point. Otherwise, the stress eventually will relax to zero. This minimum requirement causes the network to be connected throughout the entire polymer system. At this point the weight average molecular weight becomes infinity, and the gel is formed. This is the gel point. Above the gel point the modulus will relax to the value specified by Equation 6.1.1, where the number of strands N_c per unit volume is equal to Avogadro's number N_A times the mole fraction ν of the conformers that are crosslinked, and we obtain:

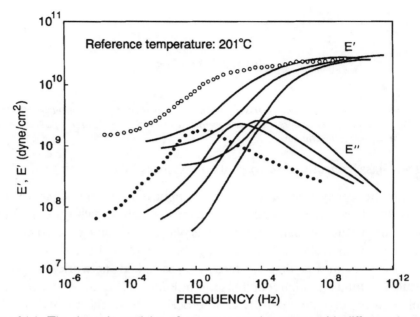

Figure 6.1.1 The dynamic modulus of an epoxy-novolac system with different degrees of crosslinking. The low frequency modulus is the relaxed equilibrium modulus. (Data from Ogata, M., Kinjo, T., Eguchi, S., and Kawata, T., *Kobunshi Rombunshu*, **46**, No. 7, 413 (1989).)

where ρ is the density (g/cm^3) and M is the number-average molecular weight of the chains between crosslink points. In the limit that M is equal to the molecular weight of one conformer (i.e., every conformer being crosslinked),[1] the shear modulus of 4×10^8 dynes/cm^2 is obtained for the values of $T = 500$ K, $M_0 = 100$, and $\rho = 1$ g/cm^3. This corresponds to a tensile modulus of 10^9 dynes/cm^2. This value is considerably less than the modulus of glassy polymers, which is typically about 3×10^{10} dynes/cm^2. In fact a fully cured glassy epoxy resin typically exhibits the glass transition,

---

1. Obviously the conditions for dynamic molecules with long-range conformational entropy are violated well before such an extremely short chain length is assumed. This calculation is for order-of-magnitude calculations only.

during which time the modulus drops from 3×10^{10} to 10^9 dynes/cm^2. An incomplete cure will result in a lower value for the equilibrium (relaxed) modulus, as shown in Figure 6.1.1.

The low value for the relaxed modulus should not be attributed to the methylene ether linkages that may remain free to rotate. The glass transition temperatures of these groups as independent conformers are very low, and the low modulus for the epoxy resin as a whole would have persisted well below room temperature. Instead, they should be grouped as part of the large conformers, as we did in Chapter 2.

Thus, the entropic limit on polymer molecules as dynamic chains is not sufficient to account for the extremely high modulus of the glassy state. As is true in the case of uncrosslinked glassy polymers, the glass transition should be regarded as resulting from the increasing difficulties associated with the occurrence of local relaxation at the conformer level. In addition to the decrease in conformational entropy of the dynamic chain system, the reduction in entropy by increased packing must be considered through a cooperativity model such as discussed in Chapter 2.

It was shown in Table 2.2 that a conformer at the end of a chain is at a considerably higher energy level than a similar conformer in the interior of the chain. The chain end can be alternatively described as having a "larger free volume." For a linear polymer, the decrease of the glass transition temperature with lowering of the molecular weight is quantitatively attributed to the increase in the number of chain ends for a given mass. In this vein, we can say that every time an epoxide reacts with a phenol, a certain amount of free volume is lost, and T_g rises incrementally. The loss in the enthalpy ΔH_c per conformer from before to after the reaction at reaction temperature T_r is obtained:

$$\Delta H_c = T_r \, \Delta S_c \left[\frac{\Delta C_p}{\Delta \alpha} \right]_{T_r} \tag{6.1.3}$$

per mole of the conformer, where ΔV is the volume shrinkage due to the reaction. Starting with the unreacted mixture of epoxides and hardener molecules, assuming an initial glass transition temperature of T_{g0}, the volume, entropy, and enthalpy will decrease as the fraction of reacted conformers increases. The glass transition temperature increases in the process. We term this particular glass transition temperature T_{gu}; the "u"

stands for the equivalent of the linear polymer in which all conformers are *un*restricted and free to rotate. Later on, we will add another factor attributable to the cessation of the allowed freedom when a conformer is restricted by the three links. At this point we consider only the loss of energy due to the formation of one linkage. When the fraction ξ has reacted, we obtain for the difference in the enthalpy :

$$\xi\Delta H = T_r\Delta S_c = T_r\int_{T_{g0}}^{T_r} \frac{\Delta C_p}{T}\, dT - T_r\int_{T_{gu}}^{T_r} \frac{\Delta C_p}{T}\, dT$$

$$= T_r\Delta C_p\left[\ln\frac{T_r}{T_{g0}} - \ln\frac{T_r}{T_{gu}}\right] \approx T_r\Delta C_p\left[\frac{T_{gu} - T_{g0}}{T_{g0}}\right] \tag{6.1.4}$$

and

$$\xi\Delta H \approx T_r T_{gu}\Delta C_p\left[\frac{1}{T_{g0}} - \frac{1}{T_{gu}}\right] \tag{6.1.5}$$

In the equation above, the entropy decreases in the crosslinked rubber network. (Equation 6.1.2 with increasing M is ignored for the time being.) The effect of crosslinking on long-range conformational entropy for dynamic chains will be dealt with subsequently. At present, we continue by assuming that the specific heat and the thermal expansion coefficient remain independent of the crosslinking density by calling this enthalpy "the enthalpy that is normalized against the various degrees of crosslinking." At any rate, we are dealing with the "free volume" type of contribution to the enthalpy.

Hale and coworkers[2] have derived the empirical expression based on the free volume type of model by Fox and Flory[3] and as modified by the "hole energy" theory by Uebberreiter and Kanig,[4]

2. Hale, A., Macosko, C. W., and Bair, H. E., *Macromolecules,* **24,** 2610 (1991).
3. Fox, T. G., and Flory, P.J., *J. Appl. Phys.* **21,** 581 (1950).
4. Uebberreiter, K., and Kanig, G., *J. Colloid Sci.* **7,** 569 (1952).

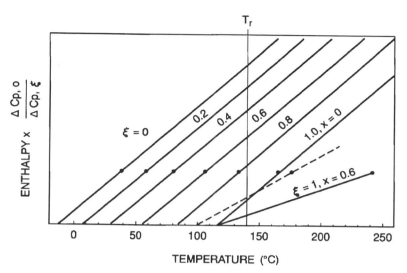

Figure 6.1.2 Normalized (by eliminating the crosslink dependence of ΔC_p) conformational enthalpy vs. temperature according to Equation 6.1.5. The dashed line is for an intermediate state between $\xi = 0.8$ and 1 (e.g., $\xi = 0.9$ and $X = 0.3$.

$$\frac{1}{T_{gu}} = \frac{1}{305.8} - 9.513 \times 10^{-4}\xi \tag{6.1.6}$$

which is identical in form to Equation 6.1.5. Substituting these empirical constants into Equation 6.1.5. Assuming 0.1 cal/gK and T_r for ΔC_p and 400 K for both T_{gu} and T_r, we obtain 15.2 cal/g for ΔH_c. This value is favorably compared to the difference of 19 cal/g between the heat of fusion of the phenyl group and that of p-phenylene group included in Table 2.2. For $\xi = 1$, T_{gu} of 431 K or 158 °C is obtained from Equation 6.1.6 above. For the cresol novolac, if we count two cresol groups and one -CH_2- group between them as two conformers, we obtain the average molecular weight of 97 for one conformer, from which T_0 of 117 °C or T_g of 167 °C is obtained. A phenol in place of a cresol will result in T_{gu} of 150 °C.

Using of 37 °C for the unreacted T_{g0}, and 167 °C for the completely reacted T_{gu} (for $\xi = 1$), the coefficient 9.5×10^{-4} is obtained. Using the "universal" value of 50 °C for $T_g - T_0$, the "normalized" enthalpy vs. temperature curve is obtained, as shown in Figure 6.1.2.

The glass transition temperature is defined by the isorelaxation time

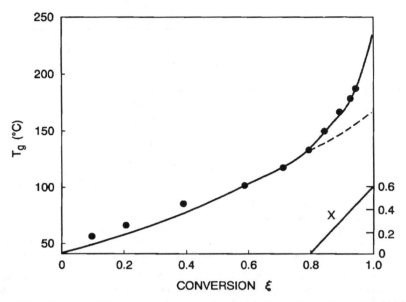

Figure 6.1.3 Glass transition temperature vs. the extent of reaction or "conversion." Lines are calculated as described in the text. The dashed line is for T_{gu}, neglecting the "pinning" of the conformers, and T_{gu} of 167 °C at $\xi = 1$ corresponds to the glass transition temperature of a linear polymer with the average conformer size equal to the that of cresol novolac conformer. (Data by H. E. Bair, *AT&T Bell Laboratories*.)

criterion such that, according to the Adam-Gibbs formula, it is the isoconformational enthalpy point. Accordingly, T_{gu} shifts from 37 °C to 58, 80, 106, 134, and 167 °C for ξ of 0, 0.2, 0.4, 0.6, 0.8, and 1, respectively. As we have emphasized, only the enthalpy decrease that is directly connected with the loss of the unreacted (end) group is accounted for. We have not accounted for the permanent loss of freedom for the rotational relaxation for the conformers that were initially in the interior of the original unreacted oligomer. For the system under consideration, the cresol and phenolic novolac oligomers are assumed to be five conformers each, including two in the end. If and when the reaction is carried to completion, 40% of all conformers remain free to rotate, but for the 60% an additional loss of enthalpy must be accounted for. With this ratio of end groups to the interior groups, all the conformers including the interior ones remain free to rotate until 80% of the reaction is completed. This is because, as long as one of the

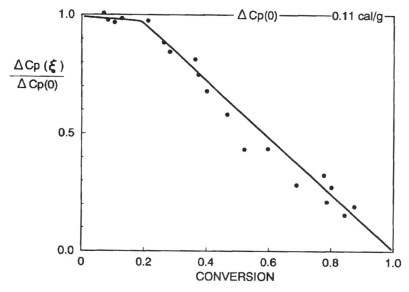

Figure 6.1.4 C_p vs. ξ for the cresol-novolac system with phenolic novolac as hardener.

conformers at either side of the link is not "locked," that particular link is able to rotate. Thus, if we define the mole fraction of conformers that are locked by three-way links as X, X is 0 at $\xi \leq 0.8$, and for $\xi > 0.8$, X increases linearly with ξ, to the final value of 0.6 at $\xi = 1$. Incorporation of this aspect of the enthalpy change will result in the final T_g of 241 °C for 100% conversion, as shown in Figure 6.1.2. In the range of ξ from 0.8 to 1, T_g is greater than T_{gu}. This is because of the "pinning" of the conformers to prevent rotational relaxation. In the range of $\xi < 0.8$, all conformers are able to rotate and, therefore, T_g is equal to T_{gu}. The calculated values of T_g are summarized in Figure 6.1.3. The rapid rise of T_g for $\xi > 0.8$ is due to this pinning of the conformers. This occurs at about the point where the glass transition temperature has reached the reaction temperature, when the reaction rate becomes controlled by the relaxation time of the polymer. T_g is dependent on the extent of the reaction ξ, but not on T_r.

The enthalpy in Figure 6.1.2 was calculated by neglecting the decrease of the long-range conformational entropy in the equilibrium ($> T_g$) state. As a result, the slopes of these curves are independent of the extent of reaction

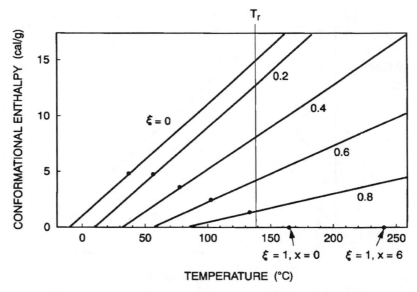

Figure 6.1.5 True conformational enthalpy vs. temperature, obtained from Figure 6.1.2 by modifying the specific heat, which depends on the amount of crosslinking.

ξ. We shall now make the correction by considering the reduction of the equilibrium entropy in the rubbery state solely from the partial loss of the conformational probability of the chain molecules by the increasing crosslinking points.

From Equation 6.1.2, for the change in the equilibrium modulus ΔG_e when the reaction has been extended by $\Delta\xi$, we obtain:

$$\frac{\Delta G_e}{G_e} = \frac{\Delta\xi}{\xi}$$

or

$$\Delta\ln G_e \mid_T = \Delta\ln\xi \mid_T \tag{6.1.7}$$

If we assume that the glassy modulus is independent of ξ, then the amplitude of relaxation $\ln G_g - \ln G_e$ is equal to $\Delta \ \tilde{} \ \ln \ \tilde{} \ \xi$. Since G_e is proportional to the enthalpy, ΔC_p should decrease proportionately with ξ after the gel point. Before the gel point, G_e is zero and ΔC_p is independent of ξ. Experimental data for the dependence of ΔC_p on the conversion ξ appear in Figure 6.1.4.

ΔC_p remains constant at 0.11 cal/g until ξ is 0.2. This value has been used to support the validity of Equation 6.1.5, in the foregoing discussion.

When ξ exceeds 0.2, ΔC_p decreases linearly with ξ toward zero at $\xi = 1$. By multiplying the "normalized" enthalpy in Figure 6.1.2 by $\Delta C_p(\xi)/\Delta C_p(0)$ from Figure 6.1.4, the true conformational enthalpy can be obtained, and the result is shown in Figure 6.1.5.

The rationale for this step is that the crosslinking-induced decrease in conformational enthalpy above T_g can be used as the scaling factor for all enthalpy values, since the crosslinked network in the rubbery state is the basic state from which further thermodynamic quantities are to be calculated. Everything including the "hole energy" and the fractional free volume becomes proportionately smaller with the smaller enthalpy and ΔC_p at a higher ξ. The critical enthalpy for the glass transition (isorelaxation time) is no longer constant but is a decreasing function of ξ. The fractional free volume diagram should show the same features displayed by this enthalpy diagram. As shown in Figure 6.1.6, $\Delta \alpha = \alpha_l - \alpha_g$ decreases proportionately with ξ as did ΔC_p.[5]

The quantity α_f or the coefficient of thermal expansion for the Doolittle free volume is really a parameter to describe the temperature dependence of relaxation time, and it is equal to the reciprocal of $\Delta \mu^*/k$, which is the activation energy for the rotation of the bond between conformers. Experimentally it turns out to be very sensitive to the conversion ξ, whereas for linear polymers it is nearly constant among many species, as shown in Chapter 2. $\Delta \mu^*$ decreases with ξ more than does $\Delta \alpha$. The WLF parameter c_2^g is really $T_g - T_0$ in the Vogel-Fulcher equation, and it increases when X increases as shown by the dashed line in Figure 6.1.2. Kinjo et al[6] have reported $c_2^g \approx 80$ as compared to the "universal" value of 50 °C. This greater value is easily understood by the dashed line for which T_0 remains the same as the conformer size is unchanged but T_g increases because more

5. Kinjo, N., Ogata, M., Nishi, K., and Kaneda, A., *Advances in Polymer Science*, Vol. 88, Springer-Verlag, Berlin, (1981) p. 1.
6. Kinjo, N. et al., *Kobunshi Ronbunshu*, **46** (7), 413 (1989).

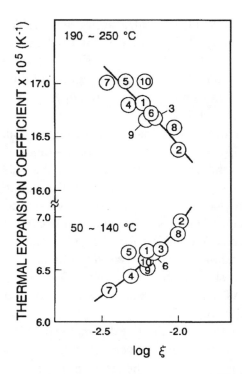

Figure 6.1.6 Linear thermal expansion coefficients below and above the respective glass transition temperatures vs. degree of crosslinking. More crosslinking results in a smaller change in the thermal expansion coefficient at the transition. The numbers indicate the different chemical structures (see note 6).

conformers are becoming pinned by the three bonds, expressed by the parameter X. Any state in which X is greater than 0 and ξ that exceeds 0.8 means an additional decrease in ΔC_p and α_f and a decrease in c_2^g. All Kinjo's data are for $\xi > 0.8$ and they fall in this category.

The volume vs. temperature data for two of Kinjo's samples are plotted in Figure 6.1.7. Both were reacted beyond 80%. The greater conversion means a higher T_g but a lower density in the glassy state. This comes about because the volume shrinkage in the rubbery state is the scaling factor for ξ, as it was for the enthalpy, and the whole specific volume curve is shifted down for a greater ξ, as represented by arrows from the uncorrected volume curve indicated by the dashed line, which should be compared to the enthalpy diagram in Figure 6.1.2.

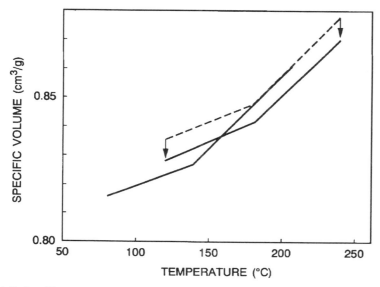

Figure 6.1.7 Specific volume vs. temperature for samples with two different degrees of cure (solid lines) and the uncorrected or "normalized" volume, which disregards the entropy decrease in the rubbery state.

The combination of all thermodynamic factors affects the end result that the more highly crosslinked glassy state is more porous. In epoxy systems, this brings out a serious moisture problem. More moisture can be absorbed in the higher T_g material, and excessive moisture in a molded package may exit with explosive force when the item is heated suddenly.

The kinetics of the curing reaction, or the time dependence of ξ at constant temperature, can be traced by the drop in the normalized enthalpy in Figure 6.1.2 with time at, e.g., 140 °C. In the early stages of reaction, the rate is virtually totally controlled by the choice of accelerator. Typical values for commercial compounds are 20 seconds for the gel time at 20% conversion at 150 °C, with an activation energy of 16 kcal/mol. As the reaction progresses further, the enthalpy decreases and T_g increases and, by the time T_g nears the reaction temperature T_r, the reaction rate will have slowed down as a result of the increasing difficulty of mating a pair of reactable conformers in juxtaposition. This is similar to the conformational relaxation observed during physical aging, discussed in Chapter 3. The time

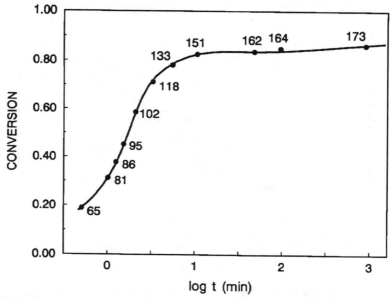

Figure 6.1.8 Conversion vs. log time for novolac epoxy resin. The numerals are the glass transition temperature (in °C) at each point of the crosslinking reaction.

"constant" (though it becomes longer progressively with the reaction) $t*$ for the enthalpic relaxation is obtained by the equation:

$$t* \approx \lambda_c \frac{\Delta\mu*}{kT_r S_c} \qquad (6.1.8)$$

where λ_c is the characteristic (e.g., dielectric) relaxation time and TS_c is equal to the normalized enthalpy. The entropy is proportional to $1 - \xi$ for less than 80% conversion, while it is proportional to $3.4 - 4\xi$ if more than 80% conversion. T_g can be evaluated as a function of time and substituted in the formula:

$$t* \approx \lambda_c \frac{\Delta\mu*}{k(T_r - T_g + 50)}$$

while λ_c depends on the current T_g, which depends on ξ. The extent of reaction is shown against the time in Figure 6.1.8.

When T_g is about equal to the reaction temperature, the process becomes controlled by the ongoing relaxation time as in the physical aging of a glassy polymer. The kinetics of this process has been published[7] and programmed in BASIC, and is included in Chapter 7.

6.2 Failure in Plastics

6.2.1 Polymers Above T_g

Fracture involves the formation and propagation of microcracks. The product of a crack length and the energy density ahead of the crack determines the instability of the crack tip and, when this product exceeds a critical value, the crack propagates.[8] In the case of a viscoelastic material, the energy density ahead of the crack tends to dissipate through relaxation while the continued application of force tends to accumulate it.

The subject of failure mechanisms is complex and even confusing, but there is a certain material aspect that is clearly related to the relaxation process. One of the most thorough studies carried out on the time-dependent fracture properties of polymers is the work of T. L. Smith[9] on crosslinked polymers above T_g. A series of stress-strain curves was obtained at various rates of strain and temperatures. Typical results are shown schematically in Figure 6.2.1. The slope of the curves increases with increasing rate of strain or with decreasing temperature. If the stress is kept at D in Figure 6.2.1, creep occurs toward the equilibrium strain at F,D, the stress continues to relax toward another equilibrium state E. Smith and coworkers found the consistent relationship among the states represented by D, E, and F through a combination of neo-Hookeian elasticity and linear viscoelasticity, with the applicability of the time-temperature superposition through the WLF or Vogel-Fulcher formula with nearly universal coefficients. At a higher stress level G, the creep meets rupture after reaching the failure envelope. Similarly, if the strain is kept constant at G, delayed rupture occurs when the stress reaches the failure envelope, even

7. Matsuoka, S., Quan, X., Bair, H. E., and Boyle, D. J., *Macromolecules,* **22**, 4093 (1989).
8. Bueche, F., and Halpin, J. C., *J. Appl. Phys.* **35**, 36 (1964).
9. Smith, T. L., *Polym. Eng. Sci.* **17**, 129 (1977).

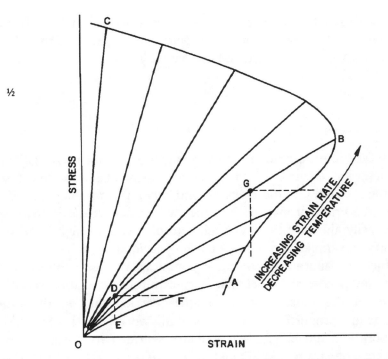

Figure 6.2.1 Stress-strain curves for a crosslinked polymer obtained at various rates of strain and/or temperatures. The curves terminate at the failure envelope. The stress at point B is about 10^7 dynes/cm^2, and the strain about 6.

though the macroscopic stress at rupture is less than the initial stress level. Smith found that time-temperature superposition can be used to obtain the master curve for fracture behavior. At very high strain levels, or at very low temperatures though still above T_g, the break occurs at high stress levels and small strains. The curve at the slowest strain rate, which passes points O, E, F, and A of Figure 6.2.1 is the stress-strain curve at the equilibrium condition representing the deformation of the completely relaxed network state. If it had not ruptured at A, the stress-strain curve would have followed the inverse Langevin equation described by Equation 4.2.16 or the experimental curve for a crosslinked rubber sample that is able to stretch, as shown in Figure 6.2.2. The Langevin equation, Equation 4.2.16', can be written with variables related to the molecular scale:

$$\frac{<r_x>}{\hat{n}l} = \mathbf{L}\left[\frac{Fl}{kT}\right] \tag{6.2.1}$$

where $\hat{n}$ is the number of conformers that make up a strand of a polymer chain between two crosslink points, F is the force per strand, and $<r_x>$ is the increase in the end-to-end distance of the strand.

For 1 cm^3 of a polymer, the number of strands equals the number of conformers per cubic centimeter $(= \rho N_A/M_0)$ divided by the number of "beads" per strand $\hat{n}$, and it is equal to the number of crosslink points per cubic centimeter $(= \nu_c)$. The strain in 1 cm^3 of polymer is:

$$\frac{\rho N_A}{M_0} \frac{<r_x>}{\hat{n}^{1/2} <\hat{n}l^2>^{1/2}} = \nu^{1/2} \frac{<r_x>}{<\hat{n}l^2>^{1/2}} = \frac{\rho N_A}{M_0} \mathbf{L}\left[\frac{Fl}{kT}\right] \tag{6.2.2}$$

where ρ is the density, M_0 is the molecular weight of the conformer ("bead"), and N_A is Avogadro's number. When the force F is increased, so is the strain. The slope $dF/d<r_x>$ increases, eventually reaching infinity as the strand becomes completely extended, and the left hand term in Equation 6.2.1 reaches 1. All strands will break before then, no matter how strong. The ultimate strain ε_u is inversely proportional to the square root of the crosslink density per unit volume:

$$\frac{\varepsilon_u}{\varepsilon_{u,r}} = \left(\frac{\nu_c}{\nu_{c,r}}\right)^{-1/2} \tag{6.2.3}$$

where the subscript r refers to a reference degree of crosslinking. The equilibrium stress-strain curves are thus compressed horizontally by the scaling factor $\nu_c^{-1/2}$.

As shown in Figure 6.2.1, however, a viscoelastic polymer breaks prematurely well before attaining the ultimate strain ε_u; how prematurely the break occurs depends on the rate of strain or the time of creep-relaxation. For example, when an extremely slow rate of strain is applied such that the equilibrium stress-strain condition is closely followed, the polymer typically breaks at a strain that is a fraction of ε_u. Under very slow strain rates, the molecular strands relax, shifting the burden of load onto a smaller number of strands. This increases the load on the remaining few active strands, and a premature break takes place. The fraction of the load-bearing strands decreases with time in proportion to the relaxation modulus, such that the

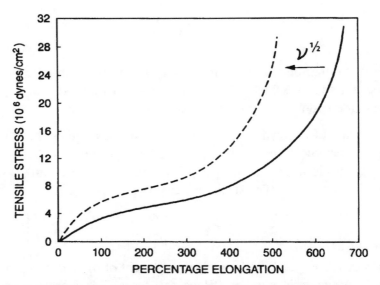

Figure 6.2.2   Stress vs. strain for rubber (solid curve, shown previously in Figure 4.5.6), has the characteristics of the inverse Langevin equation.

effective crosslink density v_{eff} is given by the relation:

$$\frac{\nu_{\text{eff}}}{\nu_c} = \frac{E(t)}{E(0)} \tag{6.2.4}$$

If we assume the power law for the relaxation modulus $E(t) \sim t^{-n}$, the effective crosslink density at $\dot{\varepsilon}$ scales with the ratio:

$$\left(\frac{\nu_{\text{eff}}}{\nu_{\text{eff},r}}\right)^{-1/2} = \left(\frac{\dot{\varepsilon}}{\dot{\varepsilon}_r}\right)^{-n/2} \tag{6.2.5}$$

where r refers to the reference rate of strain $\dot{\varepsilon}_r$. The principle of an isochronal correspondence of states is found to work among the stress and strain at break as well. This means that scaling rule 1 in Section 3.3.5 can be invoked for the stress *before* compressing the stress-strain curve horizontally with $\nu^{-1/2}$. The stress can be scaled by the strain rates:

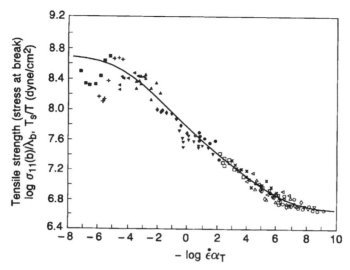

Figure 6.2.3 Log stress at break vs. the negative log strain rate exhibits the slope of 1/8 as predicted by Equation 6.2.6.

$$\frac{\sigma_b}{\sigma_{b,r}} = \left(\frac{\dot{\varepsilon}}{\dot{\varepsilon_r}}\right)^{n^2/2} \qquad (6.2.6)$$

Since $n = 0.5$ at the transition zone, the stress at break is proportional to the 1/8 power of the strain rates. This prediction is supported by the data in Figure 6.2.3, in which the change of 1 decade for the stress takes place over the 8 decades of change in the strain rate.

The fracture does not occur at the same strain for the different strain rates either. If we assume the power law for creep strain with exponent m, the strain at break ε_b can be scaled from the isochronal corresponding state, by the strain rates:

$$\frac{\varepsilon_b}{\varepsilon_{b,r}} = \left(\frac{\dot{\varepsilon}}{\dot{\varepsilon_r}}\right)^{mn/2} \qquad (6.2.7)$$

Since m is 0.33 for the transition zone, as discussed in Chapter 3, the strain at break depends on the 0.08 power of the strain rate. Smith's data are replotted on a log-log scale in Figure 6.2.4, and the predicted slope of 0.08 is in reasonable agreement with the data on the slower (longer time) side of the maximum strain.

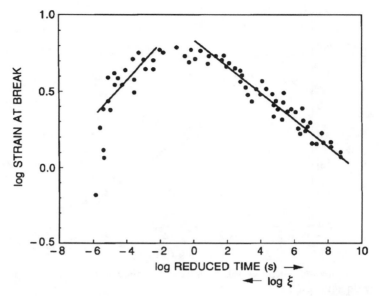

Figure 6.2.4 Log strain at break vs. negative log strain rate (or positive log time), exhibiting slopes of 0.08 on the slow side and 0.125 on the fast side from the peak strain value at 0.

On the fast side from the maximum strain, the slope reverses its sign i.e., the faster strain rate causes it to break at a smaller elongation. The stress at break, on the other hand, does not go through a maximum but continues to increase with the same slope with the value of ca. 0.125. (For $\log \dot{\varepsilon} > 6$, the scatter becomes too great and should be disregarded.) The slope for the log strain is thus opposite in sign but equal in magnitude to the slope for the log stress. It means that the product of the stress and strain at break, or the strain energy, is constant, and is independent of strain rates or the temperature.

$$\Psi = \sigma_b \varepsilon_b = \text{constant} \tag{6.2.8}$$

This relationship is found to hold below the glass transition temperature also, as discussed below.

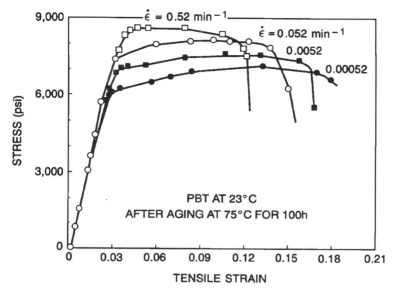

Figure 6.2.5 Stress-strain curves of polybutylene terephthalate below the glass transition temperature.

6.2.2 Polymer Solids

The strain energy criterion stated by Equation 6.2.8 apparently holds for some glassy and crystalline polymers. An example is shown with polybutylene terephthalate (PBT) in Figure 6.2.5.

The order of magnitude of elongation at break in glassy polymers is 10%, compared to 100% in the rubbery polymers. The energy at break is about 7.4×10^7 ergs/cm^3, which is about that of the rubbery polymers.

Since yield stress can be scaled by strain rate, temperature, and physical aging, as discussed in Section 3.3.5, the elongation at break also can be scaled following the energy criteria stated by Equation 6.2.8. The scaling scheme has been incorporated in a computer program for predicting various mechanical properties of polymers (see Chapter 7).

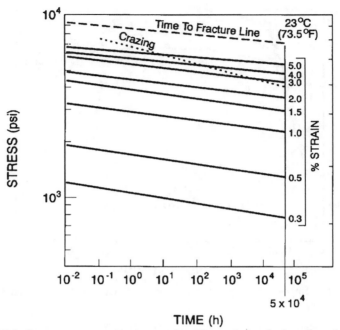

Figure 6.2.6 Stress vs. creep time to reach each strain level plotted on log-log scale. The slope is *m* for the creep compliance, which follows the power law. The slope for the craze formation is about twice as large as *m*, as discussed in the text.

6.2.3 Crazing and Stress Cracking

The notion of the strain energy as the controlling factor for time-dependent failure in solid polymers can be extended to predict the time for craze formation under creep (constant stress) conditions. Under a constant stress, the effective number of load-carrying strands decreases in proportion to the relaxation modulus. If the creep function and the relaxation function are both expressed by the power law, with exponents *m* and *n*, respectively, then the strength decreases faster than either the relaxation modulus or the creep modulus (= 1/creep compliance):

$$\Psi(t) = \Psi_0 \left(\frac{t}{t_0} \right)^{-(m+n)} \tag{6.2.9}$$

such that the slope of the log stress vs. log time to craze would be about twice that of *n* or *m*, as supported by experimental data in Figure 6.2.6 for polycarbonate. (This curve is a plot of the stress and time at which the craze appeared.)

Thus it is possible to predict a delayed craze formation time that may take months or years on the basis of a short time experiment conducted at a relatively high stress level through the scaling scheme. This scheme is also applicable to the prediction of craze formation in hostile environments, in which case the critical energy is reduced and the time to craze is shifted to the shorter time. Similarly, this scheme is found to work in predicting the stress cracking time from an accelerated test near but below the yield stress, preferably under multiaxial loading to suppress uniaxial elongation, which dissipates the strain energy easily. The stress cracking time in air is fairly accurately predicted for polyethylene from the yield stress and ultimate elongation. The latter is dependent on the molecular weight. When the molecular weight is below the critical value M_c for entanglement, the polymer breaks without delay. Cracking time improves progressively with increasing molecular weight.

6.2.4 Impact Strength and the Brittle-Ductile Transition Temperature

The ability to withstand a sudden application of a highly concentrated stress makes many polymers suitable materials for mechanical parts that require high impact strength. The impact strength of a material deteriorates at low temperatures. Low molecular weight as a result of chemical degradation also results in poor impact strength. The notched Izod test is a well-known engineering test in which a notched specimen serves for the stress concentration feature. A pendulum swings from a specified height to strike at the sample, cantilevered at the bottom of the path of the striking head, and the loss of kinetic energy after breaking the sample is recorded. This test obviously includes too many coupled variables to permit a clear and simple analysis, and comparing the "energy" thus measured among generically different polymers may result in misleading conclusions.

We have found, however, that a set of reproducible and sensible data can be obtained if one modifyies the apparatus to measure the dynamic force as experienced each moment by the striking head, and incorporates the possibility for a wide range of variables in temperature, speed, notch radius, sample thickness, high speed photoelastic photography, and scanning microscopic examination of the fractured surface. On the materials side, 23

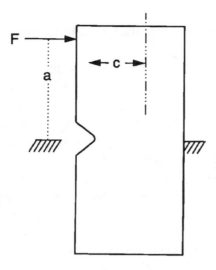

Figure 6.2.7 Schematic diagram for
the notched Izod test. Dimensions
are not to the scale.

generic polymers of varying molecular weight, sometimes with fillers and
plasticizers and impact modifiers, have been tested.

The basic configuration of the sample geometry for Izod test is shown
schematically in Figure 6.2.7. The stress in this cantilever sample is tensile,
tending to pull apart at the valley of the notch, where the stress can be
substantially higher than the "nominal" stress. The nominal stress term σ_n is
used to calculate the theoretical stress at the bottom of the notch if there
were no stress concentration effect. The nominal stress then is the stress in a
cantilever with a beam depth of the actual sample minus the depth of notch.
The nominal stress is given by the formula:

$$\sigma_n = \frac{3a}{2bc^2}F \tag{6.2.10}$$

where b is the thickness, I is the moment of area of the cantilever beam, and
c is the distance from the bottom of the notch to the neutral axis. The
question of where to place the neutral axis is difficult but essential if the true
stress concentration factor is to be evaluated. Without the effect from the
notch, the neutral axis would be near the center between the notch and to
the back surface, since the uniaxial compressive modulus is only 5% greater

than the tensile modulus, as discussed in Chapter 3. However, the presence of the notch causes for neutral axis to shift extremely far toward the back, since the tensile failure initiated in the front is so much easier to compress at the other side. From a number of high speed photoelastic photographs and from examination of the fractured surface, we concluded that the neutral axis is close to the surface opposite the blow, only 0.02 inch away, for a specimen 0.4 inch deep. This "hinging effect" at the opposite surface is found to be true when the sample breaks, but if the sample does not break and the striking hammer bounces back, the neutral axis is near the center. For the dimensions of $a = 0.8$, $b = 0.125$, and $c = 0.4$ inch, the nominal stress of

$$\sigma_n \approx 60\,F \qquad (6.2.11)$$

is obtained with the strain rate of

$$\frac{d\varepsilon}{dt} = \frac{3c}{a^2} \qquad (6.2.12)$$

where x is the distance of travel by the striking head from the point of contact with the specimen. For polycarbonate at 25 °C, for example, $F = 80$ lb was measured at $dx/dt = 11.4$ ft/s, or $\dot{\varepsilon} = 1.5 \times 10^4$ in./in./min. The nominal stress in this case, then, is 4800 psi. However, the stress that this polycarbonate sample can withstand at this strain rate can be calculated from the scaling scheme described in Chapter 3, i.e.,

$$\sigma^* = \sigma^* \mid_{5\%/min} \left(\frac{\dot{\varepsilon}}{0.05} \right)^n \qquad (6.2.13)$$

and for $n = 0.03$, the strength is 12,700 psi. The ratio of σ^* to σ_n is the stress concentration factor K_b, which in this case has been evaluated at 2.65 for a notch radius r of 10 mils.

The original definition of the stress concentration factor was introduced by Inglis[10] in 1913 for the notch of depth $2d$ and radius of r:

---

10. Inglis, S,, *Trans. Inst. Naval Arch.* **55**, 219 (1913).

$$K_b = \frac{\sigma^*}{\sigma_n} = \left[1 + \frac{2\sqrt{d}}{\sqrt{r}} \right] \qquad (6.2.14)$$

and later the coefficient 2 was changed by a number of researchers to range widely between 2 and 0.5. A smaller number is indicative of the blunting of the tip radius due to the plastic or other energy-dissipating deformation. Our example of polycarbonate with $K_b = 2.65$ for the notch radius $r = 10$ means $2\sqrt{d} = 5.22$, or the effective depth of notch $2d = 13.6$ mils. Actually this value is fairly constant against the variation in r from 5 to 30 mils, as shown with data below. The notch radius of 30 mils results in K_b of nearly unity, and the test is equivalent of no notch.

The molecular weight of the polymer is an important factor. A sample with low molecular weight may fail with little or no impact strength while the same generic polymer with higher molecular weight may exhibit a respectable impact strength. The threshold depends on the number of effective strands v_{eff}, according to the concept applied to the understanding of the strength of crosslinked polymers in the preceeding section. For a linear polymer with no crosslinks, the points of entanglement act as temporary crosslinking points. Since the terminal relaxation time may be months or years, strands the size of the "blob" can be considered to be permanent where fracture strength is concerned. When the molecular weight is less than the critical molecular weight M_c for entanglement (see Table 4.1), which is the size of the blob, the temporary crosslink is zero. Thus the effective crosslink density is:

$$\nu_{\text{eff}} = \frac{M}{M_c} \qquad (6.2.15)$$

and the breaking stress is proportional to the square root of v_{eff}. Since the melt viscosity depends on $M^{3.4}$, the stress σ_b can be calculated by the previously introduced scaling factor:

$$\frac{\sigma_b}{\sigma_{b,r}} = \left[\frac{M/M_c}{M_r/M_c} \right]^{1/2} = \left[\left(\frac{\eta}{\eta_r} \right)^{1/2.4} \right]^{1/2} \approx \left[\frac{\eta}{\eta_r} \right]^{1/5} \qquad (6.2.16)$$

where η is the melt viscosity measured in the linear viscoelastic range, and the subscript r refers to a standard benchmark polymer sample of known molecular weight and viscosity. The melt flow rate (MFR) test devised by the American Society for Testing and Materials (ASTM) is applied to

Table 6.1 Impact Properties of
Injection-Molded Polycarbonates:
Notched Izod Specimens

Ductile-Brittle Transition Temperature (°C)					
Notch radius(mils)	5	10	15	20	30
MFR					
.8	-56	-76	-85	-90	-97
2.4	-28	-53	-64	-71	-79
3.2	-19	-46	-58	-65	-73
4	-12	-40	-53	-60	-69
4.8	-6	-37	-48	-56	-65
6	2	-29	-43	-51	-60
8	13	-21	-35	-44	-54
12	30	-8	-24	-33	-44
16	30	2	-15	-25	-37
32	30	30	9	-2	-16

Table 6.2 After annealing
at 125 °C for 10 hours

Ductile-Brittle Transition Temperature (°C)					
Notch radius(mils)	5	10	15	20	30
MFR					
.8	-28	-53	-64	-71	-79
2.4	8	-24	-38	-47	-56
3.2	20	-16	-31	-39	-50
4	29	-8	-24	-33	-44
4.8	30	-2	-19	-28	-40
6	30	6	-11	-22	-34
8	30	17	-2	-13	-25
12	30	30	14	1	-13
16	30	30	25	12	-3
32	30	30	30	30	24

30 °C has been set as the upper limit of brittleness temperature.

polymer samples. It is essentially inversely proportional to the viscosity, and we have found about 3.5 to fourth-power dependence on the molecular weight. The experimental data on the brittleness temperature for polycarbonate are shown in Figure 6.2.8. The line is the calculated cure for the 10-mil notch.

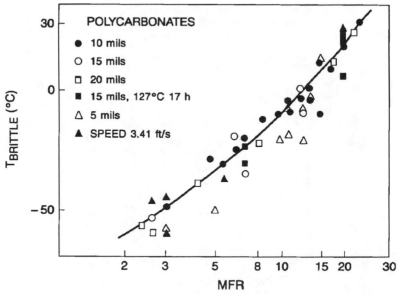

Figure 6.2.8 Brittle-to-ductile transition temperature vs. melt flow rate (MFR) for polycarbonate.

The stress for the corresponding states between two different strain rates or temperatures is given by the formula:

$$\frac{\sigma}{\sigma_r} = \left(\frac{\dot{\varepsilon}}{\dot{\varepsilon}_r}\right)^n = \exp\left[\frac{nH}{R}\left(\frac{1}{T} - \frac{1}{T_r}\right)\right] \qquad (6.2.17)$$

and the apparent activation energy H for the relaxation process is:

$$H = \frac{\Delta\mu^* \, T_g}{(T_g - T_0)} \approx \frac{\Delta\mu^* \, T_g}{50} \qquad (6.2.18)$$

from which 30 kcal/mol is obtained for polycarbonate with T_g of 420 K. Thus the temperature at which a polymer turns brittle can be calculated by scaling the brittle temperature T_b by combining the equations above. For the reciprocal of viscosity, the above mentioned melt flow rate can be substituted. The computer program in Chapter 7 was used to calculate the examples that follow and to generate the data in Tables 6.1 and 6.2.

The effect of physical aging has been incorporated in the computer program, invoking the related scaling formula given in Chapter 3. The example below is for polycarbonate that has been annealed at 125 °C for 10 hours. Physical aging can have a devastating effect at times, although this result is often mistakenly attributed to chemical degradation. These two causes can be sorted out by measuring the melt viscosities before and after molding. Finally, the effect of chemical degradation can also be calculated from the change in the molecular weight:

$$\frac{M}{M_r} = \frac{t}{t_r} \exp\left[-\frac{H_c}{R}\left(\frac{1}{T} - \frac{1}{T_r} \right) \right] \qquad (6.2.19)$$

Starting with one piece of experimental data conducted for the reference material under a reference condition referred to by the subscript r, the molecular weight of the degraded sample can be calculated, and its value is substituted to calculate the brittle temperature. The value of H_c in many degradative reactions typically is 13 to 18 kcal/mol, regardless of the type of reaction, because it corresponds to the strength of chemical bonds in the polymer main chain. Only the "front factor" varies and must be determined experimentally.

6.3 Polymer Solutions

Relaxation of polymer molecules in a concentrated solution is only a minor departure from that in the melt, in that the smaller number of strands per cubic centimeter causes the modulus to be lower, and the presence of solvent molecules causes the friction coefficient to be reduced and the relaxation time to be shorter. Intermolecular cooperativity is still an important factor, and entropy decreases rapidly when the temperature is lowered, as it does in the condensed state. The relaxation time shifts with the temperature following the familiar Vogel-Fulcher and WLF equations, with an additional parameter related to the increase in free volume by the solvent molecules.[11]

The molecular picture for the dilute solution is very different. The polymer molecules are dispersed as isolated coils, rather than as part of a continuum with uniform concentration. The true concentration within the polymer coil is determined by the expanding tendency of the polymer

---

11. Fujita, H., Kishimoto, A., and Matsumoto, K., *Trans. Faraday Soc.* **56**, 424 (1960).

molecule to increase the entropy and the contracting tendency to reduce the enthalpy, the latter tendency being prevalent in a poor solvent, which polymer conformers dislike. Individual conformers are surrounded by solvent molecules rather than by other conformers of the same kind as in the condensed state. A conformer is free from its neighbor conformers, and the segments can rotate one at a time, with the activation energy barrier $\Delta\mu$ of 4 kcal.

When a dilute solution is made to flow, the kinetic energy of the surrounding solvent is transferred to the polymer coils by frictional force. The efficiency of the transfer of momentum is measured by the difference in velocity between the solvent and the polymer. Although many solvent molecules are inside the coil, these solvent molecules are "trapped" within the coil and they move along with the coil rather than with the flowing solvent outside the cage.

Stokes' formula for the frictional flow of a sphere in a flowing media is:

$$\frac{F}{u} = 6\pi\eta_0 R_e \qquad (6.3.1)$$

where F is the frictional force, u the *relative* velocity, η_0 the viscosity of the flowing media or the solvent in our case, and R_e the radius of a sphere, which, in our case, is the hydrodynamic radius of the polymer coil. The molecular frictional coefficient is, according to the Einstein velocity relation,

$$\frac{\eta - \eta_0}{\eta_0} = 2.5\frac{N_c}{V}V_e \qquad (6.3.2)$$

where N_c/V is the number of polymer molecules per unit volume, V_e is the hydrodynamic volume, and $V_e = 4\frac{\pi}{3}R_e^3$. The number of molecules per unit volume is proportional to the concentration c in grams per unit volume but inversely proportional to the molecular weight M, and we obtain:

$$\frac{\eta - \eta_0}{\eta_0} = 2.5\frac{cN_A}{M}V_e = 10.5\frac{cN_A R_e^3}{M} \qquad (6.3.3)$$

where N_A is Avogadro's number. The intrinsic viscosity $[\eta]$ is thus defined as the slope of the plot of relative viscosity against concentration. Assuming that the molecular volume is proportional to the hydrodynamic volume, we obtain:

$$[\eta] = \Phi \frac{<r^2>^{3/2}}{M} \tag{6.3.4}$$

where Φ is the Flory constant, having an experimental value of about 2.1×10^{23}. This means that R_e is about one-third of the rms end-to-end distance of the molecule. Since the radius of gyration is $1/\sqrt{6}$ of the end-to-end distance, the hydrodynamic volume is very close to the volume of the coil, supporting the assumption of a nondraining molecular coil.

Aside from its predominant dependence on molecular weight, hydrodynamic volume becomes larger in a good solvent; this is because entropic expansion is favored when the polymer-solvent interaction is enhanced. When this interaction is exactly the same as the polymer-polymer interaction, the coil takes up its natural volume, and in such a case,

$$<r^2>^{1/2} \propto M^{1/2} \tag{6.3.5}$$

which is of course the Θ condition. Usually the solvent is a good solvent, and the polymer molecule expands beyond the natural volume such that we define

$$M^\nu \propto <r^2>^{1/2} \tag{6.3.6}$$

and $\nu > 1/2$ when in good solvent. The equation for the intrinsic viscosity, Equation 6.3.4, is written for the non-Θ condition:

$$[\eta] = KM^{3\nu - 1} \tag{6.3.7}$$

where K is a constant.

Patel and Takahashi[12] have obtained an extensive collection of dielectric data on dilute solutions of polyisoprene in an alkane solvent known as Isopar-G. Polyisoprene is a unique polymer because its conformer, arranged head-to-tail, has about equal strength in dipole moments lying parallel and perpendicular to the chain direction. Because of this feature, this polymer is ideal for studying the short range segmental relaxation of stage 1 (Stockmayer's type B relaxation) and the long-range relaxation of dynamic molecules, as in melt rheology (type A) of stages 2 and 3 by

---

12. Submitted to *Macromolecules* for publication.

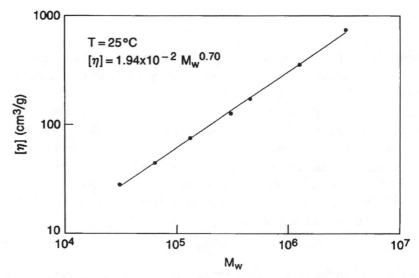

Figure 6.3.1 Intrinsic viscosity vs. molecular weight for polyisoprene in an alkane solvent. (Patel and Takahashi.)

dielectric means. Watanabe and coworkers[13] as well as Kremer[14] have carried out dielectric relaxation studies on such polyisoprenes in the condensed state. In a flowing polymer solution, the frictional shear stress exerted on the polymer coil is equal to the elastic stress within the polymer coil and, as described by Equation 1.3.8, the stress is equal to the product of the modulus, relaxation time, and flow rate. The elastic strain in the coil, therefore, is equal to the relaxation time multiplied by the flow rate. At the cessation of flow, the polymer coil will resume its original isotropic shape, and the time constant for this recovery process is the relaxation time. If it were possible to obtain dynamic mechanical data up to the megahertz range at which the dielectric data were taken, the dynamic modulus would reflect

13. Watanabe, H., to be published in *Macromolecules*; also, Yoshida, H., Watanabe, H., Adachi, K., and Kotaka, T., *Macromolecules*, **24**, 2981 (1991).

14. Kremer, F., *Macromolecules*, **23**, 829 (1990).

this relaxation time, and the loss peak would be observed at the characteristic frequency. For the dielectric experiment on polyisoprene, the time range is such that one is observing the relaxation process of the *dynamic* molecule , i.e., the relaxation process related to the change in the vector sum of the dipole in the chain direction. Deformation in the manner described for the viscoelastic relaxation of the coil should be manifested in the dielectric data with the same kind of response. The response is linear, and the mathematics is equivalent. One complication is that the dielectric constants consist of the coefficient for charge over voltage, which corresponds to the viscoelastic compliance, rather than the modulus. The retardation spectrum for the compliance increases with the retardation time, for example, in the transition zone for the melt, whereas the relaxation spectrum for the modulus decreases with relaxation time. The sign of the exponent in the power law is opposite for the dielectric spectrum and the relaxation spectrum. In either case, though, the intensity of relaxation is increased by concentration. The number of molecules per unit volume is cN_A/M, as stated in Equation 6.3.3, and the modulus is proportional to the number of molecules per unit volume.

The molecular weight dependence of the intrinsic viscosity for Patel and Takahashi's solution system is shown in Figure 6.3.1, with the value of $3\nu - 1$ = 0.70 or $\nu = 0.57$.

To interpret dielectric relaxation data in dilute solutions by comparison with solution viscosity and viscoelasticity, we continue discussion of the molecular picture of polymer in dilute solution. When the polymer solution is flowing, the field of shear stress causes the polymer molecule to deform and tumble.[15] Because of the velocity gradient, the tumbling polymer molecules undergo periodic deformation with a frequency equal to twice the velocity gradient,

---

15. The originally spherical coil deforms to an ellipsoid, which will maintain its shape and the angle of inclination to the flow direction at steady state. The molecule will rotate inside the ellipsoid. K. Amundson compares this to a caterpillar track.

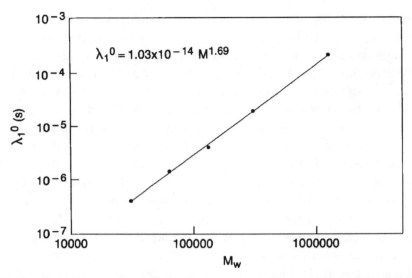

Figure 6.3.2   Relaxation time at infinite dilution vs. molecular weight of polyisoprene. (Patel and Takahashi.)

$$\omega = 2\frac{\partial v}{\partial y} = 2\dot{\gamma} \tag{6.3.8}$$

where $\dot{\gamma}$ is the shear rate in the solvent. Since the polymer is viscoelastic, the maximum deformation occurs not at a 45° angle to the flow direction but some degrees beyond. The lag in the deformation is equal to the "loss angle" δ for $\tan \delta = G''/G'$. The shape-altering (deviatoric) stress σ is

$$\sigma = G'\gamma_a \sin \omega t + G''\gamma_a \cos \omega t \tag{6.3.9}$$

where

$$G' = G_0 \frac{\omega^2 \lambda^2}{1 + \omega^2 \lambda^2} \tag{6.3.10}$$

and

$$G'' = G_0 \frac{\omega \lambda}{1 + \omega^2 \lambda^2}$$

and γ_a is the maximum strain that the molecule experiences. The maximum stress or the stress amplitude σ_a is equal to the terminal stress that the molecule would experience if strained at a constant rate $\dot{\gamma}$, i.e.,

$$\sigma_a = G_0\dot{\gamma}\lambda \tag{6.3.11}$$

The entropy of cN_A/M molecules changes upon elongation to the elongation ratio α:

$$\Delta s = -\frac{1}{2}\frac{cN_A}{M}k\left(\alpha^3 + \frac{2}{\alpha} - 3\right) \tag{6.3.12}$$

and

$$\sigma = -T\frac{\partial s}{\partial\alpha} = \frac{cN_AkT}{M}\left(\alpha - \frac{1}{\alpha^2}\right) = \frac{cRT}{M}\gamma \tag{6.3.13}$$

and

$$G_0 = \frac{\partial\sigma}{\partial\gamma} = \frac{c}{M}RT \tag{6.3.14}$$

From Equations 6.3.11 and 6.3.14, we obtain

$$\sigma = G_0\dot{\gamma}\lambda = \frac{c}{M}RT\dot{\gamma}\lambda \tag{6.3.15}$$

but

$$\sigma = (\eta - \eta_0)\dot{\gamma} \tag{6.3.16}$$

and we obtain

$$\lambda = \frac{(\eta - \eta_0)}{cRT}M \tag{6.3.17}$$

From Equation 6.3.3, we obtain:

$$\lambda = \frac{[\eta]M}{RT}\eta_0 \tag{6.3.18}$$

According to this equation, the relaxation time should be *independent* of the concentration. The experimental results, however, show a clear and consistent concentration dependence. Actually, if one takes the definition of the intrinsic viscosity to be:

$$[\eta] = \lim_{c \to 0} \frac{\eta - \eta_0}{c\eta_0} \tag{6.3.19}$$

the relaxation time at infinite dilution λ^0 is, from Equation 6.3.17,

$$\lambda^0 = \lim_{c \to 0}\lambda = \lim_{c \to 0}\frac{\eta - \eta_0}{cRT}M = \phi[\eta]\frac{M}{RT}\eta_0 \tag{6.3.20}$$

For a polymer with molecular weight M,

$$\lambda_M^0 = \frac{KM^{3\nu}}{RT}\eta_0 \tag{6.3.21}$$

where λ_M^0 denotes the relaxation time of this polymer with molecular weight M at 0 concentration. Equation 6.3.18 is compared with the empirical equation from the data shown in Figure 6.3.2:

$$\lambda_M^0 = 4.49 \times M^{1.69} \tag{6.3.21'}$$

The value of ν is in close agreement with the value obtained from the intrinsic viscosity in Figure 6.3.1.

Patel and Takahashi found that λ_M increases slightly but consistently with concentration, with a more pronounced effect for higher molecular weight polymers. Thus the ratio of λ_M to λ_M^0 is molecular weight dependent. Their data are shown in Figure 6.3.3.

This behavior can be interpreted to be a result of the *effective* hydrodynamic volume fraction in the solution, which increases faster than the real volume fraction of the coils, $v_h = cV_e/M$, possibly because the effective hydrodynamic volume of two coalesced coils is larger than twice the volume of each coil.[16] The probability of coalescence increases with the

---

16. We have taken this view rather than the view based on classical hydrodynamic interaction between particles because in the dielectric experiment (1) the solvent is not flowing in one direction, and (2) the coils will rotate in random directions under the field, cancelling out mutual hydrodynamic interactions. The quantitative verification of the volume boundary for coalescence is difficult and speculative at best, but the lowest measured value of $v_h{}'$ appears to be about 0.05% of the solution volume, and the end-to-end volume fraction is 1.5%. Hence the probability of one molecule coming into the sphere of influence of another is substantial even in the lowest molecular weight, lowest concentration case.

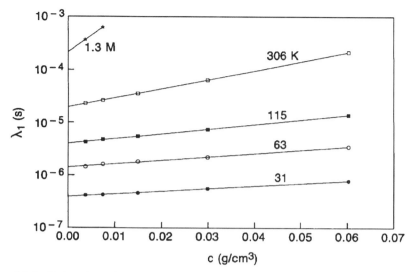

Figure 6.3.3 Relaxation time vs. concentration for polyisoprene solutions of differing molecular weights. (Patel and Takahashi.)

volume fraction of the polymer. We shall calculate the effective volume fraction by taking this effect into consideration.

We introduce the parameter α_{sw}, the linear swelling ratio, which is equal to $R_e/M^{1/2}$. The ratio α_{sw} depends on the solvent species but is independent of c or M in dilute solutions. Thus, the real hydrodynamic volume fraction v_h (without coalescing) is written using the swelling ratio:

$$v_h = \frac{cV_e}{M} = c\alpha_{sw}^3 \frac{M^{3/2}}{M} = c\alpha_{sw}^3 M^{1/2} \tag{6.3.22}$$

We now introduce a variable $x = cM^{1/2}$ so that $v_h = \alpha_{sw}^3 x$. The *effective* hydrodynamic volume fraction $v_h{'}$ (with coalescence), that results from a change in x, Δx, because of a small change in c and/or M, is:

$$v_h{'} = v_h + \frac{dv_h{'}}{dx}\Delta x \tag{6.3.23}$$

If we assume the probability of coalescence to be proportional to the volume fraction of the polymer coils, we can write

$$\frac{dv_h{'}}{dx} = k{'}v_h \tag{6.3.24}$$

where $k{'}$ is a proportionality constant, and we obtain:

$$\int_{\ln v_h}^{\ln v_h{'}} d \ln v_h = k{'} \int_0^x dx$$

or

$$\frac{v_h{'}}{v_h} = e^{k{'}x}$$

and we obtain for the effective hydrodynamic volume fraction:

$$\left(\frac{cV_r}{M}\right)_{\text{eff}} = k\alpha_{sw}^3 M^{1/2} \exp[k{'}M^{1/2}c] \tag{6.3.25}$$

which is now substituted for the hydrodynamic volume fraction in Equation 6.3.17 to give:

$$\lambda = \frac{\eta - \eta_0}{cRT} M = \frac{k\alpha^3 M^{3/2}}{RT} \exp[M^{1/2}c] \tag{6.3.26}$$

or

$$\log \lambda_M = \log \lambda_M^0 + k{'}M^{1/2}c \tag{6.3.27}$$

This is compared with the empirical formula from data:

$$\log \lambda_M = \log \lambda_M^0 + 2.1 \times 10^{-2} \tag{6.3.27'}$$

By combining the equation above with Equation 6.3.18, the dependence of λ_M on molecular weight and concentration is obtained, as shown in Figure 6.3.3.

We considered in Chapter 5 the distribution of relaxation times in polymer melts in terms of harmonics of higher orders. To repeat the results, the {p}-th mode is represented by part of a chain molecule which is 1 pth as long as the whole chain. The molecular weight of this subsection is M/p. Both the intensity of the pth harmonics and the modulus G_p are independent of p, while the relaxation time λ_p is proportional to $1/p^2$. Hence the log *relaxation* spectrum will exhibit a slope of -1/2 against log time. Now, according to Equation 6.3.24, the shift of each relaxation time with a change

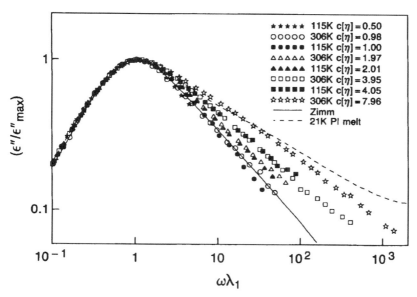

Figure 6.3.4 Dielectric loss vs. frequency adjusted to coincide at the loss peak for a dilute solution of polyisoprene. (Patel and Takahashi.)

in concentration depends on the molecular weight. With increased concentration, the fundamental mode will shift more than does the second mode, the second mode more than the third, etc. We take the state of infinite dilution as the starting point, and we take the pth mode that exhibits $\lambda_p = 10^{-2}\lambda_1$,

$$\frac{\lambda_1^0}{\lambda_p^0} = 100 = \left(\frac{M_1}{M_p}\right)^{3\nu} \tag{6.3.28}$$

from which we obtain $M_p = M_1/14.78$. In other words, a submolecule one-fifteenth as long as the whole molecule exhibits the relaxation time λ_p which is 0.01 of the fundamental mode λ_1, in the infinite dilution limit. By the way, this spectrum shows a slope of -0.58 for the *relaxation* spectrum, as compared to -0.5 for the foregoing model (and the Rouse model), while -0.67 would be obtained for the Zimm model. (This may yet be another model for the transition zone!)

The decrease in the slope of the spectrum due to increased concentration is more pronounced for larger molecular weights, as stated.

The loss curve in Figure 6.3.4 shows the broadening of the spectrum with increased concentration for the molecular weight of 306,000. By fixing the peak position for λ_1 at 1 Hz, the point on the abscissa intersected by each curve can be considered to be a measure of how much λ_p has shifted. We obtain from Equation 6.3.27′,

$$\log \frac{\lambda_1}{\lambda_p} = \log \frac{\lambda_1^0}{\lambda_p^0} + 2.1 \times 10^{-2} (M_1^{0.53} - M_p^{0.53}) \, c \qquad (6.3.29)$$

and for $m = 306{,}000$ and $c = 0.06$ g/cm^3, the shift in log λ_1/λ_p from λ_1^0/λ_p^0 is 0.76, and any value in c should scale linearly. For $M = 115{,}000$ the shift is less (i.e., 0.46 at $c = 0.06$). Thus, broadening of the spectrum occurs because the longer relaxation time mode shifts further, since the viscosity depends on the swelling but the force and deformation in a molecular coil are compensated and unaffected.

7

Computer Programs in BASIC

The following programs have been included to demonstrate how polymer properties can be calculated using the rules presented in the preceding chapters. Several other files and programs are necessary in order to run these programs. The software is available from AT&T Bell Laboratories.[1]

7.1 Engineering Properties of Glassy and Crystalline Polymers

In this section we offer computer programs with which to calculate various engineering properties. The basic approach is to scale the real stress-strain data of a polymer to predict another stress-strain curve under other conditions of strain rate, temperature, thermal history, and (for some) filler content. This is done through the methodology discussed in Chapters 3 and 5. Examples were given in Figures 3.3.2 for polycarbonate, and 3.3.3 for PVC, both at various temperatures and strain rates. An example of calculating the shear stress-strain curves from tensile data for polycarbonate appeared in Figure 3.3.12, and the stressr-strain curves in uniaxial compression were given for polyvinyl chloride in Figure 3.3.6. The effect of physical aging was shown in Figure 3.3.11. All these curves can be obtained in a graphic form with this program. The stress-strain curves for crystalline polymers are calculated with a different program, as discussed in Chapter 5. Examples were given in Figure 5.3.3 for linear polyethylene at various temperatures and strain rates, and in Figure 5.3.7 for polypropylene. The latter shows that the stress-strain curves are scaled differently below -20 °C and above 0 °C, since the glass transition temperature separates typically crystalline behavior in the latter from glassy behavior in the former. The computer program is capable of handling this aspect. Calculation of the compressive stress-strain curve from the shear data was shown for polyacetal in Figure 5.3.5.

The creep and stress relaxation curves are constructed from the given

---

1. The program was written in collaboration with J. T. Ryan, a retired member of the technical staff at AT&T Bell Laboratories.

stress-strain curve as discussed in Chapters 2, 3, and 5. Examples were given for polycarbonate in Figure 3.2.11 and for polyethylene in 5.3.2. This program is valuable for those who wish to predict long range properties from a quick, easy experiment. From his or her own stress strain data, the reader will be able to obtain creep or relaxation data through the scaling scheme in the program. As discussed in Chapter 6, time-delayed failure behavior can be predicted by inputting one data point for the time to break under a known stress at a higher temperature for the convenience of quick data acquisition. The program contains a default value for polymers included already, to predict either craze time or the time for environmental stress cracking. These data will appear as triangles on the creep curves. Craze time as a function of the stress was shown in Figure 6.2.6 for polycarbonate. This program is capable of dealing with different temperatures and thermal histories. The environmental stress cracking time depends on the molecular weight of the polymer in question. If some crucial data are not available to the user the program will calculate the values obtained in the particular grade studied by us.

The brittle-to-ductile transition temperature from an impact test is tabulated for various molecular weight values (expressed by the "melt flow rate" or MFR test of ASTM) and the stress concentration factor (by the notch radius in thousandths of inches), again for different thermal histories (physical aging) and chemical degradation experiences for some. Two example tables, as Table 6.1 and 6.2, give data for for polycarbonates with different molecular weights and different aging histories.

The program can be utilized for a variety of calculations and predictions of the reliability-related properties even for a polymer not included among the 25 generic species in our list, simply by inputting the stress-strain data conducted at 5% per minute at 25 °C. The mode of stress can be tensile, shear, or compressive, and each mode can be calculated from the others by the methodology discussed in Chapters 3 and 5. If a unique mode of loading is desired, run a test at 5% per minute at 25 °C for that loading mode, such as in flexure, and the program can be used to scale to different time-temperature conditions including the creep and stress relaxation.

This program is available from AT&T Bell Laboratories on diskette for the ATT 6386 WGS, IBM AT, or compatible computers.

7.1.1 NOMENCLATURE FOR POLYMER1.BAS - June 1991

"A1" etc. are originally read as "A(1)," etc. The latter remains unchanged while the former is changed depending on the temperature etc.

A1~:   n, This is a power for the formula $E(t)~E0*time^{-n}$. It is experimentally obtained from the ratio of the yield stress at two different rates(e.g., 5% per minute and 0.5% per minute). It can be derived from Equations 3.3.4, 3.2.12 and 3.3.31. For crystalline polymers, *n* is a complicated number illustrated in Figure 5.3.1, but it is usually about 0.05.

A2~:   Ha/R, / where Ha is the activation energy (cal/mol) for physical aging

A3~:   Draw stress (not used).

A4~:   Ta Annealing temperature in °C. for the stress-strain curve in our database.

A5~:   Tb Brittleness temperature in °C.

A6~:   ta Annealing time in hours for the stress-strain curve in our database.

A7~:   MFI Melt flow index per ASTM for the sample used for our database.

A8~:   Ultimate elongation (0 for the brittle failure is necessary)

A9~:   Hg/R Not used.

A10:   Temperature extrapolated for the yield stress to fall to zero; see Figures 3.3.5 and 5.2.12 for glassy and crystalline polymers, respectively.

A11:   This parameter is 0 for glassy polymer and 1 for crystalline.

A12:   Hc/R Hc is chemical degradation activation energy (cal/mole).

A13:   dM/M with MFI Change in molecular weight per change in melt flow index.

A14:   Tc Degradation temperature in °C for the database polymer.

A15:   Tg in °C.

A16:   tc Time for degradation in the database (hours)

A18: ε dot % per minute strain rate for the database. A18x is used for the current strain rate.

A19:   yield strain (%).

A20:   brittleness stress (not used).

A21:   LGT(yield stress) kpsi.
A22:   LGT(modulus) at 2% strain at 5% per min.
A23:   MU Poisson ratio at 2% strain 5% per min.
A24:   dLGT(E)/de (not used).
A27:   A10 for T<Tg (not used).
A29:   Glass factor (the stress multiplier per % glass filler).

7.1.2 Nomernclature in the Program

Numbers in parentheses following some definitions represent line numbers in th eprogram.

BETA: Modified KWW parameter (1900)

C1:   New yield stress (thermal history) (770)
CC: Color number for the curve
CREEP: Flag for creep and relaxation (700)

ELONG: Elongation before break at ST condition (1530)

FFILE$:   File for A1-A30
FILE$:   "ST"+P1$ File for stress-strain data for polymer P1

GL: =1 if glass filled (390)
IO: =1 for customer's data, =2 for Polymer1's database

K: Degradation reaction constant

LNTC: ln t for craze time (1940)
LNTAU: ln τ; at T/s-2/dg/u/s+2 it is 1 hour (1900).

MP: Multiple polymer plot is activated when MP=1 (240)
MS: Multiple strain rates plot (1150)

N1:   Power for the relaxation power law; for creep N1/1.5 (1440)
NX(1):   Number of points in the ST database (960)

P1:   Polymer number (e.g., 1 for polycarbonate, 4 for HD polyethylene, etc.) (350)
P3:   Program number (e.g., 3 for Stress-strain, 4 for Creep, etc.) (930)
   =1 -> (790) thermal history
   =2 -> (2820) Impact properties

= 3 -> (940) stress-strain curves

= 4 -> (1810) creep

= 5 -> (2480) relaxation

PL: (550) when data are unavailable, polycarbonate stress-strain data are used for the
  glassy polymers and HDPE data for crystalline polymers

R0: Stress multiplier for temperature (1460)

R1: Stress multiplier for strain rates (1480)

R2: Stress multiplier for annealing history (760)

R3: Strain multiplier calculated from stress multipliers (1480)

R4: Strain multiplier used in creep and relaxation (1520)

RELAXN: Flag for relaxation (2490)

STRAIN0: Starting strain for creep curve, obtained from stress-strain data (950)

STRESS0: Starting stress for relaxation curve (2570)

ST˜file: Stress-strain database file

STC: Craze stress (1840)

T10: Temporary variable for A10 zero yield stress temperature (560)

TC: Tensile or uniaxial compression plot (980)

TCR: Temperature to crack (1840)

TIMEC: Time to craze or crack (1840)

TMIN: Minumum temperature

TMAX: Maximum temperature

XR(J): Strain in database (960)

YR(J): Stress in database (970)

Y2: Temporary variable for A4, annealing temperature (740)

Y3: Temporary variable for A6, annealing time (740)

Y4: Temporary variable for annealing time (760)

Y9: Temporary vertical shift factor for modulus to compensate for aging (880)

z(1,i): MFI

z(2,i): Degraded MFI by chemical reaction

7.1.3 Optional Subroutines

Several programs can be activated by simply removing the apostrophes (') in the appropriate lines shown below. Make a copy of Polymer1.bas, and edit accordingly and run on GWBASIC.

1. Curves for many polymers can be shown in one graph by removing the ' from lines 270 and 280.
2. Tensile and (uniaxial) compression curves can be compare in one graph by removing ' from 240, 250, and 260.
3. Mechanical properties of glass-filled compounds can be calculated by removing ' from 420, 430, and 440.
4. Effects of physical aging following two different aging histories can be compared in one graph by removing ' from 1080.
5. Shear stress-strain creep relaxation can be calculated by removing ' from 1010.

7.1.4 Function Keys

1. When Text Page is on (SCREEN 0),
   F1: Run Program.
   F2: Plot ST tensile curve.
   F3: Plot SC compression curve.
   F7: Plot figures that were saved in data files.
2. When Text Page is on (SCREEN 0) for Impact or Modulus tables or when Graphics page is on (SCREEN 9) for Modulus logarithmic plots.
   F1: Run Program.
   F3: END and exit to DOS.
3. When Graphics Page is on (SCREEN 9),
   F1: Add data points to the plot being displayed.
   F2: Add labels to the plot on displayed.
   F3: Connect data points with line.
   F4: Add data points to displayed line.
   F5: Replot with new coordinates Xmax, Ymax, etc.
   F6: Dump screen to printer.
   F7: Save the plot to a file.

F9: Run program.

F10: END and exit to DOS.

4.   When Graphics Page is on (SCREEN 9) and a multiplot
        is being made,

     F8: Returns the names of the polymers.

7.2 The Program

Below is a copy of Polymer1.bas program in GWBASIC. Explanatory remarks are interspersed from time to time between lines of the program marked by three asterisks ***. One asterisk means a start of a subprogram (e.g. *SUB).


```
10 'POLYMER1.TXT 9/09/91
20 KEY OFF:SCREEN 0:WIDTH 40:'COLOR 14,1,10
25 CLS:LOCATE 5,10:PRINT" AT&T POLYMER PROGRAM":LOCATE
7,20:PRINT"BY":LOCATE 9,9:PRINT"S. MATSUOKA & J. T. RYAN"
30 PRINT:PRINT" POLYMER 1 is protected by copyright  and may not be
duplicated without     the written consent of either author."
40 PRINT:PRINT" This program provides super resolution, monochrome graphics
for   AT&T   PC6386   and   other   compatible   computers.":PRINT:PRINT
SPC(15)"ISSUE 2.03":SC=5:GOSUB 3880
50 CLEAR,,1100:SCREEN 2:SCREEN 0
55 BW=1
```

*** Make line 55 a remark if a color plot is desired.

```
60                                                                     DIM
A(30),B(15),G(10),G1(10),G3(12,100),M$(122),N(30),NF(30),NX(10),P(30)
,P$(30),P1$(30),PT(15),R(30),T1$(20),X(15,90),XR(100),XW(20),Y(15,90),YR(100),
YW(20),Y8$(15),Z(2,10),ZD(10)
70 OPEN "ALPHANUM.SR" FOR INPUT AS #1:FOR W=1 TO 122:INPUT
#1,M$(W):NEXT: CLOSE #1
```

*** This is a special lettering font Ryan has created, and is applicable for GWBASIC. For other graphic programs, you must create your own; though we have one for NEC BASIC.

```
80 KEY 1,"Progrm":KEY 2,"PlSTFi":KEY 3,"PlSCFi":KEY 4,"":KEY 5,"":KEY 6,"":
KEY 7,"RdData":KEY 8,"":KEY 9,"":KEY 10,"":KEY(1) ON:KEY(2) ON:KEY(3)
ON:KEY (7) ON
90 KEY ON:ON KEY(1) GOSUB 150:ON KEY(2) GOSUB 4170:ON KEY(3)
```

GOSUB 4160:ON KEY(7) GOSUB 3580:ON KEY (8) GOSUB 270:GOTO 130
100 IF P3=-1 OR P3=2 THEN KEY 1,"Rerun":KEY 2,"":KEY 3,"End":KEY 7,"":KEY(1) ON:KEY(2) OFF:KEY(3) ON:KEY(7) OFF:ON KEY(1) GOSUB 3850:ON KEY(3) GOSUB 3840: GOTO 130
110 P3=0:KEY 1,"AdData":KEY 2,"Label":KEY 3,"DrawLn":KEY 4,"DrawPt":KEY 5, "Replot":KEY 6,"Print":KEY 7,"SvPlot":KEY 8,"":KEY 9,"Rerun":KEY 10,"End": KEY(1) ON:KEY(2) ON:KEY(3) ON:KEY(4) ON:KEY(5) ON:KEY(6) ON:KEY(7) ON:KEY(9) ON:KEY(10) ON
120 ON KEY(1) GOSUB 4190:ON KEY(2) GOSUB 3820:ON KEY(3) GOSUB 3800:ON KEY(4) GOSUB 3810:ON KEY(5) GOSUB 3630:ON KEY(6) GOSUB 4010:ON KEY(7) GOSUB 3540:ON KEY(9) GOSUB 3850:ON KEY(10) GOSUB 3840
130 KEY ON:PRINT:PRINT"Press [F] key for action desired"
140 IF INKEY$ = "" THEN 140 ELSE 130
*** The program waits here for you to press the F key.

150 KEY OFF:KEY(1) OFF:KEY(2) OFF:KEY(3) OFF:KEY(4) OFF:KEY(7) OFF:CLS
160 PRINT:PRINT:PRINT"   MECHANICAL PROPERTIES OF MOLDED AND EXTRUDED PLASTICS":PRINT:PRINT"PART   I. ESTABLISHING EQUIVALENT THERMAL HISTORY OF YOUR PROCESSING CONDITIONS"
170 PRINT"PART II. IMPACT PROPERTIES - BRITTLENESS TEMPERATURE OF NOTCHED IZOD SPECIMENS":PRINT"PART III. GENERATING STRESS-STRAIN CURVES"
180 PRINT"PART IV. GENERATING CREEP CURVES AND PREDICTING TIME-DEPENDENT CRAZING OR   STRESS CRACKING BEHAVIOR":PRINT"PART V. STRESS-RELAXATION CURVES"
*** You choose one of the five programs here.

190 M=1:KX=1:PRINT:INPUT"Enter 1, 2, 3, 4, or 5 to select desired program else press ENTER to run   stress-strain program ",P3:CLS:P4=P3:IF P3=0 THEN P3=3 ELSE IF P3<3 THEN 250 ELSE IF P3>5 THEN BEEP:GOTO 160
200 'PRINT:PRINT"Compare tensile and compression";:GOSUB 3790:IF YES THEN CT=1:TC=1:GOTO 240
210 'PRINT:INPUT"Tensile(1) or compression(2)? Type 1 or 2 ",TC:IF TC<1 OR TC>2 THEN 210 ELSE TC=TC-1
*** If you wish to base your calculations on the uniaxial compression data, then remove the apostrophes (') from lines 200 and 210.

220 'IF M>1 AND CT=1 THEN 270
230 'PRINT:PRINT"Multi-polymer plot";:GOSUB 3880
240 'CLS:IF YES THEN MP=1
*** For a comparative plot which includes different polymers in the same plot,

remove (') from lines 230 and 240.

*** Reads parameter file for the polymer you have chosen.
250 IF TC THEN OPEN "CPL" FOR INPUT AS #1 ELSE OPEN "TPL" FOR
INPUT AS #1
260　INPUT　#1,NPL:DIM　A$(NPL):FOR　K=0　TO　NPL:INPUT
#1,A$(K):NEXT:CLOSE #1:AP=0 :GOTO 280
270 'IF MP=2 THEN SCREEN 0:RP=2:I=I+1:COLOR 15,1:ERASE A$:GOTO
250
275 IF MP=2 THEN SCREEN 0:RP=2:I=I+1: ' For color remove ' from 270 and
add '
　to 275
280　CLS:PRINT:IF　TC　THEN　PRINT　SPC(5)　"UNIAXIAL
COMPRESSION":PRINT　ELSE　PRINT　SPC(5)　"TENSILE
DEFORMATION":PRINT
290 FOR N=AP TO AP+17:PRINT A$(N):IF N=NPL THEN N=N+1:GOTO
310
300 NEXT
310 PRINT:INPUT"Select polymer above or press ENTER to see additional group
of plastics ",C$:IF C$="" THEN 330 *** Now choose the polymer from the list.

320 C=VAL(C$):IF C$>CHR$(58) OR C<0 OR C>NPL THEN 280 ELSE
P1$=C$:IF PL=-2 THEN PL$=C$:GOTO 530 ELSE IF FL=2 THEN 470 ELSE
350
330 IF N=NPL+1 THEN AP=0:GOTO 280 ELSE AP=N:GOTO 280
340 STT=0:INPUT"Select polymer by number ",P1$:IF P1$="" OR P1$>CHR$(58)
OR VAL(P1$)<0 OR VAL(P1$)>NPL THEN 340
350　P1=VAL(P1$):FL=2:IF　P1>0　THEN　FFILE$="PF"+P1$:ON　ERROR
GOTO 3850:OPEN FFILE$ FOR INPUT AS #1:FOR N1=1 TO 30:INPUT
#1,A(N1):NEXT:CLOSE #1:ON ERROR GOTO 0
*** Reads the name of the polymer you chose.

360 TA3$="CURVE NUMBERS ARE ":FILE$="ST"+P1$:P1=VAL(P1$):IF TC
THEN FILE$="SC"+P1$
370 IF A(29)=0 AND GL AND MP THEN PRINT"NO DATA":GOSUB
3870:GOTO 3900
380 'IF　GL　OR　P3<3　OR　MP　OR　A(29)=0　THEN　410　ELSE
PRINT:PRINT"Glass filled compound";:GOSUB 3880:IF YES THEN G=1 ELSE
410
390 'IF G AND MP<2 THEN PRINT:INPUT"Enter % glass by weight ",GL:IF
GL<0 OR GL>50 THEN 390
400　'GL$=STR$(GL):GL1$="　WITH"+GL$+"%　GLASS":T1$(5)=TA3$+"%
GLASS":IF MP>0 THEN T1$(5)=""
*** If glass-reinforced compound is what you want, then remove (') from lines

380,390, and 400.

410 IF P1=0 AND MP THEN I=1:GOTO 450 ELSE IF P1=0 THEN 420 ELSE 620

*SUB TO ENTER DATA FOR NEW POLYMER 420-630
420   P2X=1:CLS:PRINT:PRINT"TO   ESTABLISH   THE   MECHANICAL PROPERTIES OF A POLYMER NOT IN THE DATABASE OF THIS PROGRAM YOU MAY SELECT ONE OF THE FOLLOWING:"
430 PRINT:PRINT"1. You may use your tensile data at a known temperature in C and a strain rate in %/min":PRINT"2. If you do not wish to use your test data, ours will be used."
440 PRINT:INPUT"SELECT 1 or 2 ",I0:IF I0<1 OR I0>2 THEN 440 ELSE IF I0=2 THEN 550
450 KEY(8) OFF:PRINT:PRINT"Has your data been entered into a file";:GOSUB 3790:IF YES THEN 460 ELSE 3340
460 IF MP=2 THEN SCREEN 0:RP=2:I=I+1:COLOR 15,2
470 CLS 2: FL=2:IF TC THEN FILES "SC*." ELSE FILES "ST*."
490 PRINT"Type name of desired data file (Number is the same as the polymer number. Letter at the end designates a variation of the polymer type.) To see polymer list,   type -3. Press ENTER to return to menu.":input" ",FILE$", FILE$
500 IF FILE$="" THEN CLS:KEY ON:FL=0:PST=0:ELSE IF VAL(FILE$)=-3 THEN 4216 ELSE GOSUB 960:IF PST THEN 980 ELSE 510
510 PL=0:PRINT:PRINT"Enter number for polymer that most resembles your plastic, glassy, crystalline, ductile, etc."
520 PRINT"Enter -1, if you don't know":PRINT"Enter -2, if you wish to see the polymer   table   again":PRINT:INPUT"SELECT   ",PL$:IF   PL$=""   OR PL$>CHR$(58) THEN
510
530 PL=VAL(PL$):IF PL=-1 THEN 550 ELSE IF PL=-2 THEN 280 ELSE IF PL>NPL OR PL=0 THEN 510 ELSE P1=PL:P1$=PL$:FFILE$="PF"+P1$
540 R$=A$(P1):OPEN FFILE$ FOR INPUT AS #1:FOR N1=1 TO 30:INPUT #1,A(N1):NEXT: CLOSE #1:GOTO 570
*** Reads all parameters for the polymer selected.

550 PRINT:INPUT"Is experimental polymer glassy(3) or crystalline(4)? ENTER 3 OR 4 ",PL:IF PL=3 THEN P1=4:FFILE$="PF1":P1=1 ELSE IF PL=4 THEN P1=4: FFILE$="PF4" ELSE 550
560 PRINT:INPUT"In C enter Tg OR Tm of your polymer ",T10$:IF T10$="" THEN 560 ELSE T10=VAL(T10$):GOTO 540
570 IF I0=2 OR LEN(T4$)=0 THEN 610 ELSE PRINT:PRINT"For this plot":PRINT"1. You may give polymer a code name":PRINT"2. Use polymer type abbreviation "T3$: PRINT"3. Use material designation "T4$:PRINT
580 NST=0:INPUT"Select number ",NST:IF NST<1 OR NST>3 THEN 570 ELSE

IF NST = 1 THEN 610
590 IF NST = 2 THEN A$(P1) = "   " + T3$:A$(0) = T3$ ELSE A$(P1) = "   "
+ T4$:A$(0) = T4$
600 GOTO 620
610 PRINT:INPUT"Enter new designation ",A$(0):IF A$(0) = "" THEN 610 ELSE
A$(P1) = "   " + A$(0):GOTO 620
620 PRINT:PRINT"YOU CHOSE " + MID$(A$(P1),12);:IF GL THEN PRINT"
WITH"GL$" % GLASS"
630 IF G > 1 THEN 700

*PARAMETERS from PF file (the file containing Tg, Tn, n, etc). The definitions
can be found in the NOMEMCLATURE
640   R(1) = 5:R(2) = 10:R(3) = 15:R(4) = 20:R(5) = 30:A1 = A(1):A2 = A(2):A3 = A(3):
A4 = A(4):   A5 = A(5):A6 = A(6):A7 = A(7):A8 = A(8):A9 = A(9):A10 = A(10):
A11 = A(11):A12 = A(12):A13 = A(13):A14 = A(14):A15 = A(15)
650 IF A1 = 0 THEN BEEP:PRINT:PRINT"We have no data for this
polymer.":GOTO 510
660   A16 = A(16):A17 = A(17):A18 = A(18):A19 = A(19):A20 = A(20):A21 = A(21):
A22 = A(22):   A23 = A(23):A24 = A(24):A25 = A(25):A26 = A(26):A27 = A(27):
A28 = A(28):A29 = A(29):A30 = A(30)
670   Z(1,1) = .2*A7:Z(1,2) = .6*A7:Z(1,3) = .8*A7:Z(1,4) = A7:Z(1,5) = 1.2*A7:
Z(1,6) = 1.5*A7:Z(1,7) = 2*A7:Z(1,8) = 3*A7:Z(1,9) = 4*A7:Z(1,10) = 8*A7 680 FOR
I = 1 TO 10:Z(2,I) = 0:NEXT
690   R2 = 1:Y2 = A4:Y3 = A6:MU = A23:RSY = 1/1.732:RSX = 2*(1 + MU)/1.732:IF
PL = -1   AND   FILE$ = "ST1"   OR   PL = -1   AND   FILE$ = "SC1"   THEN
A10 = T10 + 50:A11 = 0 ELSE IF PL = -1 AND ST$ = "ST4" OR PL = -1 AND
SC$ = "SC4" THEN A10 = T10:A11 = 1
700 IF P3 = 1 THEN 790 ELSE IF P3 = 2 THEN 2820 ELSE IF P3 = 3 THEN 940
ELSE CREEP = 1:IF P3 = 4 THEN 1810 ELSE 2480
710 'IF MP > 1 THEN 720 ELSE IF COLOR 10,5:P3 < 3 THEN ANNEAL = 1
715 IF MP > 1 THEN 720 ELSE IF P3 < 3 THEN ANNEAL = 1
*** For color, remove ' from LINE 710 and add ' to line 715.

*SUB on physical aging for lines 720 to 870.
720 IF DEGRADE THEN 760
730 IF ETH THEN 740 ELSE GOSUB 850
740 Y2$ = STR$(Y2):IF Y3 > 9.99 THEN Y3 = INT(Y3)
750   Y3$ = STR$(Y3):PRINT:PRINT"THERMAL   HISTORY   EQUIVALENT
TO"Y2"C FOR"Y3"HRS FOR"MID$(A$(P1),5,5):AN$ = "AFTER" + Y3$ + " HRS
AT" + Y2$ + "C":IF P4 = 1 THEN ET$ = "EQUIV. THERMAL HISTORY:" + Y3$ + "
HRS AT" + Y2$ + " C":T1$(6) = ET$:AN$ = ""
760 Y4 = Y3*(1 + EXP(A2*(1/(A4 + 273)-1/(Y2 + 273))))
*** Parameter R2 is the parameter for physical aging in glassy polymers.
770   R2 = Y4/A6:A5 = -273 + 1/(1/(A(5) + 273)-

LOG(R2)/A2):C1=A21+A1*(LOG(R2)/2.3): TH=3:RETURN
780 K=EXP((-1/(Y2+273)+1/(A14+273))*A12)*A13/A16:FOR N4=1 TO 10:
Z(2,N4)=(K*Y3+Z(1,N4)^(1/3.6))^3.6:NEXT:GOTO 760
790 CLS:PRINT:PRINT"PART I. ESTABLISHING EQUIVALENT THERMAL
HISTORY FOR MOLDING CONDITIONS OF YOUR SAMPLES":PRINT
800 PRINT"1. To establish equivalent temperature and time for thermal history of
your   sample, measure either the ductile-to-brittle temperatures or tensile yield";
810 PRINT"stresses of samples that have been subjected to various elevated
temperatures; then find the condition at which these properties begin to show the
effect.   Record this temperature and the time it took.":PRINT 820 PRINT"2. Or
you may measure the tensile yield stress of your sample at a known strain rate.
We'll figure out the equivalent history for you.":PRINT
830 PRINT"3. Or the thermal history of our injection molded samples will be used."
840 Y2=A4:Y3=A6:PRINT:INPUT"SELECT 1, 2 OR 3 ",I:IF I=1 THEN 850
ELSE IF I=2 THEN 890 ELSE IF I=3 THEN 920 ELSE 840
850 CLS 2:PRINT:INPUT"Specify Time in hrs & Temp in C ",Y3,Y2:IF Y3<1
THEN Y3=1:PRINT:PRINT"TIME WILL BE INCREASED TO MINIMUM 1
HR":SC=2:GOSUB 3970
860 IF Y2<A4 THEN PRINT:PRINT"TEMP IS BELOW MINIMUM
ANNEALING TEMP OF"A4"C": GOSUB 3880:IF YES THEN Y2=A4
870 IF ANNEAL THEN RETURN
880   A5=1/(1/(A(5)+273)-(LOG(Y3)-LOG(A6))/A2+1/(Y2+273)-
1/(A4+273))-273:   Y9=A1*(LOG(Y3/A6)/2.3+A2*(1/(A4+273)-
1/(Y2+273))/2.3):A21=A(21)+Y9: A22=A11+Y9:GOTO 920
890 INPUT"Specify yield stress in psi & strain rate in %/min ",Y6,Y7:IF Y6=0 OR
Y7=0 THEN 890 ELSE Y6$=STR$(Y6):Y7$=STR$(Y7)
900   Y3=A6*10^((LOG(Y6)/2.3-A21)/A1-LOG(Y7/5)/2.3):IF Y3>100 THEN
Y3=INT(Y3)
910   A5=1/(1/(A5+273)-LOG(Y3/A6)/A2)-273:A20=LOG(Y7)/2.3:
A22=LOG(Y6)/2.3-A21+A22:A21=LOG(Y6)/2.3
920 ETH=1:GOSUB 710:A4=Y2:A6=Y3
930 PRINT:INPUT"SPECIFY BY NUMBER: 2. Impact Properties, 3. Stress
Strain, 4. Creep, 5. Stress Relaxation ",P3:IF P3<2 OR P3>5 THEN 930 ELSE 700
940 'IF M>1 THEN 960 ELSE COLOR 14,12
*** Color of the screen can be specified by removing (') in line 940.

950 FL=0:A18X=A18:A18R=A18:STRAIN0=A19/100:IF LMOD=2 THEN 1010
960 ON ERROR GOTO 3850:OPEN FILE$ FOR INPUT AS #1:INPUT
#1,A18,NX(1),ZD: FOR J=1 TO NX(1):INPUT #1,XR(J),YR(J):NEXT:INPUT
#1,XMIN,XMAX,YMIN,YMAX,
DELTAX2,DELTAY2,DELTAX1,DELTAY1,T3$,T4$:CLOSE
#1:XMAXR=XMAX:IF FL=2 THEN RETURN
*** Reads the stress-strain data file.

970 IF M>1 THEN 1050
980 TN$="TENSILE ":IF CT THEN TN$="" ELSE IF TC AND CT=0 THEN TN$="COMPRESSIVE "
*** Labels for the coordinates in the plot

990 T1$(1)=TN$+"STRESS VS PERCENT STRAIN":IF PST THEN 1010
1000 'SHEAR=0:PRINT:IF TC=0 AND CT=0 THEN PRINT:PRINT"In shear";:GOSUB 3790: IF YES THEN SHEAR=1:TN$="SHEAR "
*** If shear deformation is of interest, remove (') from line 1000. It will be calculated from the tensile (default) or the compressive stress-strain data.

1010 LX$="STRAIN: %":LY$=TN$+" STRESS: KPSI":IF PST THEN 4080 ELSE IF P3=3 THEN 1040
1020 LX$="LOG TIME: HOURS":IF P3=4 THEN T1$(1)="CREEP STRAIN % VS LOG TIME HOURS":TA4$=" PSI STRESS":LY$=TN$+" STRAIN: %":GOTO 1040
1030 IF P3=5 THEN T1$(1)="RELAXATION STRESS VS LOG TIME HOURS":TA4$="% STRAIN"
1040 IF P3>3 THEN YMIN=0:YMAX=.5:XMIN=-1:XMAX=6:DELTAY1=.01:DELTAY2=.1: DELTAX1=.1:DELTAX2=1
1050 IF M>1 THEN YMAX=EYX:YMIN=EYN:DELTAY1=EY1:DELTAY2=EY2::XMAX=EXX: XMIN=EXN:DELTAX1=EX1:DELTAX2=EX2 ELSE IF G AND P3=3 THEN XMAX=10
1060 IF A11 OR M>1 OR MP OR P4=1 THEN 1080
1070 PRINT:INPUT"Enter 1 for physical aging effect, or just ENTER for none." ANNEAL:IF ANNEAL<0 OR ANNEAL>2 THEN 1070 ELSE IF ANNEAL>0 THEN GOSUB 710:' IF ANNEAL=2 THEN 1250
*** It asks if you would like to include the physical aging effect. Respond with 1 if yes. ENTER only if not interested. If you press 2 instead of 1, though it does ask for such, you will obtain a comparative plot for another thermal history.

1080 IF CREEP THEN 1210 ELSE IF MP>1 THEN 1370 ELSE IF PST THEN B=2:MT=1: GOTO 1170
1090 IF G=2 THEN 1370
1100 DIM SN(20),SR(20):IF MP=1 THEN B=1:GOTO 1210 ELSE PRINT:PRINT"Your choice of parameter is :":IF G THEN PRINT" 1. glass filler content"
1110 PRINT" 2. temperature":PRINT" 3. strain rate":PRINT" 4. or TABLE of Modulus at different temperatures":PRINT" 5. or TABLE of Modulus for different strain rates"
1120 PRINT:IF G=0 THEN INPUT"ENTER 2, 3, 4, or 5 ",B:IF B<2 OR B>5 THEN 1120
1130 IF G THEN INPUT"ENTER 1, 2, 3, 4, or 5 ",B:IF B<1 OR B>5 THEN 1130

*** Here you choose as your parameter 2. Temperature, 3. Strain Rates. You can choose a table for modulus vs. strain by pressing 4 or 5. 1 is reserved for glass-filled systems.

1140 IF B=2 THEN PRINT:INPUT"To specify temperature, type 1 and ENTER, else press [ENTER] for automatic   multi-temperature plots ",MT:IF MT<0 OR MT>1 THEN 1140 ELSE IF MT=0 THEN KX=0
*** When you choose temperature as the parametric variable, you can obtain a stress-strain curve by specifying either a new temperature time by pressing 1 or a group of curves for multiple temperatures spaced by 20C by pressing ENTER only.

1150 IF B=3 THEN PRINT:INPUT"To specify strain rate, type 1 and ENTER, else press ENTER for automatic multi-strain rate plots ",MS:IF MS<0 OR MS>1 THEN 1150 ELSE IF MS=0 THEN KX=0
*** The same applies for the strain rates, as above for temperature.

1160 IF B>3 THEN ERASE NF,M$,XW,YW:KX=0
1170 IF B=2 THEN T1$(5)=TA3$+"TEMPERATURE" ELSE IF B=3 THEN T1$(5)=TA3$+ "STRAIN RATE IN %/MIN"
1180 IF PST THEN 1260
1190 IF MT=1 THEN 1210
1200 PRINT:IF B=2 OR B=4 THEN INPUT"Enter min & max plot temps in C ",TMIN, TMAX:IF TMIN> =TMAX THEN 1200 ELSE ET=TMIN:GOSUB 3810:TMIN=ET:T1$=STR$(ET):   ET=TMAX:GOSUB 3810:TMAX=ET:T2$=STR$(ET):ZMIN=TMIN/10:ZMAX=TMAX/10:GOTO 1280
*** for the multi-temperature plot.
1210 IF LMOD THEN MT=1:GOTO 1240 ELSE IF CRAZE OR MP THEN 1230
1220 IF P3>3 AND MT<1 AND MP=0 AND G<2 AND ANNEAL<2 THEN PRINT:PRINT "Multi-temperature plot";:GOSUB 3790:IF YES THEN MT=1
1230 IF G=2 OR MP>1 THEN 1420
1240 IF ANNEAL=2 AND M>1 THEN GOSUB 730:GOTO 1440
1250 PRINT:INPUT"Enter Temp in C ",T$:IF T$="" THEN 1250 ELSE T=VAL(T$): ET=T:GOSUB 3830:T=ET:T$=STR$(T):GOTO 1270
1260 T=ZD*10
1270 Z=T/10:T$=STR$(T):IF M>1 THEN 1300
1280 TA1$="FOR "+MID$(A$(P1),12):TA2$=" AT"+T$+"C ":IF MP THEN TA1$="FOR POLYMERS" ELSE IF PST THEN TA1$="for "+T4$+T3$
1290 T1$(2)=TA1$+TA2$:IF PST THEN SR=A18:SR$=STR$(SR):GOTO 1330
1300 IF CREEP THEN 1440 ELSE IF B=2 AND MT=2 OR ANNEAL=2 AND M>1 THEN 1370

*** CREEP and RELAXATION programs also use the stress-strain data.

1310 PRINT:IF B=3 AND MS=0 OR B=5 THEN INPUT"Enter min & max strain rates %/min ",SR2,SR ELSE INPUT"Enter strain rate %/min ",SR
*** For multi-strain rates plot.

1320 SR$=STR$(SR):SR2$=STR$(SR2):IF SR=<0 OR SR2=<0 AND B=3 AND MS=0 OR SR2=<0 AND B=5 OR SR2>SR AND B=3 OR SR2>SR AND B=5 THEN 1310
1330 IF B=2 AND G=0 THEN T1$(2)=TA1$ ELSE IF GL THEN IF B=2 OR B=3 OR ANNEAL=2 THEN T1$(2)=TA1$+GL1$ ELSE IF B=1 THEN T1$(2)=TA1$+TA2$
1340 IF B<3 OR ANNEAL=2 THEN T1$(3)="AT A STRAIN RATE OF"+SR$+"%/MIN" ELSE IF B=3 THEN IF G AND ANNEAL=1 THEN T1$(3)=TA2$+AN$ ELSE IF G THEN T1$(3)=TA2$ ELSE IF ANNEAL=1 THEN T1$(3)=AN$:GOTO 1370
1350 IF ANNEAL=1 AND B<3 THEN T1$(4)=AN$ ELSE IF ANNEAL=2 AND G>0 THEN T1$(4)=TA2$ 1360 IF B>3 THEN PRINT:PRINT"PLEASE WAIT FOR CALCULATIONS"
1370 A18X=VAL(SR$):IF B=2 AND MT=0 AND MP=0 OR B=4 THEN Z=ZMIN
1380 IF PST OR KX>1 OR B>2 OR MP OR G OR TC=1 THEN 1420 ELSE FRACTURE=1:IF FRACTURE=0 THEN 1420
*** The brittle temperature depends on the molecular weight (MFI) and the notch sensitivity. If you know the brittle temperature of your material, it will help. Otherwise, either you ignore the brittle effect or just let us put in the data for our sample.

1390 PRINT:INPUT"If known, enter Brittle Temp in C else press ENTER ",TB$: IF TB$="" THEN PRINT:INPUT"If known, enter Melt Flow Rate value else press ENTER",MFI:IF MFI=0 THEN MFI=A7
1400 IF TB$="" THEN TB=INT(1/(1/(A5+273)+(.25-MFI/A7/5)/A2/A1)-273): TB$=STR$(TB)
1410 T1$(6)="BRITTLE TEMPERATURE IS "+TB$+"C"
1420 IF B=2 AND MT=0 OR B=3 AND MS=0 OR B>3 THEN KX=KX+1:M=KX
1430 IF FRACTURE>1 THEN FRACTURE=1

* SUB for the scaling factors R's) (temp), R1 (strain rate or time) lines 1440 to 1520.
1440 N1=A1:IF P3=4 THEN N1=N1/1.5
1450 IF A11=0 AND P3<>4 THEN N1=1/(1/N1+A2*(1/(273+10*Z)- 1/(273+10*ZD))/2.3)
1460 IF A11=0 THEN R0=(A10-10*Z)/(A10-10*ZD):GOTO 1500
1470   IF   10*Z>=A15   THEN   R0=((273+10*ZD)/(273+10*Z))*(A10- 10*Z)/(A10-10*ZD)   ELSE   RG=((273+10*ZD)/(273+A15))*(A10-A15)/(A10-

```
10*ZD)
1480 IF 10*Z<A15 THEN R1=(1+A29*GL)*(A18X/A18*R2)^N1*RG:R3=1/R1:
R0=(A10-10*Z)/(A10-A15):R1=R1*R0:R3=R3*R0:GOTO 1510
1500 R1=(A18X/A18*R2)^N1*R0:IF A11 AND Z*10>=A15 THEN R3=1/R1
ELSE R3=R1
1510 R1=R1*(1+A29*GL)
1520 IF CREEP THEN R4=R3:RETURN
*** R1 is the stress scaling factor, R3 is for the strain.
1530 IF FRACTURE=1 THEN ELONG=A8/R1:IF A8=0 THEN
FRACTURE=0
1540 IF FRACTURE THEN FRACTURE=FRACTURE+1
1550 IF FRACTURE=2 THEN 1440
1560 IF B=4 OR B=5 THEN SN=1
1570 FOR I=1 TO NX(1):X=R3*XR(I):Y=R1*YR(I):IF SHEAR AND SHR=0
THEN X=X*RSX:Y=Y*RSY:SHR=1
1580 X(KX,I)=X:Y(KX,I)=Y:IF FRACTURE=>2 AND X=>ELONG AND
Z*10<=VAL(TB$) THEN 1650
1590 IF Y>YMAX THEN GOSUB 3400:RP=2:GOTO 1590
1600 IF GL AND Y(KX,I)<Y(KX,I-1) THEN 1650
1610 IF B<4 THEN 1640
1620 IF Y(KX,I)<Y(KX,I-1) THEN 1650 ELSE IF X(KX,I)<SN THEN 1640
ELSE SS=Y(KX,I-1)+(Y(KX,I)-Y(KX,I-1))*(SN-X(KX,I-1))/(X(KX,I)-X(KX,I-
1)):IF
SHEAR=0 THEN MD=(INT(100*SS/SN))/100 ELSE
MD=(INT(1000*SS/SN))/100
1630 IF MD<=0 THEN MD=0 ELSE G3(KX,SN)=MD:SN(SN)=SN:IF SN=10
THEN 1640 ELSE SN=SN+1
1640 NEXT
1650 IF FRACTURE=>2 AND ELONG=>XMAX THEN X(KX,I-1)=XMAX
1660 N(KX)=I-1:SR(KX)=VAL(SR$):IF G THEN Y8$(KX)=GL$+"%"
1670 IF B=2 OR B=4 THEN B(KX)=CINT(10*Z):IF MT=0 AND
B(KX)>TMAX THEN B(KX)=TMAX
1680 IF B=4 THEN 1790 ELSE IF B=5 THEN 1770
1690 I=KX:N(I)=N(KX):IF B=2 THEN Y8$(I)=STR$(B(I))+"C" ELSE IF B=3
THEN Y8$(I)=STR$(SR(I))
1700 IF MP THEN P(KX)=NP:Y8$(I)=MID$(A$(P1),6,6):IF PL<>0 THEN
Y8$(I)=A$(0)
1710 IF ANNEAL=2 THEN Y8$(I)=Y3$+" HRS
AT"+Y2$+"C":T1$(5)=TA3$+"THERMAL HISTORY":IF M=1 AND P3=3
AND G THEN XMAX=XMAX+DELTAX2 ELSE IF M=1 THEN
XMAX=XMAX+2*DELTAX2 1720 IF MP>0 AND CT AND TC=0 THEN
Y8$(I)=Y8$(I)+" TENSILE" ELSE IF MP>0 AND CT AND TC THEN
Y8$(I)=Y8$(I)+" COMP"
1730 IF RP=2 THEN RP=1:I=I+1:SCREEN 0
```

1740 IF CT AND M=1 THEN XMAX=XMAX+DELTAX2
1750 GOSUB 2990
1760 IF B=2 AND MT=0 THEN 1790 ELSE IF B=3 AND MS=0 THEN 1770 ELSE GOTO 3990
1770 IF B=5 AND FLAG5 THEN 2640 ELSE IF FLAG5 THEN 3990 ELSE SR\$=STR\$(VAL(SR\$)/10):IF VAL(SR\$)>VAL(SR2\$) THEN IF B=3 AND KX<11 OR B=5 AND KX<9 THEN 1370 ELSE SR\$=SR2\$:GOTO 1370
1780 FLAG5=0:IF VAL(SR\$)<VAL(SR2\$) OR VAL(SR\$)=VAL(SR2\$) THEN SR\$=SR2\$: FLAG5=1:IF B=3 THEN RETURN 110 ELSE 1370
1790 IF S AND Z=ZMAX THEN 1800 ELSE IF Z<ZMAX THEN Z=Z+2:IF Z>ZMAX OR B=2 AND KX=11 OR B=4 AND KX=9 THEN Z=ZMAX:S=1:GOTO 1420 ELSE GOTO 1420 *** Go back to SUBROUTINE for R0, line 1460
1800 IF B=4 THEN 2640 ELSE RETURN 100

*** CREEP Program: part of it is used for RELAXATION also up to 2000.
1810 IF M>1 THEN 1870 'ELSE COLOR 0,3
1820 IF ETH OR MP OR G OR TC THEN 1870 ELSE PRINT:PRINT:PRINT"Craze or Crack Time";:GOSUB 3880:IF YES THEN CRAZE=1 ELSE 1870
1830 IF A11 THEN T1\$(6)="TRIANGLE IS CRACKING POINT" ELSE T1\$(6)="TRIANGLE IS CRAZING POINT"
1840 PRINT:INPUT"If known, enter Craze Stress in psi else press [ENTER] for ours ",STC:IF STC=0 THEN STC=10^A21:TCR=25:TIMEC=1:GOTO 1860
1850 PRINT:INPUT"Enter Time in min and temp in C to craze or crack(t,T) ", TIMEC,TCR:IF TIMEC= <0 OR TCR= <0 THEN 1850
1860 LNTC0=LOG(TIMEC)
1870 DAT=5:GOSUB 950
*** Line 950 is SUB for R0, R1.
1880 IF A11 AND Z>A115/10 THEN A10A=A10-50 ELSE A10A=A15
1890 IF CRAZE THEN LNTC1=LNTC0+A2*(1/(T+273)-1/(TCR+273))
1900 LNTAU=4.09+A2*(1/(T+273)-1/(A10A+273)):BETA=1/(LNTAU+.22):IF A11 THEN BETA=A1
1905 IF P3=4 THEN BETA=BETA/1.5
1910 IF SHEAR AND SHR=0 THEN R3=R3*RSX:R1=R1*RSY:SHR=1
1920 IF P3=4 AND STRESS=0 THEN STRESS=50000!:GOTO 1940
1930 IF MP=2 OR G>1 OR MT>1 OR ANNEAL=2 AND M>1 THEN 2000 ELSE IF RELAXN THEN 1960 ELSE PRINT:INPUT"Enter stress in psi ",ST:STRESS=ST:ST\$=STR\$(ST): IF ST< =0 THEN 1930 ELSE IF M=1 THEN STS=ST:M4=1 ELSE IF STS>ST THEN STS=ST: M4=M
1940 IF CRAZE THEN LNTC=LNTAU+LOG(EXP(2*BETA*(LNTC1-LNTAU)-LOG(STRESS/STC)))/ BETA/2:FLCR=1
1950 IF FLAG5 THEN 2010
1960 T1\$(2)=TA1\$+TA2\$:IF G AND MT OR ANNEAL=2 AND G THEN

T1$(2) = TA1$ + GL1$ ELSE IF MT THEN T1$(2) = TA1$ + " AT" + ST$ + TA4$
1970 T1$(3) = " AT" + ST$ + TA4$:IF ANNEAL = 0 AND MP = 0 AND G = 0 THEN
T1$(3) = "" ELSE IF ANNEAL = 1 AND MP = 0 AND G = 0 THEN T1$(3) = AN$
ELSE IF ANNEAL = 2 AND G THEN T1$(3) = T1$(3) + TA2$
1980 IF ANNEAL = 1 THEN IF MP OR G THEN T1$(4) = AN$
1990 IF MP = 1 THEN 2000 ELSE IF MT = 1 THEN
T1$(5) = TA3$ + "TEMPERATURE" ELSE IF G = 1 AND MT = 0 THEN
T1$(5) = TA3$ + "% GLASS" ELSE T1$(5) = TA3$ + TA4$
2000 IF RELAXN THEN 2020

* SUB to find the maximum stress SF, lines 2010 to 2060.
2010 LOGT = XMIN:DLOGT = .1
2020 IF ANNEAL = 0 THEN R2 = 1
2030 IF RELAXN GOTO 2530
2040 FOR J = 1 TO NX(1):SX = INT(R1*YR(J)*1000):IF SF < SX THEN SF = SX
ELSE IF SX < SF AND SF < STRESS THEN 2070
2050 IF STRESS < = SX THEN SF = 0:GOTO 2080
2060 NEXT

*SUB CREEP STRAIN calculation.
2070 PRINT:PRINT"YIELD OR MAXIMUM STRESS
IS";SF;"psi":SF = 0:SC = 1:GOSUB 3970: IF M = 1 THEN 1920 ELSE KX = KX-
1:M = KX:BEEP:FLAG0 = 0:GOTO 4070
2080 STRAIN0 = R3*XR(J-1) + (XR(J)-XR(J-1))/(YR(J)-YR(J-
1))*(STRESS/1000/R1- YR(J-1))*R3
2090 STRAIN = STRAIN0*EXP(-EXP(BETA*(LOG(STRAIN0/A18) + 1.78-
LNTAU)) + EXP(BETA* (LOGT*2.3 + 1.78-LNTAU)))
2100 IF LOGT < XMIN THEN 2160
2110 IF FLCR = 0 OR LOGT < LNTC/2.3 THEN 2130
2120 SR(KX) = LOGT:SN(KX) = STRAIN:G1(KX) = STRESS:FLCR = 0
2130 JX = JX + 1
2140 X(KX,JX) = LOGT:Y(KX,JX) = STRAIN:G3(KX,JX) = STRESS/STRAIN
2150 IF STRAIN > YMAX THEN GOSUB 3400:RP = 2:GOTO 2150
*** GOTO plotting routine 2990 via 1700 for creep curves. From here down is for
creep modulus.

2160 B(KX) = STRESS:LOGT = LOGT + DLOGT:IF ANNEAL = 2 AND M > 1
AND LOGT = TGOL OR CT AND LOGT = TGOL THEN 2170 ELSE IF
LOGT < = XMAX THEN 2090 ELSE IF M = 1 THEN TGOL = LOGT
2170 N(KX) = JX-1
2180 I = KX:M = KX:N(I) = JX:Y8$(I) = STR$(B(I)):IF G AND MT = 0 THEN
G(KX) = GL: Y8$(I) = STR$(G(I)) ELSE IF MT THEN
B(KX) = CINT(10*Z):Y8$(I) = STR$(B(I)) + "C"
2190 GOTO 1700

*** Lmod = 1 means log modulus.

2200 BW = 0:AZE THEN 2210 ELSE CLS 2:PRINT:PRINT"Plot Creep Modulus";:GOSUB 3880:IF YES THEN LMOD = 1:GOTO 2220 ELSE RETURN 110 'FOR COLOR DELETE BW = 0

2210 CLS 2:PRINT:PRINT"Plot Log Creep Stress Vs Log Hours";:GOSUB 3880:IF YES THEN CRAZE = 0 ELSE RETURN 110 2220 IF LMOD THEN T1$(1) = "LOG CREEP MODULUS VS LOG HOURS":LY$ = "LOG MODULUS: KN/SQ MM" ELSE T1$(1) = "LOG CREEP STRESS VS LOG HOURS":LY$ = "LOG CREEP STRESS: PSI":T1$(5) = "":'BW = 0

2230 GOTO 2250

2240   PRINT:INPUT"Enter   Ymin   and   Ymax ",YMIN$,YMAX$:YMIN = VAL(YMIN$):   YMAX = VAL(YMAX$):IF YMIN > YMAX OR YMIN$ = "" OR YMAX$ = "" THEN BEEP:GOTO 2240 ELSE 2260

2250 IF LMOD THEN YMIN = -1:YMAX = 1 ELSE YMIN = 2.5:YMAX = 4

2260 DELTAY1 = .1:DELTAY2 = .5

2270 RS = 1:IF LMOD = 0 THEN 2360 ELSE RP = 1

2280 FOR I = 1 TO KX: FOR J = 1 TO N(I):Y(I,J) = (LOG(G3(I,J))/2.3)-3.17:NEXT:NEXT

2290 DELTAY2 = .4:SCREEN 0:GOSUB 3000

2300 RESTORE 4230:FOR J4 = 1 TO 25:READ Y

2310 IF LOG(Y)/2.3 < YMIN OR LOG(Y)/2.3 > YMAX THEN 2340

2320 IF BW THEN CC = 15 ELSE CC = 14

2330   Y9$ = STR$(Y):PX3 = PX1 + 35:PX4 = AX:PY = PY1-((LOG(Y)/2.3)-YMIN)*YA/DELTAY1: LINE(PX4,PY)-(PX3,PY),14:DRAW"BL2":GOSUB 3340

2340 NEXT:CRAZE = 2

2350 IF PT THEN 4020 ELSE IF LMOD OR CRAZE = 2 THEN RETURN 110

2360 SCREEN 0

2370 RESTORE 4240:FOR I4 = 1 TO 8:READ STRAIN5

2380 I = M4:FOR J = 1 TO N(I)

2390 IF X(I,J) < XMIN THEN 2410 ELSE IF X(I,J) > XMAX THEN 2430

2400 Y(I,J) = LOG(G3(I,J)*STRAIN5)/2.3

2410 NEXT

2420 Y8$(I) = STR$(STRAIN5):IF I4 = 1 THEN GOSUB 3000 ELSE GOSUB 3100:IF I5 > M THEN 2460

*** At this point GOTO 3000 or 3100 for Plotting routine.

2430 IF SR(I4) = 0 THEN 2460 ELSE PY = PY1-((LOG(G1(I4))/2.3)-YMIN)*YA/DELTAY1: PX = PX1 + (SR(I4)-XMIN)*XA/DELTAX1:IF PY > PY1 THEN 2460

2440 IF BW THEN CC = 15

2450 PSET(PX,PY):DRAW "X" + VARPTR$(M$(1))

2460 NEXT

2470 PRINT"Replot";:GOSUB 3880:IF YES THEN 2240 ELSE P3 = -1:GOTO 4010

2480 'IF M > 1 THEN 2490 ELSE COLOR 15,0

*** Stress Relaxation Curves
2490 RELAXN=1:GOSUB 950
2500 IF STRAIN=0 THEN IF A11=0 THEN STRAIN=500:GOTO 2520 ELSE PRINT"MAXIMUM STRAIN ";INT(XMAXR*R4*10)/10
2510 IF MT>1 OR G>1 OR MP>1 OR ANNEAL=2 AND M>1 THEN 2520 ELSE PRINT:INPUT" Specify strain in % ",ST:IF ST<.0009 OR ST>INT(XMAXR*R4*10)/10 THEN 2510 ELSE STRAIN=ST:ST$=STR$(ST)
2520 LOGT=-.2:DLOGT=.2:IF FLAG5 THEN 2020 ELSE 1880
2530 IF A11 AND ST>XMAXR*R4 THEN PRINT:PRINT"TEST STRAIN IS TOO HIGH":GOTO 4210
2540 B(KX)=ST:FOR J=1 TO NX(1):IF YR(J)<YR(J-1) THEN PRINT:PRINT"YIELD STRAIN IS ";INT(R4*XR(J-1)*10)/10;"%":GOTO 4210
2550 IF STRAIN<R4*XR(J) THEN 2570
2560 NEXT
*** Calculation of stress as a function of time.
2570 STRESS0=(YR(J-1)+(YR(J)-YR(J-1))/(XR(J)-XR(J-1))*(STRAIN/R3-XR(J-1)))* 1000*R1
2580 STRESS=STRESS0*EXP(EXP(BETA*(LOG(STRAIN/A18)+1.78-LNTAU))-EXP(BETA* (LOGT*2.3+1.78-LNTAU))):IF ANNEAL=2 AND M>1 AND LOGT>=TGOL OR CT AND M>1 AND LOGT=TGOL THEN 2180 ELSE IF LOGT>=XMAX OR STRESS<.1*YMAX THEN TGOL=LOGT: GOTO 2180
2590 JX=JX+1:IF LOGT<XMIN THEN JX=0:GOTO 2620
2600 X(KX,JX)=LOGT:Y(KX,JX)=STRESS/1000:G3(KX,JX)=STRESS/STRAIN
2610 IF STRESS/1000>YMAX THEN GOSUB 3400:RP=2:GOTO 2610
*** To plotting routine line 2990 via line 2610. From here on down is for log modulus plot.
2620 LOGT=LOGT+DLOGT:GOTO 2580
2630 'CLS 2:PRINT:PRINT"Plot Relaxation Modulus";:GOSUB 3880:IF YES THEN BW=0:LMOD=1:T1$(1)="LOG RELAXATION MODULUS VS LOG HOURS":LY$="LOG RELAXN MODULUS: PSI":GOTO 2250 ELSE RETURN 110
2635 CLS 2:PRINT:PRINT"Plot Relaxation Modulus";:gosub 3880:IF YES THEN LMOD=1:T1$(1)="LOG RELAXATION MODULUS VS LOG HRS":LY$="LOG RELAXN MODULUS: PSI":GOTO 2250 ELSE RETURN 110
*** For color remove ' from line 2630 and add ' to line 2635.
2640 CLS:PRINT:IF SHEAR THEN PRINT SPC(15)"SHEAR"; ELSE PRINT SPC(15)" TENSILE";
*** TABLE for Secant Modulus for stress-strain relationship, Program III.
2650 PRINT" SECANT MODULUS OF"MID$(A$(P1),11):IF G THEN PRINT SPC(24)" WITH"; GL$;" % GLASS"
2660 IF ETH THEN PRINT SPC(16)ET$ ELSE IF ANNEAL THEN PRINT SPC(23)"AFTER" Y3$" HRS AT"Y2$" C" ELSE PRINT

2670 PRINT:IF B=5 THEN 2700 ELSE PRINT" TEMPERATURE C";:
2680   J=10:FOR   KX=1   TO   10:J=J+6:PRINT   TAB(J)B(KX);:IF
B(KX+1)<B(KX) THEN 2730
2690 NEXT:GOTO 2730
2700 PRINT" STN RATE %/min";
2710 J=10:FOR KX=1 TO 10:J=J+6:IF SR(KX)=0 OR SR(KX)=SR(KX-1)
THEN 2730
2720 PRINT TAB(J)SR(KX);:NEXT
*** TABLE of Secant Modulus vs. strain (B=4).
2730 PRINT:PRINT:PRINT" STRAIN   SECANT MODULUS ";
2740 IF SHEAR THEN PRINT"10E4 "; ELSE PRINT"10E5 ";
2750 PRINT"psi AT A ";:IF B=5 THEN PRINT"TEMPERATURE
OF"T$"C":PRINT" %": GOTO 2760 ELSE PRINT"STRAIN RATE OF "SR$"
%/min":PRINT" %"
2760 FOR SN=1 TO 10:IF SN(SN)=0 THEN 2781
2770 PRINT TAB(3)SN(SN);
2780 J=10:FOR KX=1 TO 10:J=J+6:IF G3(KX,SN)=0 THEN 2800
2790 PRINT TAB(J)G3(KX,SN);
2800 NEXT:NEXT
2810 PRINT:VIEW PRINT 23 TO 24:P3=-1:GOTO 4020

*** Impact strength program II.
2820 VIEW PRINT 1 TO 24:CLS:PRINT:PRINT SPC(9)"IMPACT PROPERTIES
OF INJECTION MOLDED "+MID$(A$(P1),11):IF ETH THEN PRINT
SPC(16)ET$ ELSE IF ANNEAL THEN PRINT SPC(25)"AFTER"Y3"HRS
AT"Y2"C"
2830 PRINT SPC(12)" DUCTILE-BRITTLE TRANSITION TEMPERATURE IN
C FOR NOTCHED IZOD SPECIMENS"
2840   IF   DEGRADE   THEN   PRINT   SPC(24)"SUBJECTED   TO
DEGRADATION"
2850 N1=1:PRINT:PRINT " NOTCH":PRINT" RADIUS   5   10
15   20   30 MILS":PRINT:IF DEGRADE=1 THEN N1=2
2860 I1=1:I2=10
2870 PRINT" MFI"
2880 IF P1=3 THEN 2890 ELSE IF P1=4 THEN 2900 ELSE 2910
2890 I2=6
2900 I1=4
2910 FOR N2=I1 TO I2:FOR N3=1 TO 5:Z=Z(N1,N2):ZI=1/(A5+273)-
LOG(Z/A7)/A2/A1/5:R=R(N3):RI=LOG((1+3.4/SQR(10))/(1+3.4
/SQR(R)))/A2/A1:X(N2,N3)=INT(1/(ZI+RI)-273):IF   X(N2,N3)>30   THEN
X(N2,N3)=30
2920 NEXT
2930 PRINT TAB(5)Z(1,N2);TAB(18)X(N2,1);TAB(28)X(N2,2);TAB(38)X(N2,3);
TAB(48)X(N2,4);TAB(58)X(N2,5):NEXT

2940 PRINT:PRINT"   Note: 30 C is the upper limit of this table.":VIEW PRINT 23
TO 24
2950 DEGRADE=0:IF A11 THEN 2960 ELSE GOSUB 4000:PRINT" Another
Thermal History";:GOSUB 3790:IF YES THEN ETH=0:GOSUB 710:GOTO 2820
2960 ANNEAL=0:CLS 2:PRINT" Chemical Degradation";:GOSUB 3880:IF YES
THEN DEGRADE=1 ELSE DEGRADE=0:RETURN 100
2970 INPUT"If known, type Brittle Temp in C else press [ENTER] ",TB$:IF TB$=""
THEN 2980 ELSE A(5)=VAL(TB$)
2980 GOSUB 780:GOTO 2820

* SUB Plotting Routine, lines 2990 to 3380.
2990 IF M>1 AND RP=0 THEN 3100
3000 SCREEN 9:COLOR 14,0:IF BW THEN 15,1
3010   VIEW   PRINT   22   TO
24:PX1=80:PY1=270:XX=450:YY=200:PX3=100:D=1:K=0
3020   EXX=XMAX:EXN=XMIN:EX1=DELTAX1:EX2=DELTAX2:XTS
=(XMAX-XMIN):XMA=CINT(DELTAX2/DELTAX1):PSET(PX1,
PY1):NX1=CINT(XTS/DELTAX1):XA=INT(XX/NX1):Y9=XMIN:
Y9$=STR$(Y9):YR=Y9:DRAW"BD8BL8":GOSUB   3260:Y9=YR:
PSET(PX1,PY1)
3030 FOR XC=1 TO NX1:DRAW"R="+VARPTR$(XA): IF XC<D*XMA
THEN DRAW"NU3" ELSE DRAW"NU6":AX=POINT(0):Y9=Y9+DELTAX2:
Y9$=STR$(Y9):YR=Y9:DRAW"BD8BL8":GOSUB
3260:Y9=YR:PSET(AX,PY1):D=D+1
3040 NEXT:AX=POINT(0):D=1:PX2=AX
3050   EYX=YMAX:EYN=YMIN:EY1=DELTAY1:EY2=DELTAY2:YTS=
(YMAX-YMIN):YMA=CINT(DELTAY2/DELTAY1):YH=1:PSET(PX1,PY1):
NY1=CINT(YTS/DELTAY1):YA=INT(YY/NY1):
Y9=YMIN:Y9$=STR$(Y9):YR=Y9:DRAW"BL2":GOSUB
3340:Y9=YR:PSET(PX1,PY1)
3060 FOR YC=1 TO NY1:DRAW"U="+VARPTR$(YA):IF YC<D*YMA THEN
DRAW"NR3"   ELSE   DRAW"NR6":AY=POINT(1):Y9=Y9+DELTAY2:
Y9$=STR$(Y9):YR=Y9:DRAW"BL2":GOSUB   3340:
Y9=YR:PSET(PX1,AY):D=D+1
3070 NEXT:AY=POINT(1):YH=0:PY2=AY
3080   Y9$=LX$:PX=PX1+(AX-PX1-LEN(Y9$)*9)/2:PY=PY1+20:
PSET(PX,PY):DRAW"S6":GOSUB   3260:Y9$=LY$:PX3=PX3-5:   PY=PY1-
(PY1-AY-LEN(Y9$)*7.4)/2:PSET(PX3,PY):   GOSUB
3290:PY=AY:DRAW"S4":PY=PY2-40
3090   K=K+1:Y9$=T1$(K):PX=PX1+(AX-PX1-LEN(Y9$)*10)/2:
PSET(PX,PY):DRAW"S6":GOSUB   3260:DRAW"S4":IF   K<4   THEN
PY=PY+10:GOTO 3090 ELSE IF K<5 THEN PY=PY1 -20:GOTO 3090

```
ELSE IF K<6 THEN PY=PY1-10:GOTO 3090
3100 IF RP=1 THEN I=I-1:IF I=1 THEN RP=0
3110 L=0:PSET(PX1,PY1):IF PST THEN CC=1 ELSE IF I<8 THEN CC=1
ELSE IF I<15 THEN CC=1 ELSE CC=1
3120 IF BW THEN CC=15
3130      IF      NW>K      THEN      K=K+1:PX=PX1+(XW(K)-
XMIN)*XA/DELTAX1:PY=PY1-(YW(K)-YMIN)*
YA/DELTAY1:PSET(PX,PY):Y9$=T1$(K):DRAW"S6":GOSUB
3260:DRAW"S4":IF K<NW THEN
3130 ELSE IF LB=1 THEN RETURN 100
3140 FOR J=1 TO N(I):PX=PX1+(X(I,J)-XMIN)*XA/DELTAX1:IF PX>AX
THEN 3200 ELSE IF PX<PX1 THEN 3190
3150 PY=PY1-(Y(I,J)-YMIN)*YA/DELTAY1:IF RS AND PY<AY THEN 3200
ELSE IF PY<AY THEN I=I+1:GOTO 3390 ELSE IF PY>PY1 THEN 3190
3160 IF L=0 THEN PSET(PX,PY):L=1
3165 CC=15
*** For color add ' to line 3165
3170 IF PT(I)=0 THEN LINE-(PX,PY),CC:GOTO 3190 ELSE W=PT(I):IF
W>10 THEN W=I-10
3180 PSET(PX,PY),CC:DRAW"X"+VARPTR$(M$(W))
3190 NEXT
3200 IF PX<PX1+10 OR RS=3 THEN 3230 ELSE IF P3=5 AND
STRESS<.1*YMAX THEN DRAW"BL150BU5"
3210 Y9$=Y8$(I):DRAW"S6BD2BR5":GOSUB 3260:DRAW"S4"
3220 IF CRAZE THEN GOSUB 3860
3230 IF RP=1 THEN 3100 ELSE IF CRAZE=2 THEN 2300 ELSE NW=K:IF
PST AND BW=0 THEN RETURN 110 ELSE RETURN
3240 'BW=0
3250 RS=1:DAT=1:I=M:LB=0:GOTO 3670
3260 FOR J=1 TO LEN(Y9$):W=ASC(MID$(Y9$,J,1)):IF W>96 AND W<123
THEN W=W-32
3270 IF W=32 OR W=45 THEN ZR=1 ELSE IF W>46 THEN ZR=0 ELSE IF
ZR=1 AND W=46 THEN DRAW"X"+VARPTR$(M$(48))+"BR3":ZR=0
3280 DRAW"X"+VARPTR$(M$(W))+"BR4":NEXT:RETURN
3290 FOR J=1 TO LEN(Y9$):W=ASC(MID$(Y9$,J,1))
3300 IF W=61 THEN W=11 ELSE IF W=94 THEN W=12 ELSE IF W=39
THEN W=13 ELSE IF W=40 THEN W=14 ELSE IF W=41 THEN W=15 ELSE
IF W=37 THEN W=16 ELSE IF W=32 THEN W=17 ELSE 3320
3310 GOTO 3330
3320 IF W>44 AND W<59 THEN W=W-27:GOTO 3330 ELSE IF W>96 AND
W<123 THEN 3333 ELSE W=W+32
3330 DRAW"X"+VARPTR$(M$(W))+"BU3":NEXT:RETURN
3340 FOR J=LEN(Y9$) TO 1 STEP -1:W=ASC(MID$(Y9$,J,1))
3350 IF J=2 AND W=46 THEN ZR=2 ELSE IF ZR=2 AND J=1 AND W=32
```

OR   ZR = 2   AND   J = 1   AND   W = 45   THEN
DRAW"BL7" + "X" + VARPTR$(M$(48)) + "BL3":ZR = 0
3360 DRAW"BL8" + "X" + VARPTR$(M$(W)) + "BL3"
3370 NEXT:IF PX3 > POINT(0) THEN PX3 = POINT(0)
3380 RETURN
3390 SCREEN 0:RP = 1
3400 READ YMAX,DELTAY1,DELTAY2:IF YMAX < EYX THEN 3400 3410 IF
RP = 1 THEN 3000 ELSE RETURN
3420 IF MP > 1 THEN SCREEN 0:RP = 2:'COLOR 15,1
3430 BEEP:PRINT:PRINT"TURN ON UPPER CASE LETTERS"
3440 PRINT:INPUT"Enter Test Speed in %/min ",SR:IF SR < = 0 THEN
BEEP:GOTO 3420 ELSE A18 = SR:SR$ = STR$(SR):IF CG THEN 3490
3450 PRINT:INPUT"Enter Test Temp in C ",T:T$ = STR$(T):Z = T/10:IF CG
THEN 3490 ELSE FLAG0 = 1:GOTO 3640
3460 PRINT:INPUT"Enter Abbreviation for your Polymer Type (e.g., ABS)
",T3$:IF CG THEN 3490
3470 PRINT:INPUT"Enter Name of your Polymer(eg. CYCOLAC T1000) ",T4$:IF
CG THEN 3490
3480 PRINT:INPUT"Assign a number nm to this file. If tensile data, type STnm
else, if compressiondata, type SCnm ",FILE$
3490 CLS:PRINT:PRINT"1. STRAIN RATE: "A18"%/min":PRINT"2. TEST
TEMPERATURE: "T"C":PRINT"3. XMIN, XMAX, YMIN, YMAX:
"XMIN;XMAX;YMIN;YMAX:PRINT"4. MAJOR X,Y TICS:
"DELTAX2;DELTAY2 3500 PRINT"5. MINOR X,Y TICS:
"DELTAX1;DELTAY1:PRINT"6. ABREVIATED NAME: "T3$:PRINT"7.
POLYMER NAME: "T4$:PRINT"8. ST or SC DESIGNATION: "FILE$
*** To change the ST or SC parameters such as A18, ZD, curve point data, etc.,
lines 3510 to 3750.
3510 CG = 0:PRINT:INPUT"TO MODIFY PARAMETERS, ENTER LINE
NUMBER OF ITEM YOU WISH TO CHANGE ELSE ENTER 0 ",CG:IF CG < 0
OR CG > 9 THEN 3510
3520 IF CG = 1 THEN 3440 ELSE IF CG = 2 THEN 3450 ELSE IF CG = 3 THEN
3640 ELSE IF CG = 4 THEN 3650 ELSE IF CG = 5 THEN 3660 ELSE IF CG = 6
THEN 3460 ELSE IF CG = 7 THEN 3470 ELSE IF CG = 8 THEN 3480
3530 OPEN FILE$ FOR OUTPUT AS #1:WRITE #1,A18,N(I),Z:FOR J = 1 TO
N(I):WRITE   #1,X(I,J),Y(I,J):NEXT:WRITE
#1,XMIN,XMAX,YMIN,YMAX,DELTAX2,DELTAX1,
DELTAY1,T3$,T4$:CLOSE #1:NX(I) = J:GOTO 510
3540 KEY OFF:INPUT"What is File Name ";FILE$:FILE$ = FILE$ + ".DAT"
3550 OPEN FILE$ FOR OUTPUT AS #1:WRITE
#1,M,NW,CRAZE,LX$,LY$,DELTAX1,DELTAX2,
DELTAY1,DELTAY2,XMIN,XMAX,YMIN,YMAX:FOR K = 1 TO NW:WRITE
#1,T1$(K),XW(K), YW(K),SN(K),SR(K):NEXT
3560 FOR I = 1 TO M:WRITE #1,N(I),PT(I),Y8$(I):NEXT:FOR I = 1 TO M:FOR

J=1 TO N(I):WRITE #1,X(I,J),Y(I,J):NEXT:NEXT:CLOSE #1:IF LMOD=0 AND P3>3 THEN 4060

3570 RETURN 130

3580   FL=1:ON   ERROR   GOTO   3940:KEY   OFF:CLS:FILES "*.DAT":PRINT:INPUT"Type your file name without [.DAT]. To return to menu, press ENTER ",FILE$:IF FILE$="" THEN CLS:KEY ON:RETURN 80 ELSE FILE$=FILE$+".DAT"

3590   OPEN   FILE$ FOR   INPUT   AS   #1:INPUT #1,M,NW,CRAZE,LX$,LY$,DELTAX1,DELTAX2, DELTAY1,DELTAY2,XMIN,XMAX,YMIN,YMAX:FOR K=1 TO NW:INPUT #1,T1$(K),XW(K), YW(K),SN(K),SR(K):NEXT

3610 FOR I=1 TO M:INPUT #1,N(I),PT(I),Y8$(I):NEXT:FOR I=1 TO M:FOR J=1   TO   N(I):INPUT   #1,X(I,J),Y(I,J):NEXT:NEXT:CLOSE #1:KX=M:RS=1:RP=1:GOSUB 3000: ON ERROR GOTO 0

3620 RETURN 100

3630 RS=1

3640   DAT=1:KEY   OFF:CC=1:I=M:LB=0:PRINT:INPUT"Enter Xmin,Xmax,Ymin,Ymax ", XMIN,XMAX,YMIN,YMAX:IF XMIN> =XMAX OR YMIN> =YMAX THEN 3640 ELSE IF CG THEN

3490 3650 INPUT"Enter Major Tic Points where Scale Numbers will be printed(X,Y) ",DELTAX2,DELTAY2:IF CG THEN 3490

3660 INPUT"Enter Minor Tic Points between Numbers ",DELTAX1,DELTAY1:IF CG THEN 3490

3670 IF RS=1 THEN SCREEN 0:RP=1:I=I+1:GOSUB 3000:rs=0:RETURN

3680 I=M:J=0:KEY OFF

3690 ID=1:CLS 2:PRINT:PRINT"Enter Data Points separated by a Comma (X,Y). When through, enter Value off   scale. Press [ENTER] key after each pair of values."

3700 I=I+1:CC=1

3710 J=J+1:INPUT" X,Y values ",X(I,J),Y(I,J)

3720 IF X(I,J)>XMAX OR Y(I,J)>YMAX THEN 3730 ELSE 3710

3730   J=J-1:N(I)=J:CLS:PRINT:PRINT"YOUR   XY   DATA   POINTS ARE:":PRINT"   NUMBER X   Y":FOR J=1 TO N(I):PRINT SPC(5) J,X(I,J),Y(I,J):NEXT:JG=J

3740 PRINT:PRINT"TO REPEAT THE XY DATA ENTRY, ENTER 100 ":PRINT"TO CHANGE A DATA VALUE, ENTER THE NUMBER OF THE PAIR YOU WISH TO MODIFY ":PRINT"TO CONTINUE PROGRAM, PRESS ENTER ":INPUT"ENTER ",CG

3750 IF CG=100 THEN I=I-1:CC=1:J=0:GOTO 3700 ELSE IF CG<0 OR CG>J THEN 3740 ELSE IF CG=0 THEN 3780

3760 IF BW THEN CC=15

3770   INPUT"WHAT   ARE   THE   NEW   X   AND   Y VALUES";XC,YC:J=CG:X(I,J)=XC:Y(I,J)=YC: J=JG:GOTO 3730

3780 M=I:PT(I)=M:IF FLAG0 THEN M=KX:GOTO 3380 ELSE IF DAT=O

THEN GOSUB 3110 ELSE I = I + 1:GOSUB 3000

3790 PRINT"Do you wish to input more data";:GOSUB 3880:IF YES THEN 4190 ELSE RETURN 110

3800 RP = 1:RS = 3:FOR I = 1 TO M:PT(I) = 0:NEXT:GOTO 3100

3810 RP = 1:RS = 3:FOR I = 1 TO M:PT(I) = I:NEXT:GOTO 3100

* SUB to place label (title) at a specified XY coordinate, lines 3820-3830.

3820 KEY OFF:LB = 1:K = K + 1:NW = K:LN1 = 0:INPUT"Enter label ",T1$(K):IF T1$(K) = "" THEN 3820

3830 INPUT"Enter X,Y Coordinates for the start of your Label(X,Y) ",XW(K), YW(K):IF XW(K) < XMIN OR XW(K) > XMAX OR YW(K) < YMIN OR YW(K) > YMAX THEN BEEP: GOTO 3830 ELSE K = K-1:GOTO 3130

3840 KEY OFF:BEEP:PRINT:PRINT"ARE YOU SURE YOU WISH TO TERMINATE THIS PROGRAM";:GOSUB 3880:IF YES THEN SYSTEM ELSE RETURN 100

3850 RUN 50

3860   PY = PY1-(SN(I)-YMIN)*YA/DELTAY1:PX = PX1 + (SR(I)-XMIN)*XA/DELTAX1:IF SR(I) = 0 THEN RETURN

3870 PSET(PX,PY),CC:DRAW "X" + VARPTR$(M$(1)):RETURN

3880 INPUT"(Y/Enter = N)";Y1$:YES = 0:IF Y1$ = "Y" OR Y1$ = "y" THEN YES = 1 ELSE IF Y1$ = "" OR Y1$ = "N" OR Y1$ = "n" THEN 3890 ELSE BEEP:GOTO 3880

3890 RETURN

3900 IF A11 = 0 AND ET < A5-50 THEN ET = INT(A5-50) ELSE 3920

3910 BEEP:PRINT:PRINT"TEMPERATURE IS TOO LOW AND WILL BE INCREASED TO "ET"C": GOSUB 3960:RETURN 3920 IF A11 = 0 AND ET > A15-10 THEN ET = INT(A15-10) ELSE IF A11 AND ET > A10-10 THEN ET = INT(A10-10) ELSE RETURN

*** Above line is for the upper limit of temperature. Above Tg the amorphous polymer must be dealt with as melt, which is the subject of another program.

3930 BEEP:PRINT:PRINT"TEMPERATURE IS TOO HIGH AND WILL BE REDUCED TO"ET"C.": GOSUB 3960:RETURN

3940 CLS:BEEP:IF ERR = 53 THEN SCREEN 0:'COLOR 15,1

3945 LOCATE 13,31:PRINT"FILE NOT FOUND.":GOSUB 3960:RESUME 3950

3950 ON ERROR GOTO 0:IF FL = 1 THEN 3580 ELSE IF FL = 2 THEN 460 ELSE IF MP THEN 270 ELSE GOTO 50

3960 SC = 1

3970 INIT = TIMER

3980 TI = TIMER:IF TI < INIT + SC THEN 3980 ELSE RETURN

* SUB for another curve at another temperature, strain rate, stress, etc., lines 3990 to   4040.   3990   FLAG0 = 0:SHR = 0:IF   KX = 10   THEN   4000   ELSE PRINT:PRINT:PRINT"Another Curve";: GOSUB 3880:IF YES THEN 4070

4000 IF P3 = 3 THEN RETURN 110 ELSE CLS 2:PRINT:PRINT"Do you wish to print this plot";: GOSUB 4040:IF YES = 0 THEN 4020 ELSE IF P3 = 2 THEN 4020

4010 'PT = 1:IF BW = 0 THE BW = 1:GOSUB 3250

4020 KEY(1) OFF:KEY OFF:RN=1:INPUT"Press ENTER once to remove this note, press Print Scrn to print graphics, then press ENTER again to continue this program",C

4030 PRINT:IF INKEY$ = "" THEN 4030

4040 PT=0:IF P3=2 THEN CLS 2:RETURN ELSE IF P3=0 THEN RETURN 110 ELSE IF P3=-1 THEN RETURN 100

4050 CLS 2:PRINT:PRINT"Do you wish to save this plot";:GOSUB 3880:IF YES THEN 3540

4060 IF P3=4 THEN 2280 ELSE 2630

4070 FL=0:M=M+1:KX=M:GL$=STR$(GL):JX=0:IF MP THEN MP=2:KEY(8) ON:PRINT"To see Polymer List again, press KEY F[8] and RETURN or":IF PL>0 THEN A$(P1)=R$: PL=0

4080 IF CT THEN 210

4090 IF ANNEAL=2 THEN A18=A18R:GOTO 4150

4100 IF MP THEN 340

4110 IF G AND MT=0 AND MS=0 THEN G=2:GOTO 390

4120 IF MT THEN MT=2:GOTO 4150

4130 IF MS THEN 1310

4140 FLAG5=1:IF P3=4 THEN 1920 ELSE IF P3=5 THEN 2500

4150 IF P3=3 THEN 1230 ELSE IF P3=4 THEN 1870 ELSE 2490

4160 TC=1

4170 KEY OFF:PST=1:GOTO 470

4180 KX=1:M=1:NW=1:CC=1:R1=1:R3=1:T$=STR$(ZD*10): SR$=STR$(A18):T1$(2)="FOR "+ T4$+" "+T3$+" AT"+T$+" C":T1$(3) ="AT A STRAIN RATE OF"+SR$+"%/MIN":T1$(5)= "FILE IS "+FILE$:GOTO 1570

4190 SCREEN 0:RP=1:DAT=1:CC=1:GOTO 3680:'CC=CC+1:COLOR 14,1

4195 GOTO 3680

4200 ON ERROR GOTO 0:CLOSE #1:GOTO 250

4210 SC=2:GOSUB 3970:IF M=1 THEN 2500 ELSE KX=KX-1:M=KX:BEEP:FLAG0=0:GOTO 4070

4216 IF VAL(A$(NPL))>0 THEN ERASE A$

4217 GOTO 250

4220 DATA 1,.1,.5,2,.1,.5,3,.1,1,5,.1,1,10,1,5,15,1,5,20,1,5,25,1,5,30,1,10, 50,1,10,75,5,25,100,5,25,200,10,50,500,10,100,600,10,100,700,10,100,800,10, 100,1000,100,500,1500,100,500,2000,100,500   4230   DATA .0002,.0004,.0006,.0008,.001,.002,.004,.006,.008,.01,.02,.04,.06,   4240   DATA .3,.5,1,1.5,2,3,4,5

7.3 Thermodynamic Recovery

This program creates the volume-time curves such as Figures 3.1.3 and 3.1.6, the memory effect as in Figure 3.1.4, and the most challenging log λ vs. δ curves of Figure 3.1.5 in Chapter 3. It can also create a plot of log λ vs. log t

such as shown in Figure 3.1.7. The program is shown here to illustrate the methodology of computation and the values of parameters used, for those readers who are interested.

```
10 ' MODEL DEMO PROGRAM 9/13/91 20 KEY OFF:SCREEN 0:WIDTH
40:COLOR  14,1,10:CLS:LOCATE  5,7:PRINT"  AT&T  MODEL  DEM  O
PROGRAM":LOCATE 7,19:PRINT"BY":LOCATE 9,9:PRINT"S. MATSUOKA &
J. T. RYAN"              ,
30 LOCATE 13,1:PRINT" MODEL DEMO is protected by copyright   and may
not be dup licated without the   written consent of either author."
40 PRINT:PRINT" This program provides super resolution, color graphics for
AT&T PC6386 and    other compatible computers."
50 PRINT:PRINT SPC(13) "ISSUE 1.6":SC=4:GOSUB 2520
60 CLEAR,,900:SCREEN 2:SCREEN 0:COLOR 15,1
70            DIM            F(50),LTAU(50),N(21),ND(15),NF(100),
NX(20),N$(123),PT(21),PX(20),PY(30),T$(10),
TF(50),TF0(50),TF1(50),T1$(50),T2$(2),
WT(30),X(15,170),XD(17),X0(50),XW(30),
XWP(30),Y(15,250),YD(17),YW(30),YWP(30),Y8$(21)
80 OPEN "ALPHANUM.SR" FOR INPUT AS #1: FOR W=1 TO 122:INPUT
#1,N$(W):NEXT:CLOSE #1
90 '* KEYS *
100  KEY  1,"MODEL":KEY  2,"":KEY  3,"":KEY  4,"":KEY  5,"":KEY  6,"":KEY
7,"RDDATA":KE Y 8,"":KEY 9,"":KEY 10,"":KEY(1) ON:KEY(7) ON
110 KEY ON:ON KEY(1) GOSUB 270:ON KEY(7) GOSUB 2570:GOTO 150
120   KEY    ON:COLOR    14:KEY   1,"ADDATA":KEY    2,"LABEL":KEY
6,"PRINT":KEY 7,"":KEY 8, " CONSCV":KEY 9,"RERUN":KEY 10,"END"
130 KEY(1) ON:KEY(2) ON:KEY (6) ON:KEY (8) ON:KEY (9) ON:KEY (10)
ON
140 ON KEY (1) GOSUB 2670:ON KEY (2) GOSUB 2110:ON KEY (6) GOSUB
2060:ON KEY (8)
 GOSUB 2140:ON KEY (9) GOSUB 2200:ON KEY (10) GOSUB 2180
150 IF RN=1 OR ID=1 THEN KEY ON:CLS 2:RN=0:ID=0
160 PRINT:PRINT"Press KEY F[7] to start the program. Press [ENTER] to
continue e ach step."
170 IF INKEY$="" THEN 170
180 CLS 2:GOTO 150
190 '********** MATH 2 **********
200 DIM GS(10)
210      'L=2    DIELECTRIC    DATA    220    DATA    -1,.0015,-
.5,.006,0,.028,.5,.14827,1,.134857,1.5,.065676
230 DATA 2,.0369159,2.5,.021,3,.0136,3.5,.00822,4,.0067,4.5,.00514853,5,.0029
```

```
240      GSUM=0:FOR      J=1      TO      13:READ
XD(J),YD(J):GSUM=GSUM+YD(J):NEXT
250 J=0:RETURN
260 '********** MATH 16 **********
270 FCN=16:I1=1:YI2=0:LP=0:IF K=0 THEN K=1
280   GOSUB   200:IF   DAT=0   THEN   K=1:T1$   ="PHYSICAL
AGING":J1=1:J2=0:GR16=0:CV=1
290 '*********** J *************
300 KEY 1,"":KEY 7,"":KEY(1) OFF:KEY(7) OFF
310   ALPHA=.000386:DTG=11:   HW=1700:TOR=-14.5:IF   DAT=0   THEN
MM=-1
320   PRINT:PRINT"Do  you  wish  to  print  parameters  "; :COLOR
10:PRINT"N":COLOR 14:LP=0
330 IF INKEY$="" THEN 330
340 PRINT:PRINT"Select: Isothermal(0), Memory Effect(1), Specifying Quench
History(2), dT/dt(3). Type 0,1,2, or 3 and press [ENTER]. ";: COLOR
10:PRINT"0":COLOR 14:MEM=0:MEM$=STR$(MEM):MM=MEM
350 IF INKEY$="" THEN 350
360 IF DAT=2 THEN 380 ELSE IF MEM=0 THEN T1$(K)=T1$+"
ISOTHERMALLY" ELSE IF MEM= 1 THEN T1$(K)=T1$+" MEMORY
EFFECT" ELSE IF MEM=2 THEN T1$(K)=T1$+" QUENCH HISTOR Y"
ELSE IF MEM=3 THEN T1$(K)=T1$
370 IF I1>1 AND DAT<2 THEN 410
380 PRINT:INPUT"What is the Tg from DSC? Press [ENTER] for default value.
",TG1$ :TG1=43:TG1$=STR$(TG1):PRINT:PRINT"DSC Tg default is ";:COLOR
10:PRINT"43 C":COL OR 14
390 TG=TG1-8:PRINT:INPUT"What is Tg? Press [ENTER] for default value.
",TG$:TG=3   5:TG$=STR$(TG):PRINT"Tg   default   is   ";:COLOR
10:PRINT"35C":COLOR 14
400 TOR=TG-50.5:LOGTAUG=.83:DELOGT=.05:DETEMP=.1:IF K=1 THEN
K=2
410 IF MEM=0 OR MEM>2 THEN 440
420 PRINT:INPUT"What is the last temperature T1 or Tmax for heating? ",T1$:IF
T1 $="" THEN 420 ELSE T1=VAL(T1$)
430 IF MEM=2 THEN PRINT:INPUT"How many hours after quench? ",
HRSQ:IF   HRSQ<=0   THEN   430   ELSE   HRSQ$=STR$(HRSQ):
LOGTQ=LOG(HRSQ)/2.3:K=K+1:NW=K:T1$(K)="HOURS   AFTER   Q
UENCH"+HRSQ$:IF I1>1 THEN H=1:GOSUB 1850:H=0
440 READ T0$,T$
450 PRINT:PRINT"What are the initial and final temp. in C? Type T0,T and press [
ENTER]. ";:COLOR 10:PRINT T0$+","+T$:COLOR 14
460 IF INKEY$="" THEN 460
470 T0=INT(VAL(T0$)*10)/10
480 T=INT(VAL(T$)*10)/10:K=K+1:NW=K:CC=14
```

490 IF M>0 THEN CLS 2:PRINT"PLEASE WAIT FOR CALCULATIONS"

500 IF MEM=3 THEN T1=T0

510 IF MEM<3 THEN 530 ELSE PRINT:INPUT"What is the heating or cooling rate in C/ min? Type a + value for heating and a - value for cooling. Press [ENTER]. ",Q1$:IF Q1$="" THEN 510 ELSE Q1=INT(VAL(Q1$)) 520 Q=Q1*60:IF Q<0 THEN DETEMP=-.1 ELSE IF Q1>0 THEN DETEMP=.1

530 IF T0>TG+DTG THEN T0=TG+DTG

540 TF=T0:IF Q<0 THEN T=T0

550 FOR J=1 TO 13:TF(J)=T0:NEXT

560 TE=T:IF TE<TOR THEN TE=TOR

570 IF GR16=1 THEN 860 'A16

580 LOGTMIN=-2:LOGTMAX=3

590 IF MEM=3 THEN PLOT16=4:GOTO 680

600 PRINT:PRINT"What are min and max Log Time values for your plot? Type min,max

 and press   [ENTER] or type a comma and press [ENTER] for default values. "; :COLOR   10:PRINT"-2,3":COLOR   14:LOGTMIN=- 2:LOGTMIN$=STR$(LOGTMIN)

610 IF INKEY$="" THEN 610

620 LOGTMAX=3:LOGTMAX$=STR$(LOGTMAX)

630 IF LOGTMIN>LOGTMAX THEN 600

640 IF MM=2 THEN PLOT16=4:GOTO 700

650 IF PLOT16=2 AND MM<3 THEN 680

660 PRINT:PRINT"Select Delta vs. logt(1), -log tau vs. Delta(2), log tau vs. t(3), or dDelta/dT(4).Type   1,2,3,   or   4   and   press   [ENTER].   ";:COLOR 10:PRINT"2":COLOR 1 4:PLOT16=2:PT(0)=PLOT16

670 IF INKEY$="" THEN 670

680 KEY OFF:IF PLOT16=1 THEN T1$(2)="DELTA VS LOGT":GOTO 760 ELSE IF PLOT16=2 TH EN T1$(2)="-LOG TAU VS DELTA":GOTO 740 ELSE IF PLOT16=3 THEN T1$(2)="LOG TAU VS LOG T":GOTO 760 ELSE IF PLOT16=4 THEN T1$(2)="DELTA CP/DELTA T":GOTO 700 ELSE 66 0

690 '*********** K16 ***********

700 PRINT:INPUT"What are the minimum and maximum temperatures for your plot? Typ e Tmin, Tmax. ",XMIN$,XMAX$:IF XMIN$="" OR XMAX$="" THEN 700 ELSE XMIN=VAL(XMIN$):XMAX=VAL(XMAX$):IF XMIN>XMAX THEN 700

710 YMIN=0:PRINT:INPUT"What is Cp scale? Default=1 ",YMAX$:IF YMAX$="" THEN YMAX =1 ELSE YMAX=VAL(YMAX$)

720 LOGTMIN=-2:LOGTMAX=10:LX$="TEMPERATURE C": LY$="DELTA CP   CAL/G/C":DELTAX1=1:D ELTAX2=10:DELTAY1=.1:DELTAY2=.5:GOTO 830' Plot

730 '*********** C16 **********

740 XMIN=-4.5:XMAX=4.5:YMIN=-3:YMAX=2:LX$="DELTA x 1000":LY$="- LOG TAU (HRS)":G OTO 820 'D16

750 '*********** B16 **********
760   XMIN = LOGTMIN:LOGTMIN = XMIN-
1:XMAX = LOGTMAX:ALPHA = .00034
770 IF YMAX > YMIN THEN 800
780 PRINT:INPUT"What are Ymin, Ymax in Delta*1000 or Log tau? Type min,max
and p ress [ENTER] or type a comma and press [ENTER] for default values.
";YMIN$,YMAX$:IF YMIN$ = "" THEN YMIN = 0 ELSE YMIN = VAL(YMIN$)
790 IF YMAX$ = "" THEN YMAX = 5 ELSE YMAX = VAL(YMAX$)
800 LX$ = "LOG T HRS":IF PLOT16 = 1 THEN LY$ = "delta x 1000" ELSE IF
PLOT16 = 3 THEN LY $ = "log tau (hrs)"
810   '***********   D16   ***********   820
DELTAX1 = .1:DELTAX2 = 1:DELTAY1 = .1:DELTAY2 = 1   830   IF   I1 = 1   AND
DAT = 0 THEN GOSUB 1670:CC = 15 'Plot
840 CLS 2:PRINT:PRINT"PLEASE WAIT FOR CALCULATIONS"
850 '*********** A16 **********
860 IF PLOT16 = 4 AND MM > 1 THEN 870 ELSE 890
870 KEY 2,"[REVS]":KEY 3,"[HOLD]":KEY 4,"":KEY 7,"": KEY (2) ON:KEY (3)
ON:ON KEY(2) GOSUB 1550:ON KEY(3) GOSUB 1630
880 COLOR 10:PRINT:PRINT"Press [F2] for reverse temp plot or [F3] for hold at
te mp where plot was stopped for time in hrs followed by a reverse temp
plot.":COLOR 14
890 IF PLOT16 = 2 THEN DELOGT = .04
900 IF PLOT16 = 4 AND MEM = 0 THEN T = XMIN
910 IF PLOT16 = 4 AND Q < 0 THEN T = T0
920 LOGT = LOGTMIN:GR16 = 1
930 '*********** H16 ************
940   TFTOT = 0:LTAUMAX = LOGTAUG + (HW/(TF-TOR)*(TF + 273)/(T + 273)
-HW/(TG-TOR))/2.3:LTAUMAX = LTAUMAX + HW*(TG + 273)/(TG-TOR)
2(1/(T + 273)-1/(TG + 273))/2.3
950 FOR J = 1 TO 13:LTAU(J) = LTAUMAX-XD(J)/(TF(J) + 273)*(TF + 273)
960 IF RAMP = 1 OR PLOT16 = 4 AND MEM = 0 THEN 980
970   TF(J) = TF(J)-(TF(J)-TE)*(1-EXP(-(10^(LOGT + DELOGT)
-10^LOGT)/10^LTAU(J))):GOTO 990
980 IF   Q = 0   THEN   TF(J) = TE   ELSE   TF(J) = TF(J)-(TF(J)-TE)   *(1-EXP(-
(DETEMP/Q/10^LTAU(J))^.5))
990 TFTOT = TFTOT + (TF(J)-TOR)*YD(J):NEXT
1000 TF1 = TF:TF = TFTOT/GSUM + TOR
1010 IF MEM < 2 THEN 1040
1020 IF LOGT < LOGTQ THEN 1420 'G16
1030 IF LOGT > = LOGTQ THEN 1050 1040 IF MEM = 0 OR TF > T1 THEN 1200
1050 IF MEM < > 1 THEN PLOT16 = 4
1060 IF LP = 0 THEN 1100
1070 LPRINT I1;")";10^LOGT;"HRS AT";T;"C, QUENCHED FROM",T0;"C."
1080 IF PLOT16 = 1 OR PLOT16 = 3 THEN LPRINT "AND BROUGHT UP TO

THE FINAL T:";T1;"C. "
1090 LPRINT "TF=";TF
1100 IF HOLD=0 THEN T=T1:T0=TF
1110 IF MEM=1 THEN TE=T
1120 MEM=0:J1=1:LOGT=LOGTMIN:IF LP=0 THEN 1160
1130 LPRINT "Ltaumax=";LTAUMAX
1140   FOR   J=1   TO   13:LPRINT   J;"Tf(";J;")=";TF(J);
"Ltau(J)=";"LTAU(TF(J))=";(LOGTAUG+(HW/(TF-TOR))
*(TF+273)/(T+273)-HW/(TG-TOR))/2.3)-XD(J):NEXT
1150 IF PLOT16=4 THEN LPRINT"";"Heating rate from this point
is";Q/60;"C/min."
1160 IF HOLD=0 THEN 940 'H16
1170 HOLD=0:GOSUB 1550 'REV16
1180 TE=T:IF TE<TOR THEN TE=TOR
1190 GOTO 940 'H16
1200 IF PLOT16<>4 AND LOGT<XMIN THEN 1490
1210 IF PLOT16=1 OR PLOT16=3 THEN X(I1,J1)=LOGT
1220 IF PLOT16=1 THEN Y(I1,J1)=(TF-TE)*1000*ALPHA/(T+273)*(TF+273)
1230 IF MEM=1 OR MEM=2 THEN 1420 'G16
1240 IF PLOT16=2 AND MEM=0 THEN X(I1,J1)=(TF-T)*1000*(ALPHA-(T0-
TG)*1.4/10^5) '*
 for plot16=2 X input *
1250 IF PLOT16=4 AND MEM=0 THEN X=T:Y=(TF-TF1)/DETEMP*.15:IF
Y<=YMIN OR X<XMIN O R X=TT1 OR X>XMAX THEN
J=1:LN1=0:GOTO 1440
1260 IF Y<YMIN THEN 1330
1270 IF PLOT16<4 THEN 1340
1280 IF CC=8 OR CC=15 THEN CC=9
1290 PX=PX1+(X-XMIN)*XA/DELTAX1:PY=PY1-(Y-YMIN)*YA/DELTAY1
1300 IF LN1=0 THEN LN1=-1:PSET(PX,PY):GOTO 1330 ELSE IF LN1=-1
THEN PSET(PX,PY): LN1=1
1310 LINE-(PX,PY),CC
1320   X(I1,J1)=X:Y(I1,J1)=Y:J1=J1+1:IF   J1=250   THEN
I=I1:N(I)=J1:J1=1:I1=I1+1:' * Plot16=4 plot *
1330 IF PLOT16=4 AND MEN=0 THEN 1440
1340 IF PLOT16=2 AND J1=1 THEN 1420 'G16
1350 IF PLOT16=3 AND MEM=0 THEN Y(I1,J1)=LTAU(4) '* center relaxn
time *
1360 IF PLOT16<>2 THEN 1420
1370 IF X(I1,J1-1)=0 THEN 1490
1380 YI1=((-(X(I1,J1)-X(I1,J1-1))/(10^LOGT-10^ (LOGT-DELOGT))/X(I1,J1-
1))):IF YI1<=0 AND YI2=0 THEN J1=1:GOTO 1420 ELSE IF YI1=0 AND YI2
THEN 1500'* for plot16=2 Y input *
1390   Y(I1,J1)=LOG((-(X(I1,J1)-X(I1,J1-1))/   (10^LOGT-10^(LOGT-

DELOGT))/X(I1,J1-1)))/2.3:YI2 = 1
1400 IF PLOT16 = 2 AND MM = 1 THEN J2 = J2 + 1:X(I1,J2)
= X(I1,J1):Y(I1,J2) = Y(I1,J1)
1410 '*********** G16 ************
1420 IF MEM = 0 THEN J1 = J1 + 1
1430 GOTO 1490
1440 T = T + DETEMP:IF T > TOR THEN TE = T
1450 IF T < = TOR THEN TE = TOR
1460 IF MEM > 0 THEN 940 'H16
1470 IF PLOT16 = 4 AND T < = XMIN OR PLOT16 = 4 AND T > = XMAX THEN
1500 1480 IF T < XMAX THEN 940 ELSE GOTO 1500
1490 LOGT = LOGT + DELOGT:IF LOGT < = LOGTMAX OR MEM = 1 OR
MEM = 2 OR PLOT16 = 2 AND ABS(X(I1,J1)) > .1 THEN 940 'H16
1500 I = I1:X(I,1) = X(I,2):Y(I,1) = Y(I,2):LN1 = 0: N(I) = J1-1:PT(I) = 0:IF MM = 1
AND PLOT16 = 2 THEN N(I) = J2:GOTO 1520
1510 IF MM > 1 OR PLOT16 = 4 THEN 2540
1520 DAT = 0:ID = 1:GOSUB 1950 '*CURVE PLOTTING*
1530 GOTO 2540
1540 '************* REV16 **************
1550 Q = -Q:QT = Q:CC = CC + 1:H = 1:K = K + 1:NW = K:DETEMP =
-DETEMP:DT = DETEMP:IF CC > 15 THEN CC = 8
1560 PRINT:INPUT"If a simple reverse, type a comma and press [ENTER]. For
another rate, specify Q(T/hr) and DeltaTemp ",Q$,DETEMP$: IF Q$ = "" THEN
Q = Q:Q$ = STR$(Q) ELSE Q = VAL(Q$):IF QT < 0 AND Q > 0 OR QT > 0 AND
Q < 0 THEN Q = -Q
1570 IF DETEMP$ = "" THEN DETEMP = DETEMP:DETEMP$ =
STR$(DETEMP) ELSE DETEMP = VAL(DETEMP$):IF DT < 0 AND
DETEMP > 0 OR DT > 0 AND DETEMP < 0 THEN DETEMP = -DETEMP
1580 COLOR 10:PRINT:PRINT"Press [F2] for reverse temp plot or [F3] for hold at
t ime in hrs at temp where plot was stopped followed by a reverse temp
plot.":COLOR 14
1590 IF DETEMP > 0 THEN T1$(K) = "REV TEMP INCRS FROM" +
STR$(CINT(T)) + "C":GOSUB 1870
1600 IF DETEMP < 0 THEN T1$(K) = "REV TEMP DECRS FROM"
+ STR$(CINT(T)) + "C":GOSUB 1870
1610 H = 0:KEY (3) ON:PLOT16 = 4:N(I1) = J1:M = M + 1:I1 = I1
+ 1:J1 = 1:J = 1:LN1 = 0:RETURN 1440
1620 '*********** HOLD16 **************
1630 KEY (3) OFF:CLS 2:PLOT16 = 1:H = 1:HOLD = 1:INPUT"What is the time in
hrs to be k ept at temperature T? ",HRS:IF HRS < = 0 THEN 1630 ELSE
HRS$ = STR$(HRS):CLS 2
1640 K = K + 1:NW = K:T1$(K) = "HELD" + HRS$ + " HRS AT" + STR$(CINT(T)) + "
C":GOSUB 1870:H = 0
1650 LOGTQ = LOG(HRS)/2.3:LOGTMIN = LOGTQ-2:MEM = 2:RETURN 560

```
1660 '************* GRAPHICS *************
1670 SCREEN 9:COLOR 14,0:IF BW THEN COLOR 15
1680        VIEW        PRINT        22        TO
24:PX1=80:PY1=270:XX=500:YY=248:CC=8:PX3=100:D=1
1690 '* FOR DRAWING X-AXES *
1700
EXN=XMIN:EXX=XMAX:EX1=DELTAX1:EX2=DELTAX2:XTS=(XMAX-
XMIN):XMA=CINT(DELTAX2/ DELTAX1)
1710                    PSET(PX1,PY1):NX1=CINT(XTS/DELTAX1):
XA=INT(XX/NX1):Y9=XMIN:Y9$=STR$(Y9):YR=
Y9:DRAW"BD8BL8":GOSUB 2230:Y9=YR:PSET(PX1,PY1)
1720 FOR XC=1 TO NX1:DRAW"R ="+VARPTR$(XA):  IF  XC<D*XMA
THEN        DRAW"NU3"        ELSE        DRAW"NU6":AX=POINT(0):
Y9=Y9+DELTAX2:Y9$=STR$(Y9):YR=Y9:DRAW"BD8BL8":GOSUB    2230:
Y9=YR:PSET(AX,PY1):D=D+1 ' * drawing X-axis *
1730 NEXT:AX=POINT(0):D=1:X2=AX-PX1:PX2=AX
1740 '* FOR DRAWING Y-AXES *
1750            EYN=YMIN:EYX=YMAX:EY1=DELTAY1:EY2=DELTAY2:
YTS=(YMAX-YMIN):YMA=CINT(DELTAY2/DELTAY1)
1760                    YH=1:PSET(PX1,PY1):NY1=CINT(YTS/DELTAY1):
YA=INT(YY/NY1):Y9=YMIN:Y9$=STR$(Y9):YR=Y9:DRAW"BL2":  GOSUB
2370:Y9=YR:PSET(PX1,PY1)
1770 FOR YC=1 TO NY1:DRAW"U ="+VARPTR$(YA):  IF  YC<D*YMA
THEN           DRAW"NR3"          ELSE          DRAW"NR6":
AY=POINT(1):Y9=Y9+DELTAY2:Y9$=STR$(Y9):
YR=Y9:DRAW"BL2":GOSUB  2370:Y9=YR:PSET  (PX1,AY):D=D+1  '  *
drawing Y-axis *
1780 NEXT:AY=POINT(1):YH=0:Y2=PY1-AY:K=0:LAY=20:PY2=AY
1790 LINE(PX1,PY2)-(PX2,PY2):LINE(PX2,PY2)-(PX2,PY1)
1800     IF     PLOT16=1     THEN     AY1=PY1-(0-YMIN)*Y2/(YMAX-
YMIN):PSET(PX1,AY1):DRAW"NR ="+VA RPTR$(X2) ELSE IF PLOT16=2
THEN        AX1=PX1+(0-XMIN)*X2/(XMAX-XMIN):PSET(AX1,PY1):DR
AW"NU ="+VARPTR$(Y2)
1810 '* PRINTING TITLE AND LABELING X & Y AXES *
1820     K=K+1:Y9$=T1$(K):PX=PX1+(AX-PX1-LEN(Y9$)*7.4)/2:PY=AY-
LAY:PSET(PX,PY):DRAW"  S6":GOSUB  2230:DRAW"S4":IF  K=1  THEN
LAY=10:GOTO 1820 '* TITLE *
1830                              Y9$=LX$:PX=PX1+(AX-PX1-
LEN(Y9$)*7.4)/2:PY=PY1+20:PSET(PX,PY):DRAW"S6":GOSUB
2230:DRAW"S4" '* LABEL X-AXIS *
1840                         Y9$=LY$:PX3=PX3-5:PY=PY1-(PY1-AY-
LEN(Y9$)*7.4)/2:PSET(PX3,PY):DRAW"S6":GOSU B 2300:DRAW"S4" '*
LABEL Y-AXIS *
1850 IF M=0 THEN YP=AY+10
```

1860 FOR K=3 TO NW
1870 'PX=PX1+(XW(K)-XMIN)*XA/DELTAX1:PY=PY1-(YW(K)-YMIN)*YA/DELTAY1
1880 IF XW(K)=0 AND YW(K)=0 THEN PX=100:PY(K)=YP+10: PY=PY(K):YP=PY ELSE PX=PX1+(XW(K)-XMIN)*XA/DELTAX1: PY=PY1-(YW(K)-YMIN)*YA/DELTAY1:YP=PY
1890 Y9$=T1$(K):PSET(PX,PY):DRAW"S6":GOSUB 2230: DRAW"S4":XW(K)=XMIN+(PX-PX1)*(XMAX-XMIN)/(AX-PX1): YW(K)=YMIN+(PY-PY1)*(YMAX-YMIN)/(AY-PY1):IF LB=1 THEN RETURN 120 ELSE IF H=1 THEN RETURN' * Labels, new and read file saved with this program.
1900 NEXT:K=NW:IF FCN=1 OR DAT=2 THEN 1930
1910 IF FCN>0 THEN RETURN
1920 '* PLOTTING POINTS & CURVES *
1930 FOR I=1 TO M
1940 IF DL=1 AND K=NW THEN LB=1
1950 CC=CC+1:IF CC>15 THEN CC=8+1
1960 IF BW THEN CC=15
1970 NUM=1:FOR J=1 TO N(I)
1980 PX=PX1+(X(I,J)-XMIN)*XA/DELTAX1:IF PX>AX OR PX<PX1 OR J=N(I) AND X(I,J)<X(I,J-1) AND PT(I)=0 THEN LN1=0:GOTO 2010
1990 PY=PY1-(Y(I,J)-YMIN)*YA/DELTAY1:IF PY<AY OR PY>PY1 THEN LN1=0:GOTO 2010 ELSE IF LN1=0 THEN PSET(PX,PY),CC:PX2=PX:PY2=PY:LN1=1
2000 IF PT(I)=0 THEN LINE-(PX,PY),CC ELSE W=PT(I): PSET(PX,PY),CC:DRAW"X"+VARPTR$(N$(W))
2010 NEXT:LN1=0:LB=0
2020 IF ID=1 AND DAT=0 THEN 2540 ELSE IF ID=1 AND DAT=1 THEN RETURN
2030 NEXT
2040 RN=1:IF BW=1 THEN 2070 ELSE GOTO 2540
2050 '*********** PRINT SCREEN *************
2060 CLS:BW=1:RS=1:RP=1:GOTO 1670
2070 KEY OFF:CLS 2:RN=1:INPUT"Press [PRINT SCRN] to print plot after pressing [E NTER] to remove this note.   After printing plot press [ENTER] again to continu e.",A:CLS 2
2080 IF INKEY$="" THEN 2080
2090 RN=1:IF BW THEN BW=0:CLS:RS=1:RP=1:GOTO 1670 ELSE RETURN 120
2100 '* LABELING CURVES *
2110 CLS 2:KEY OFF:FCN=0:K=K+1:NW=K:LN1=0:LB=1:INPUT"WHAT IS THE LABEL";T1$(K):I F T1$(K)="" THEN 2110
2120 INPUT"What are the X,Y coordinates of the start of your label(X,Y) ";XW(K), YW(K):IF XW(K)<XMIN OR XW(K)>XMAX OR YW(K)<YMIN

OR YW(K) > YMAX THEN BEEP:GOTO 212 0 ELSE GOTO 1870

2130 '* CONSTRUCTING CURVE *

2140   ID = 1:DAT = 0:J = 0:I = I + 1:PT(I) = 0:M = M + 1:X = XMIN:DX = (XMAX-XMIN)/100 ' equation

2150 Y = X + 13:IF Y > YMAX THEN 2170

2160 J = J + 1:N(I) = J:X(I,J) = X:Y(I,J) = Y:LN1 = 0

2170   X = X + DX:IF   X = < XMAX   THEN   2150   ELSE   GOSUB 1950:LN1 = 0:RETURN

2180 '* RERUN PROGRAM *

2190 CLS 2:PRINT:PRINT"ARE YOU SURE THAT YOU WISH TO TERMINATE THIS PROGRAM ";:G
OSUB 2440:IF YES THEN SYSTEM ELSE RETURN 150

2200 RUN 60

2210 '* FOR DRAWING NUMBERS AND WORDS *

2220 '* FOR DRAWING FROM LEFT TO RIGHT *

2230 FOR J = 1 TO LEN(Y9$):W = ASC(MID$(Y9$,J,1)):IF W > 96 AND W < 123 THEN W = W-32

2240 IF W = 32 OR W = 45 THEN ZR = 1

2250 IF W > 46 THEN ZR = 0

2260 IF ZR = 1 AND W = 46 THEN DRAW"X" + VARPTR$(N$(48)) + "BR3":ZR = 0
' * FOR INSERTING A ZERO BEFORE A DECIMAL LESS THEN ONE *

2270 DRAW"X" + VARPTR$(N$(W)) + "BR4" ' * DRAWING FROM LEFT TO RIGHT *

2280 NEXT:RETURN

2290 '* FOR DRAWING FROM BOTTOM TO TOP ON VERTICAL AXIS *

2300 FOR J = 1 TO LEN(Y9$):W = ASC(MID$(Y9$,J,1))

2310 IF W = 61 THEN W = 11 ELSE IF W = 94 THEN W = 12 ELSE IF W = 39 THEN W = 13 ELSE IF W = 4 0 THEN W = 14 ELSE IF W = 41 THEN W = 15 ELSE IF W = 37 THEN W = 16 ELSE IF W = 32 THEN W = 17 ELSE 2330

2320 GOTO 2340

2330 IF W > 44 AND W < 59 THEN W = W-27:GOTO 2340 ELSE IF W > 96 AND W < 123 THEN 2340 ELS E W = W + 32'* FOR CONVERTING LETTERS TO A VERTICAL SCALE USING THE ASCII LOWER CASE
 POSITIONS *

2340 DRAW"X" + VARPTR$(N$(W)) + "BU3":ZR = 0

2350 NEXT:RETURN

2360 '* FOR DRAWING FROM RIGHT TO LEFT ON VERTICAL AXIS *

2370 FOR J = LEN(Y9$) TO 1 STEP -1:W = ASC(MID$(Y9$,J,1))

2380 IF J = 2 AND W = 46 THEN ZR = 2

2390 IF ZR = 2 AND J = 1 AND W = 32 OR ZR = 2 AND J = 1 AND W = 45 THEN DRAW"BL7" + "X" + VARPTR $(N$(48)):ZR = 0 ' * FOR INSERTING A ZERO BEFORE A DECIMAL LESS THAN ONE ON THE Y SCALE *

2400 DRAW"BL8" + "X" + VARPTR$(N$(W)) + "BL3" '* FOR DRAWING FROM RIGHT TO LEFT (NUMBE RING Y AXIS) *

2410 NEXT:IF PX3 > POINT(0) THEN PX3 = POINT(0)
2420 RETURN
2430 '* CONVERT "Y" OR "y" TO YES OR "N" OR "n" TO NO *
2440   YES = 0:PRINT"(Y/N)   or   Enter = N)   ";:COLOR 10:PRINT"Y":YES = 1:COLOR 14
2450 IF INKEY$ = "" THEN 2450
2460 RETURN
2470 '* ERROR HANDLING ROUTINE *
2480 CLS:BEEP:IF ERR = 53 THEN LOCATE 13,31:PRINT"FILE NOT FOUND.":GOSUB 2510:CLS 2:RESUME 2490 ELSE RUN 60
2490 ON ERROR GOTO 0:GOTO 2570
2500 '* TIMER FOR DISPLAY OF MESSAGE *
2510 SC = 1
2520 INIT = TIMER
2530 TI = TIMER:IF TI < INIT + SC THEN 2530 ELSE RETURN
2540 FCN = 0:RP = 0:IF M = 23 THEN RETURN 120 ELSE CLS 2:FCN = 16:PRINT"Do you want more
 curves ";:GOSUB 2440:IF YES THEN 2550 ELSE RETURN 120
2550 J1 = 1:PT(I1) = 0:YI2 = 0
2560 IF DAT = 2 THEN 270 ELSE I1 = 1:M = M + 1:GOTO 410
2570 KEY 1,"":KEY(1) OFF:SCREEN 0:ON ERROR GOTO 2480:KEY OFF:CLS:COLOR 15,1,10:F ILES"*.DAT":PRINT:PRINT"Enter your file name without [.DAT]. ";:COLOR 14:PRINT"P VA23B":COLOR 15:FILE$ = "PVA23B"
2580 IF INKEY$ = "" THEN 2580
2590 IF FILE$ = "" AND M = 0 THEN CLS:RETURN 100 ELSE IF FILE$ = "" AND M > 0 THEN CLS:G OTO 1670 ELSE FILE$ = FILE$ + ".DAT"
2600 K1 = K:OPEN FILE$ FOR INPUT AS #1:INPUT #1,MN,NW,LX$,LY$,DELTAX1,DELTAX2,DELT AY1,DELTAY2,XMIN,XMAX,YMIN,YMAX
2610 FOR K = 1 TO NW:INPUT #1,T1$(K),XW(K),YW(K):NEXT
2620 FOR I = 0 TO MN:INPUT #1,N(I),PT(I):NEXT
2630 FOR I = 0 TO MN:FOR J = 1 TO N(I):INPUT #1,X(I,J),Y(I,J)
2640 NEXT:NEXT:CLOSE #1
2650 ON ERROR GOTO 0
2660 PLOT16 = PT(0):MM = N(0):MEM = MM:M = M + MN:NW = K1 + NW:ID = 0: DAT = 2:RP = 1:GOTO 1670
2670 I = M:J = 0:KEY OFF
2680 ID = 1:DAT = 1:CLS 2:PRINT:PRINT"Enter data points seperated by a comma (X,Y). When through, enter value off   scale. Press [ENTER] key after each pair of v alues."
2690 I = I + 1: 'ADD DATA
2700 J = J + 1:INPUT" X,Y values ",X(I,J),Y(I,J)
2710 IF X(I,J) > XMAX OR Y(I,J) > YMAX THEN 2720 ELSE 2700
2720 J = J-1:N(I) = J:PT(I) = M:GOSUB 1950

2730 PRINT"Do you wish to input more data";:GOSUB 2440:IF YES THEN 2670 ELSE RET URN 120

2740   DATA   30,40,32.5,40,35,40,37.5,40.5,30,35,33,35.5,37.5,35,40,35,32.5,30,35,3 0,37.5,30,40,30

Nomenclature

The equation numbers are shown in parentheses.

A	Cross-sectional area.
A	Helmholtz free energy (4.1.2).
a	Segment length (1.4.7).
C_0	Vacuum capacitance (1.4.15).
c_1, c_2	Williams-Landel-Ferry (WLF) parameters (2.1.12).
c_2^g	WLF parameter with T_g as the reference temperature
c	Concentration in g/cm^3 (6.3.3).
c_1	Number of configurations that a conformer can take (2.1.1).
C_p	Specific heat at constant pressure per mole of conformer.
ΔC_p	Specific heat relative to the excess enthalpy (2.1.7).
E	Tensile modulus (See the shear modulus, G, below).
E	Electrical field (1.4.10).
E_h	Hole energy at T_g (2.1.17).
F	Force (1.2.1).
f	Free volume fraction (2.1.13).
f_g	Free volume fraction f at T_g (3.3.2).
G	Shear modulus (See below).
G_0	Unrelaxed modulus (1.3.1).
$G(t)$	Relaxation modulus (1.3.4).
$G'(\omega)$	Storage or elastic modulus (1.5.4).
$G''(\omega)$	Loss modulus (1.5.6).
G_e	Plateau modulus (4.4.1).
g^*	Critical size for nucleation (5.1.10).
H	Enthalpy
ΔH_u	Heat of fusion (5.1.2).
H_c	Conformational enthalpy (2.1.5).
$H(\ln\lambda)$	Relaxation spectrum (1.5.1).
h^*	Conformational enthalpy without cooperativity (2.1.5).
h	Planck's constant (1.4.14).
I_1	Invariant of the first kind (3.3.36).
I_2	Invariant of the second kind (3.3.37).
I_2'	Deviatoric invariant (3.3.38).
$J(t)$	Creep compliance (1.3.9).
$J'(\omega)$	Dynamic storage compliance (1.5.7).
$J''(\omega)$	Dynamic loss compliance (1.5.7).

K	Compressive modulus, the reciprocal of the compressibility (4.2.13).
K_b	Stress concentration factor for fracture (6.2.14).
k	Boltsmann constant
l	Length of a segmental unit (4.2.5).
M	Molecular weight of conformer (2.1.19).
M	Molecular weight of polymer (4.2.12).
M_c	Molecular weight between crosslinks (4.2.14b).
M_0	Molecular weight of special conformer with $T_0 = 0$ K (1.4.9).
M_c	Critical molecular weight for 3.4 power behavior (4.4.3).
M_e	Molecular weight between entanglement or size of a blob (4.4.3).
m	Power law exponent for creep data (4.5.18).
m_x	Electric moment (1.4.10).
N	Number of chain molecules per unit volume (4.2.11).
N_A	Avogadro's number
N_z	Number of cooperative domains (2.1.1).
n	Exponent for power law (1.4.4, 3.3.4, 3.3.29).
n	Number of beads in a chain (4.2.5).
P	Statistical probability (1.4.6).
p	Pressure
Q	Charge
R	Gas constant (1.4.9)
R_e	Effective hydrodynamic radius (6.3.1).
$<r^2>^{1/2}$	Rms end-to-end distance of a molecule (4.2.5).
ΔS_u	Entropy of fusion (5.1.2).
S_c	Conformational entropy (2.1.1)
s^*	conformational entropy without cooperativity
T	Temperature.
T_c	Critical temperature at which the yield stress is zero (5.3.1a).
T_f	Fictive temperature (3.1.8).
T_{ref}	Reference temperature (2.1.12).
T_g	Glass transition temperature
T_{gu}	Glass transition temperature of uncrosslinked polymer (6.1.6).
T_m	Melting point (5.1.2).
T_0	"Zero entropy" temperature in the Vogel equation (1.4.3).
T^*	High temperature limit for relaxation (2.1.5).
t	Time.
t^*	Characteristic time constant for reaction or aging (6.1.8).
U	Internal energy (4.1.2).
V	Potential energy (1.4.6).
V	Voltage(1.4.16)

V_0	Volume extrapolated to T_0 (2.1.23).
V_e	Effective hydrodynamic volume (6.3.2).
V_g	Volume at T_g (2.1.23).
v	Sound velocity in media (5.3.11).
v_h	Hydrodynamic volume fraction (6.3.22).
ΔV_u	Volume of fusion (5.1.6).
W	Conformational probability (4.2.2).
z	Number of conformers in a cooperative domain (2.1.4).
z_c	The critical z that corresponds to λ_c (2.2.1).
α	Thermal expansion coefficient
α_f	α for the free volume fraction (2.1.13).
α	Extension ratio (4.2.11).
α	Swelling ratio (6.3.25).
$\Delta\alpha$	Difference in α between liquid and glassy states (2.1.16).
β	Kohlrausch-Williams-Watts (KWW) parameter, used later for domain model (1.4.2, 3.3.3).
β	Pre-exponential factor for conformational probability (4.2.2).
β_g	KWW β at T_g (3.2.5).
γ	Shear strain (1.3.8).
$\dot{\gamma}$	Rate of strain in shear (1.3.8).
$\dot{\gamma}^*$	Critical strain rate for plasticity (1.6.3).
γ_e	Recoverable shear strain (1.3.3).
δ	Thermodynamic perturbation (3.1.1).
ε	Tensile strain (see shear strain γ) (1.4.9).
ε_0	Static dielectric constant (1.4.15).
ε_∞	Dielectric constant at high frequency limit (1.4.15).
ς	Frictional coefficient (1.4.20, 4.3.1).
ς_0	Monomeric frictional coefficient (4.3.4).
η	Viscosity (1.3.1, 4.3.3).
η^*	Dynamic viscosity (a complex quantity) (1.6.11).
η_s	Steady state viscosity (4.5.1, 4.5.2).
$[\eta]$	Intrinsic viscosity (6.3.4).
θ	Angle between the dipole and the field (1.4.6).
λ	Relaxation time (1.3.2, 4.3.2).
λ^*	Relaxation time at T^* (2.1.9).
λ_c	Characteristic relaxation time (1.4.2, 1.4.4, 3.3.1).
μ	Dipole moment (1.4.10).
$\Delta\mu$	Activation energy for rotational relaxation of one conformer without cooperativity (2.1.8).

$\Delta\mu^*$	$\Delta\mu$ for conformer with $T_0 = 0$ K (2.1.11).
$\Delta\mu_e$	$\Delta\mu$ for external viscosity (2.2.13).
ν	Poisson's ratio (3.3.15).
ν	crosslinking density (6.2.3).
ξ	Extent of crosslinking reaction (6.1.4).
ρ	Density (1.4.9).
σ or σ_{ij}	Stress
σ_0	Unrelaxed stress (1.3.2).
σ^*	Yield stress (1.6.1, 3.3.16).
σ_d^*	Steady state stress after yield (1.6.7).
σ_b	Stress at break (6.2.6).
σ_e	End surface free energy (5.1.12).
σ_n	Normal stress (1.2.1).
σ_s	Shear stress (1.2.4).
σ_s	Lateral surface free energy (5.1.12).
σ_{ss}	Steady state stress (1.6.5).
$\phi(t)$	Relaxation function (e.g., $G(t)/G_0$) (1.3.11).
Ψ	Gibbs free energy (1.1.3, 4.1.3).
ω	Circular frequency (1.3.7).

Subject Index

Author Index